A Treasury of HUMOR
and TOASTMASTER'S HANDBOOK

A TREASURY OF

Humor

AND

Toastmaster's

Handbook

Compiled by

MARJORIE BARROWS
MATHILDA SCHIRMER
BENNETT CERF

Chicago

SPENCER PRESS, *Inc.*

COPYRIGHT ACKNOWLEDGMENTS

*The compilers and the publishers wish to thank the following authors, agents and
publishers for granting permission to reprint the copyrighted selections specified:*

BRANDT & BRANDT for permission to reprint *Dr. Atwood and Mr. Ed*
by Walter Brooks, Copyright 1943 by The Curtis Publishing Company; *Mr. Pottle and the One Man Dog* by Richard Connell, Copyright 1922 by Richard Connell.

CROWN PUBLISHERS for permission to reprint *The Alienist* by Keith
Preston, from "Top O' the Column" by Keith Preston, and *The
Pensive Pen* by Keith Preston, Copyright 1925 by Pascal Covici.
Reprinted by permission of Crown Publishers.

CURTIS BROWN, LTD. and the Author's Estate for permission to reprint *Constable Sam and the Ugly Tyke* by Eric Knight, from "Sam
Small Flies Again" by Eric Knight, Copyright 1941 by Eric Knight.

DODD, MEAD & COMPANY, INC. for permission to reprint *Ring Out,
Wild Bells* by Wolcott Gibbs, from "A Bed of Neuroses" by Wolcott Gibbs, Copyright 1936 by Dodd, Mead & Company, Inc.; *On
Riding* by Cornelia Otis Skinner, from "Excuse It, Please!" by
Cornelia Otis Skinner, Copyright 1929 by Cornelia Otis Skinner;
The Body Beautiful by Cornelia Otis Skinner, from "Soap Behind
the Ears" by Cornelia Otis Skinner, Copyright 1941 by Cornelia
Otis Skinner; *The Need of Change* by Julian Street, Copyright
1909 by Dodd, Mead & Company, Inc.

DOUBLEDAY & COMPANY, INC. for permission to reprint *A Pair of
Sexes, Tact in Entertaining, Those Two Boys,* and *To a Thesaurus*
by Franklin P. Adams, from "The Column Book of F.P.A." by
Franklin P. Adams, Copyright 1911, 1928 by Doubleday & Company, Inc.; *Pigs Is Pigs* by Ellis Parker Butler, Copyright 1906 by
Doubleday & Company, Inc.; *The Ransom of Red Chief* by O.
Henry, from "Whirligigs" by O. Henry, Copyright 1910 by Doubleday & Company, Inc.; *Aunt Agatha Speaks Her Mind* by P. G.
Wodehouse, from "Jeeves" by P. G. Wodehouse, Copyright 1923
by Doubleday & Company, Inc.

HAROLD MATSON for permission to reprint *My Next Girl* by Max Shulman, Copyright 1946 by Hearst Magazines, Inc.

HAROLD OBER for permission to reprint *The Kennel and the Cat Coop* by Ellis Parker Butler, Copyright 1926 by Crowell-Collier Publishing Company.

G. P. PUTNAM'S SONS for permission to reprint *A Vision for Willy* by Marion Sturges-Jones, from "Babes in the Woods" by Marion Sturges-Jones, Copyright 1941, 1942, 1944 by Marion Sturges-Jones.

RANDOM HOUSE, INC. for permission to reprint *How Beautiful with Mud* by Hildegarde Dolson, from "We Shook the Family Tree" by Hildegarde Dolson, Copyright 1946 by Hildegarde Dolson; *Calling Dr. Kildare! Calling Dr. Pasture!* by Arthur Kober, from "My Dear Bella" by Arthur Kober, Copyright 1941 by Arthur Kober.

RINEHART & COMPANY, INC. for permission to reprint *The Treasure Hunt* by Mary Roberts Rinehart, from "The Book of Tish" by Mary Roberts Rinehart, Copyright 1926 by The Curtis Publishing Company, Copyright 1931 by Mary Roberts Rinehart.

SYDNEY A. SANDERS for permission to reprint *Spring over Brooklyn* by Zachary Gold, Copyright 1939 by Zachary Gold.

CHARLES SCRIBNER'S SONS for permission to reprint *Zenobia's Infidelity* by H. C. Bunner, from "The Stories of H. C. Bunner."

THE VIKING PRESS, INC. for permission to reprint *Experience* and *Fighting Words* by Dorothy Parker, from "The Portable Dorothy Parker," Copyright 1926, 1936, 1944 by Dorothy Parker.

ANN WATKINS, INC. for permission to reprint *How Does It Feel?* by David Burnham.

A. P. WATT AND SONS, LTD. (and Houghton Mifflin & Company) for permission to reprint *Fowl Play* by Ian Hay, from "The Lucky Number" by Ian Hay.

WHITTLESEY HOUSE for permission to reprint *The Complete Dangler* by John Mason Brown, from "Insides Out" by John Mason Brown, Copyright 1947 by the McGraw-Hill Book Company, Inc.

THE FOLLOWING AUTHORS for permission to reprint these selections:

FRANKLIN P. ADAMS for *The Rich Man* and *To a Lady Troubled by Insomnia*, from "Innocent Merriment."

RICHARD ARMOUR for *Anecdotage* and *The Ladies*, from THE SATURDAY EVENING POST.

LAURA LEE RANDALL for *A New Year Wish*.

PUBLISHER'S FOREWORD

HERE IS A BOOK of fun and laughter for all the family. It is a collection of gay stories, amusing, real adventures, bright, sparkling verse, and rollicking cartoons.

Here is an illustrated humor anthology that bends over backwards to avoid the dated humor of yesteryear while still remembering the ageless humor of such master storytellers as Mark Twain, O. Henry and Frank R. Stockton.

Our compilers have remembered that too many short humorous selections read at one sitting are too much, and have therefore, for the most part, included longer short stories of wide appeal. A number of these stories have never before appeared in anthologies, while others are well-known. But new or old, Tish, Constable Sam, Beauty, My Next Girl, Willy's Vision, young Joey, the twins, Eileen and Ruth, and all the others are a parade of characters guaranteed to delight and amuse laughter-loving Americans.

All members of the family are invited to partake of this book for leisure moments in their often serious, busy lives; and we hope you will all find this book a festival of fun, worthy of a permanent place on the bedside table.

The last section of the book is filled with anecdotes collected by Bennett Cerf. A toastmaster will revel in these amusing stories and everyone will enjoy them.

The compilers are deeply grateful for the help they have received from the editorial staff of this publishing house and for the amusing pictures or cartoons by Clarence Biers, Henry Boltinoff, Bo Brown, Charles Cartwright, Barbara Clyne, Corka, Aubrey Dutton, Frances Eckart, Eric Erickson, Hazel Frazee, Martin Garrity, George Hamilton Green, Alan Hindmarch, John Janeck, Will Johnson, Reamer Keller, Marion Kunzelman, Lawrence Lariar, Stan Lilstrom, Louise Lyman, Barbara Maynard, J. Monahan, Ed Nofziger, Bill O'Malley, Eric Peters, Robinson, Al Ross, Schus, Sue Simons, Robert Sinnott, Diana Thorne, Barney Tobey, Don Ulsh, Fritz Wilkinson, George Wolfe, Lillian Wuerfel, and Milt Youngren. They are especially grateful for the editorial help of Lois Williams Stein.

CONTENTS

PUBLISHER'S FOREWORD   vii

PART ONE

THE BODY BEAUTIFUL	*Cornelia Otis Skinner*	1
ROOF SITTER	*Frances Eisenberg*	9
THE FIREFLY	*Ogden Nash*	22
BEWARE THE BRAZILIAN NAVY	*Ruth McKenney*	23
THOSE TWO BOYS	*Franklin P. Adams (F.P.A.)*	32
THE ALIENIST	*Keith Preston*	32
FIGHTING WORDS	*Dorothy Parker*	33
HI, ROVER, OR, OLIVER AMES WANTS A DOG	*Phyllis McGinley*	34
TACT IN ENTERTAINING	*Franklin P. Adams (F.P.A.)*	36
MY NEXT GIRL	*Max Shulman*	39
EXPERIENCE	*Dorothy Parker*	53
CONSTABLE SAM AND THE UGLY TYKE	*Eric Knight*	54
A VISION FOR WILLY	*Marion Sturges-Jones*	73
A NEW YEAR WISH	*Laura Lee Randall*	80
FILLING THAT HIATUS	*Robert Benchley*	81
THE TREASURE HUNT	*Mary Roberts Rinehart*	84
WANTED: ONE CAVE MAN WITH CLUB	*Margaret Fishback*	119
ZENOBIA'S INFIDELITY	*H. C. Bunner*	120
TO A YOUNG MAN SELECTING SIX ORCHIDS	*Margaret Fishback*	132
HOW DOES IT FEEL?	*David Burnham*	133
TO A THESAURUS	*Franklin P. Adams (F.P.A.)*	150
THE GREAT PANCAKE RECORD	*Owen Johnson*	152
A PAIR OF SEXES	*Franklin P. Adams (F.P.A.)*	168
ANTHOLOGISTICS	*Arthur Guiterman*	170
PIGS IS PIGS	*Ellis Parker Butler*	171
EIGHT BOTTLES OF LINIMENT	*Frances Eisenberg*	181
MONEY	*Richard Armour*	187
DR. ATWOOD AND MR. ED	*Walter Brooks*	188
SPRING OVER BROOKLYN	*Zachary Gold*	206
SPRING TONIC	*Margaret Fishback*	217
THE HIPPOPOTAMUS	*Ogden Nash*	218
THE COMPLETE DANGLER	*John Mason Brown*	219
HELL'S BELLS	*Margaret Fishback*	227

THE WIDOW'S CRUISE — *Frank R. Stockton* — 228
THE LAST DAY — *Robert Benchley* — 241
THE THREE MUSKETEERS — *Rudyard Kipling* — 246
SONG OF THE OPEN ROAD — *Ogden Nash* — 250
AUNT AGATHA SPEAKS HER MIND — *P. G. Wodehouse* — 251
THE RICH MAN — *Franklin P. Adams (F.P.A.)* — 269
TRIAL AND ERROR — *Phyllis McGinley* — 269
THE LADIES — *Richard Armour* — 270
MR. POTTLE AND THE ONE MAN DOG — *Richard Connell* — 271
THE CHRISTMAS OF THE FUTURE — *Frank Sullivan* — 294
VERSES FOR A GREETING CARD — *Phyllis McGinley* — 297
BEAUTY'S SISTER — *Owen Johnson* — 298
A ROMAN GUIDE — *Mark Twain* — 314
RING OUT, WILD BELLS — *Wolcott Gibbs* — 320
THE KENNEL AND THE CAT COOP — *Ellis Parker Butler* — 324
TO A SMALL BOY STANDING ON MY SHOES
  WHILE I AM WEARING THEM — *Ogden Nash* — 340
THE TERMITE — *Ogden Nash* — 341
THE PENSIVE PEN — *Keith Preston* — 342
THE TRANSFERRED GHOST — *Frank R. Stockton* — 343
MOMENT MUSICALE — *Margaret Fishback* — 354
ANECDOTAGE — *Richard Armour* — 354
UNCLE PODGER HANGS A PICTURE — *Jerome K. Jerome* — 355
A CHANGE OF TREATMENT — *W. W. Jacobs* — 357
CALLING DR. KILDARE! CALLING DR. PASTURE! — *Arthur Kober* — 365
TO A LADY TROUBLED BY INSOMNIA — *Franklin P. Adams (F.P.A.)* — 369
AWAKE, AWAKE! — *Robert Benchley* — 370
THE NEED OF CHANGE — *Julian Street* — 372
FOWL PLAY — *Ian Hay* — 397
HOW BEAUTIFUL WITH MUD — *Hildegarde Dolson* — 401
THE RANSOM OF RED CHIEF — *O. Henry* — 408
ON RIDING — *Cornelia Otis Skinner* — 419
HORSES — *Richard Armour* — 425

PART TWO

TOASTMASTER'S HANDBOOK — *Bennett Cerf* — 427
TITLE INDEX — 565
AUTHOR INDEX — 569
TOASTMASTER'S HANDBOOK INDEX — 573

PART ONE
A TREASURY OF HUMOR

THE BODY BEAUTIFUL

CORNELIA OTIS SKINNER

AT LEAST three times a year the average woman tries on dresses in a shop. She finds herself standing before one of those fitting-room mirrors with movable side-panels suggestive of a primitive triptych . . . that is, if she has sufficient imagination to turn the triple reflection of herself in a pink slip into a trio of medieval saints. Such mirrors afford one a lot of seldom beheld angles of one's self and the sudden sight of them comes in the nature of a shock. You find you're staring at yourself rather than at the clothes you're buying; at your profile which somehow isn't at all the way you'd remembered it; at that curious three-quarter view when your face appears to be the shape of a Jordan almond, and at that alarming, almost indecent exposure of the back of your neck. When, furthermore, your eye travels earthward from the nape and is suddenly arrested, not without horror, by the reflection of that portion of the anatomy of which you catch a good glimpse only on these sartorial occasions, and which since the last shopping trip appears to have taken on distressing prominence, you reach the grim conclusion that it's almost too late for clothes to matter.

1

A recently beheld panorama of myself in the clear cold light of Bloomingdale's most relentless mirror filled me with such panic, I felt I must do something immediately. Recalling the ads of those numerous "slimming salons" which assure you that within a few weeks and for a price unnamed they can change you from a model for Helen Hokinson into a stand-in for Katharine Hepburn, I decided to take my troubles and my protuberances to one of them. Ever since the days of boarding-school, when I used to send for every free sample from henna rinses to stove-polish, I have always fallen for ads. The sweetheart of J. Walter Thompson, I have a peasant-like belief in whatever miracle they profess to effect.

I made inquiries among my better-shaped acquaintances and was told that an establishment in the East Fifties was among the best. The place, though small, was impressive. The façade was what is known as "moderne." Instead of the usual show window it had sort of portholes in which terra-cotta dryads (they might even have been hamadryads) danced amid bottles of perfume. On the ground floor was a sales and reception room where were displayed cosmetics, evening bags and (although a blizzard was raging outside) dark glasses and suntan oil. The place, decorated in Louis something style, had such an air of luxe and "parfum" about it you felt that, instead of streamlining you, they ought to turn you out looking like a Boucher. (Why didn't I live at that time, anyway?) A marquise disguised as a saleswoman was sitting behind the sort of table at which De Sévigné must have written her letters. It now held an enormous appointment book, some atomizer bottles and a very pure white phone. She asked if there were anything she could do for me and I said, "Yes. Reduce my rear," which shocked her very much; but, being of the aristocracy, she managed to smile politely. "Have you made an appointment for a consultation with Mme. Alberta?" "Mme. Alberta?" I echoed. "I'm afraid I haven't heard about her." From the expression of the marquise I might have said I hadn't heard about the Duchess of Windsor.

"I don't think I need any consultation," I said. "I just want to reduce my . . ." her eyebrows flickered ever so slightly and I ended lamely, "I just want to lose a few inches."

"All our clients have a consultation first with Mme. Alberta," was her reply. "She happens to be disengaged at the moment. If you'll please go upstairs I'll phone her you're coming." I climbed a mauve-carpeted stair, wondering what sort of consultation lay in store for me.

Would Mme. Alberta greet me with a stethoscope or would she be discovered gazing into a crystal? A pretty woman, youngish and frighteningly smart, was seated at another period table. I gathered she was Mme. Alberta for she said "How do you do?" She had a very strenuous smile and her accent was so determined to be English it broadened every "a" . . . even in the case of such words as *hand* and *ankle*. It was hard to know how to address her. "Mme. Alberta" sounded embarrassing. She didn't look much like an Alberta and to call her plain *Madam* was unthinkable. She was one of those women who are so well-groomed they are positively "soignée." . . . In their immaculate presence you feel as if you had several runs in your stockings. She motioned me to a chair and listened to the story of my proportions as if it were a case history. She then quoted me prices and after accepting my check took out a card resembling a hospital chart. On it she wrote my name and address and some things that struck me as being singularly irrelevant in the matter of hip reduction . . . when my child was born, what sicknesses I'd ever had, the current lie about my age, and my blood pressure which, like my Social Security number, is something I can never remember.

"Now, then, we'll see about your weight."

"I know what I weigh," I said, and added recklessly, "and I don't care. All I'm after is to reduce my . . . "

"Weight and measurements must be taken every treatment." Her tone, though polite, implied she didn't think I was quite bright. "There's the dressing room. Will you disrobe kindly?" I went to what seemed to be a daintily furnished sentry box and disrobed kindly. I felt somehow I was up for a woman's branch of the Army. A trim mulatto brought me a sheet and pair of paper slippers that were the shape and texture of peanut bags. I tried to drape the sheet so I'd look like a Tanagra figure but it wouldn't work, so I arranged it along the more simple lines of a Navajo blanket and emerged with caution. Mme. Alberta, who was waiting, told me to "come this way" and I followed her down a corridor, not without a vague apprehension that at the finish of the trip I might find myself confronted by an anaesthetist. She led me behind a screen, whisked off my sheet in the manner of a mayor unveiling a statue and placed me on a scale, naked as Lot's wife . . . nakeder, because that lady could at least boast of a good coating of salt.

"But I tell you, I *know* what I weigh," I protested weakly and told her. She shed on me the indulgent smile a night nurse might give a

3

psychopathic patient, took my weight which turned out to be exactly what I'd said and then told *me*. "Now for those measurements," she said. "Miss Jones, will you please come here?" Miss Jones proved to be a lovely young thing in a wisp of sky-blue tunic. She was of such bodily perfection one had the suspicion that "Miss Jones" was incognito for "Miss America." We were formally introduced . . . Miss Jones in her bright blue suit, I in my bright pink skin. She handed Mme. Alberta a tape measure in exchange for which Mme. Alberta gave her a pencil and my hospital chart.

"Please mark as I call them, Miss Jones," and as if she hadn't already sufficiently humiliated me, Mme. Alberta began calling out my measurements to the world at large. She measured everything. She even measured my neck, my ankle and the length of my arm. I began to wonder if a suit of acrobat's fleshings were thrown in with the course.

"I hardly think you need go to all that trouble," I interposed. "It's just my . . ."

"We take all measurements," Mme. Alberta said somewhat acidly and continued to encompass me with the tape measure, which was a flexible metal affair . . . very cold and with a tendency to tickle. She accompanied her work with a flow of exclamations that might be taken any way. "Well, *well!*" she'd murmur, or "I *thought* so!" and at times shook her pretty head and went "Tsk! Tsk!"

Having completed her survey, she turned me over to Miss Jones, who had me don a baggy little lemon-colored suit . . . the sort of thing that in my girlhood was known as an Annette Kellerman. It contrasted cruelly with her own trim tunic, and I felt more humble than I had in my recent nakedness. She led the way to an exercise room that contained a mat, a gramophone and far too many mirrors, ordered me onto the mat and proceeded to put me through twenty minutes of hard labor. I rolled and thumped. I stretched and kicked. I jumped and pranced. I also puffed and panted. I stood on my shoulders with my

4

feet in the air; that is, Miss Jones hoisted my feet into the air while I rose up onto a fast-breaking neck and screamed. She never paused to allow me to catch a breath, which by now was of such a weakened quality it hardly seemed worth while trying to catch it. I tried to take time out . . . to divert her with harmless chatter. But Miss Jones is very strict. Now and then when total collapse seemed imminent, using the therapy of the brass band spurring on exhausted troops, she'd play a lively record on the gramophone, calling out "one *and* two *and* three *and* four" as if it were a battle cry. She herself was tireless. She'd do awful things such as picking up her ankle with one hand and holding her foot above her head like a semaphore, and expected me to do like-wise. I'm one of those rigid types who, since early childhood, has never been able to lean over and touch my toes—not that I've ever wanted to especially. Moreover, I not only can't raise my foot above my head, I can't even bend far enough to get my hand anywhere near my ankle. Miss Jones tells me I am seriously hamstrung . . . a nasty expression that makes me feel they've been keeping me in the smokehouse all these years.

It's hard to feel cozy with Miss Jones. She is not only strict, she's exceptionally refined. What I call "middle" she calls *diaphragm*, what I call *stomach* with her goes whimsey and becomes *tummy*, and what I call something else she refers with averted eyes to as *derrière*.

The time dragged almost as heavily as my limbs. Finally Miss Jones said I was a good girl and had done enough for the day (the dear Lord knows the day had done enough for me!) and I might go have my massage. I staggered out and into the capable arms of a Miss Svenson, who looked like Flagstad dressed up as a nurse. She took me into a small room, flung me onto a hard table and for forty-five minutes went to work on me as if I were material for a taffy-pulling contest. She

ONE and TWO and

5

kneaded me, she rolled me with a hot rolling pin, she did to me what she called "cupping"—which is just a beauty-parlor term for good old orthodox spanking. After she'd gotten me in shape for the oven she took me into a shower room and finished me up with that same hose treatment by which they subdue the recalcitrant inmates of penitentiaries.

I was then permitted to return to my sentry box and my clothes. Once I'd recaptured my breath I felt extraordinarily full of radiant health and rugged appetite. It was time for lunch and visions of beef-steak danced in my head. But Mme. Alberta was lying in wait for me outside. "Here is your diet," she said, handing me an ominous little slip of paper which I fully expected to be marked ℞.

"I don't really care about a diet," I stammered. "You see, it isn't my weight, it's just my . . . "

"We'd like you to try it," she said.

It was a tasty little menu with the usual well-done dab of chopmeat, a few fruit juices and some lettuce garnished by a rousing dressing made with mineral oil. I was to dine at the Colony that evening and could just imagine Eugene's expression if I were to ask him to bring me an order of green salad mixed with Nujol. However, I pocketed the darn thing and used the back of it for a shopping list.

Part of the system at Mme. Alberta's consists in doing quite a lot of extracurricular work. Employing the honor system, Miss Jones expects one to go through a daily routine of prescribed gymnastics at home. For this end (that end I've been referring to) she has tried to lure me into purchasing a mat of purple satin but with Jeffersonian simplicity I maintain that I can gyrate just as unsuccessfully on the moth-honored surface of my old college blanket. Exercise in the privacy of one's own domicile is a brisk and splendid idea provided one has any amount of

domicile and any modicum of privacy. Space in my apartment is by no means magnificent and the only reasonable expanse of it is in the living-room, which in lieu of a door has an open archway and is exposed in every portion to the hall. Having no yellow Annette Kellerman at home, I generally gird myself for my exertions in nothing more confining than a pair of old pink rayon bloomers. This means that whenever the doorbell rings I am obliged to leap for sanctuary behind the sofa and I don't always hear the bell—which makes it pretty fascinating for whoever comes to the door. Once, in all innocence and semi-nudity, I gave a private performance for the window-cleaner; since when, on the occasions of his monthly visit, if we have the misfortune to meet, we pass each other with lowered eyes.

A problem that confronts me more, perhaps, than most people is that much of my time is spent in travel. The rooms in the newer of what are known as the "leading" hotels are often of dimensions akin to those of a Pullman roomette. To find a sufficient number of square feet in which to spread out one's blanket and one's self becomes a problem in engineering. Often as not I have to lie with head and shoulders under the bed, one arm beneath the bureau and the other halfway across the sill of the bathroom—a pretty picture indeed for the chambermaid or house detective, should they take the notion to enter with their pass-keys. The overshadowing proximity of furniture is a constant menace. During the course of leg-flinging, rolling upside-down, bicycling, and the rest of Miss Jones' required antics, I have cracked shins on the corners of tables, dislocated digits on the rockers of chairs, stunned myself into momentary insensibility against radiators and kicked cuspi-dors about like medicine balls. An important feature in reducing the —well, you know—is the thump—double thump, single thump and just plain boomps-a-daisy. When executed with sufficient enthusiasm, thumping can produce considerable strain on the structure of the room and there is always the fear that the plaster in the ceiling underneath will start falling and prove fatal to some distinguished traveler like Mrs. Roosevelt or Nelson Eddy.

Reducing, if one goes by the doctrines of the Mme. Alberta school, is a twenty-four hour job. Aside from the list of more or less stereo-typed exercises, one is shown any number of everyday contortions that can, supposedly, be indulged in anywhere, any time. You can, for example, improve your posture by straightening out your spine along the edge of the nearest available door, even if, to the casual observer,

7

you appear to be scratching an itching back. You can also, while standing, do those thumps against the handiest walls—say those of the elevator, thereby bringing a moment of diversion into the monotonous life of the operator. Then there are a few less inconspicuous numbers such as standing on tiptoe and stretching up the hands ("Reaching for cherries" is Miss Jones' pretty term for it), leaning over sideways from the waist, deep-knee bending and a movement dignified by the name of "abdominal control" that curiously resembles the beginnings of the "danse du ventre." These you are expected to burst forth with at odd hours of the day and night even at the risk of starting the grim rumor that you're coming down with St. Vitus. Then one must "Walk like a goddess" is Miss Jones' advice. So I do. I walk like mad if not particularly like a goddess. Walking in New York is a simple pursuit but in strange towns it leads to any number of surprises. Setting out for the residential section, I suddenly find myself in the thick of the colored population; or, aiming for a public park, discover that, with the unerring instinct of the homing pigeon, I'm back at the railroad yards. At other times I realize I'm striding enthusiastically down one of those streets of a nature that isn't even questionable. There remains nothing to do but hasten back to the hotel and walk round and round the block until the local policeman begins to grow suspicious.

However, all things come to she who weighs and I discover that I'm tipping the scales to a much lesser degree. Thanks to Miss Jones and Miss Svenson and my own shining determination, the last time Mme. Alberta encircled me with that glacial little measuring tape she found signs of considerable shrinkage and told me she was pleased with me— which made me glow with pride. I doubt if anyone viewing me from the neck down would as yet mistake me for Hedy Lamarr but I'm no longer so horrified by the reflection of myself in a triple mirror and what is more satisfying my clothes are beginning to look like the hand-me-downs of an older and fatter sister. And that is *déjà quelque chose*.

8

ROOF SITTER

FRANCES EISENBERG

FROM the very beginning there were two things wrong with my brother Joe. He was shy and he was stubborn. This is the way he did. If somebody tried to make him not shy, then he got stubborn. Like the time when he was only four years old and he was supposed to be a butterfly in the Sunday school entertainment, and Miss Willson tried and tried to push Joe out on the stage and make him flutter his wings, but Joe lay down on the floor of the stage and wouldn't get up no matter how much the other butterflies stepped on him.

And when he started to kindergarten and his teacher kept asking him to come up in front and tell the other children about his pets, Joe ran out of the room and hid downstairs in the boys' toilet until they had to call the janitor to get him out.

My mother had tried her best to make Joe not like he was, but when he was six years old she had to give up. She said she hoped he would outgrow it. And she asked Joe's teacher please not to try to draw Joe out any more because of the way it made him act. So after that everybody let him alone.

One morning in June just after school was out we got a telegram from Nashville saying that my father's Aunt Sadie was in a dying condition, and for them to come quick. At first my mother didn't know what to do, because she knew they wouldn't want any children there,

9

and there wasn't anybody to leave us with. And she thought a while, and then all of a sudden she said, "Sarah Blevins."

"Who is that?" I asked. I was standing there watching my mother.

"She is a College Student," said my mother. "She is Mrs. White down the street's niece, and she is staying with her and earning her way through college by taking care of children and things like that this summer."

So my mother hurried down to Mrs. White's house, and I went too, and Mrs. White was out in the yard, and she said that Sarah Blevins would be glad to take care of us while my mother and father were gone. "She is very good with children," Mrs. White said. "She has had some courses in child training at the College, and she knows all about them. She will try out some new ideas on your children."

Then Mrs. White called Sarah Blevins out and she was a tall skinny girl with glasses on and a serious look. She told my mother that she would be glad to stay with us, and would give us the best of care. "How old are these children?" Sarah Blevins asked, looking at me, and stretching her mouth a little, like a smile.

"This is Helen," my mother said. "She is nine. And Joe, her little brother, is six."

"Oh, that's very fortunate," Sarah Blevins said, "because I have just finished a course in the child from six to twelve years, and that includes both of your children."

"Yes," said my mother. "But please be careful with little Joe. He is a very shy child, and doesn't like to be noticed. As long as he's left alone though, he's very nice. Just so you don't try to draw him into the limelight."

Sarah Blevins looked interested. "I'm very good on behavior problems," she said. "I will try to adjust your little boy. I have done a lot of field work on problem children."

My mother looked worried. "Oh, there's nothing wrong with Joe," she said. "He's just a little young for his age. If you let him alone he'll be all right."

"I'm sure we'll get along splendidly together," said Sarah Blevins, stretching her mouth at me again. She went into her aunt's house and came out with her clothes in a little bag, and we all hurried back to our house because my mother had to meet my father in town and catch the one o'clock train.

When we got to our yard Joe was playing under the sweet-gum tree.

10

He had some rocks and little sticks, and when he saw Sarah Blevins he stared at her for a minute and went on playing.

"This is Joe," said my mother in a hurry. "Joey this is Sarah Blevins. She is going to take care of you while mother is gone, and you must be a good little boy and do what she says." Then my mother went into the house to get ready.

Joe stared at Sarah Blevins again, and then he began to hammer a stick into the ground with a rock. Sarah Blevins went over to Joe and held out her hand. "How do you do, Joe," she said.

Joe began to look nervous. He twisted his head around so he couldn't see her, but she kept on holding her hand out for him to shake. When she saw he wasn't going to shake hands with her finally she put her hand down. She looked at the sticks and the rocks he was playing with.

"Oh, a house," she said. "Joe is building a nice house. Who will live in your house when it is built? Is it a fairy house? Will a tiny fairy live in it?"

Joe put his arm up and hid his face. Then he went over and stood behind a bush where Sarah Blevins couldn't see him. All you could see was a piece of his head.

"He doesn't like for people to talk to him," I told Sarah Blevins. "Just the family. He's shy of people."

Sarah Blevins looked a little mad. "Yes, but that's very wrong to encourage him in it," she said. "That way he'll get conditioned and then it will be hopeless. He should be drawn out."

"He doesn't like to be drawn out," I told her. "That just makes him worse."

"Not if it's done right," she said. She began to pretend that she didn't know where Joe was. "There was a little boy here a minute ago," she said. "Where did he go? Maybe he had on a pair of magic shoes, or maybe he changed into a flower or a butterfly?"

Joe heard what she was saying and he squatted down quickly behind the bush. He tried to crawl into it, but it was full of stickers.

Just then my mother came out of the house with her hat on. She kissed me good-bye. "Joe is behind the bush," I told her.

My mother went over and kissed him good-bye. "Be a good boy," she told him. "Good-bye," she said to Sarah Blevins. "I know you're going to be fine with the children. Just take charge of things, and order what you need from the grocery. We'll be back by Wednesday at least,"

Then she got into the taxi and rode away.

It seemed very lonely without her. Sarah Blevins stood still a minute, then she said, "I will just leave your little brother alone for the time being." And she took her bag and we went into the house and I showed her where to put her things.

After a while, when she had looked in the icebox to see what food there was, she got a piece of paper and began to write on it. She told me she was writing out what for me to do every hour of the day and beginning tomorrow I must do exactly what it said. She stuck the paper on the kitchen door with some thumbtacks.

"Now you must take care of everything for a few minutes," she said. "I am going to run down to the grocery store and get some celery. Your little brother seems to be lacking in iron."

While she was gone I went out and hunted for Joe. He was digging holes in the back yard.

"Is she gone yet?" he asked. I knew he meant Sarah Blevins.

"She is gone, but she is coming back in a minute," I told him. "She has gone to get something for you to eat to give you iron."

"I don't want iron," Joe said.

"But listen, Joe," I told him. "She is supposed to take care of us, and we are supposed to mind her while mother and father are away. So don't be stubborn. Do what she says, and maybe they will bring us something nice."

"I don't like her," Joe said.

I didn't know what else to say to Joe. I could see that he was going to be stubborn, but I didn't know how to make him not be.

Pretty soon I could hear Sarah Blevins in the kitchen fixing the supper, and after awhile she called us in to eat it.

It was mostly lamb chops and celery and carrots with nothing for dessert. All through supper Sarah Blevins talked to Joe. She asked him things like did he like furry kittens, and did he ever see a brownie, and things like that. But Joe was so hungry that he didn't hide anywhere. He would take a bite of whatever it was, and then he would put his head under the table to chew it so he wouldn't have to look at Sarah Blevins. And just as soon as he got through eating he went into the living room and turned on the radio to the Krunchy Krispy Kiddies hour and I went in there too, and we listened to it.

It had got to the place where the twins had sailed to the moon in their rocket ship and found the palace of King Zoozag, the moon king. While

12

the twins were looking around for the moon pearl, King Zoozag's magician had caught them and locked them up in a dungeon with a ceiling that kept coming down closer and closer to crush the twins to pieces. It was very exciting. The roof was just above their heads and you could hear it giving awful creaks, and you could hear the king laughing an awful laugh, hahahaha, when all of a sudden Sarah Blevins came rushing in there looking like she was going to faint. She ran over and turned off the radio.

"My goodness," she said. She sat down in a chair and got her breath. "No wonder," she said. "No wonder your little brother has got a complex if your mother lets him listen to such things as that. Especially at night."

Joe had been sitting up close to the radio listening with his mouth open, but when Sarah Blevins turned it off, he turned around and stared at her with his mouth still open.

"Now," Sarah Blevins said, after a minute, in a cheerful voice. "Let's tell stories. Shall we? First I'll tell a story, then Helen will tell one and then Joe will. Or maybe Joe would tell his first."

Joe kept looking at her for just a minute, and then he shook his head. But Sarah Blevins paid no attention to that. "Joe's going to tell us a story, Helen," she said. "Won't that be nice? I wish Joe would tell us a story about a little white rabbit. Don't you?"

"Yes, but he won't," I told her. "He doesn't like to talk before people."

"Oh, yes, Joe will, I know he will," Sarah Blevins said. She gave me a kind of a mad look. "Joe will tell us a story."

Joe put his head down in a corner of the chair, and pulled a cushion over it.

13

"You see," I said. "He won't."

"Shhhh," hissed Sarah Blevins, frowning at me. "Yes he will," she said out loud. "Just as soon as he thinks awhile he will. Let's be quiet and let him think. Oh, what a nice story Joe is going to tell us."

For a little while we were quiet and Joe didn't take his head out.

"Now," Sarah Blevins said finally. "Now I think Joe is ready to begin. But where is Joe?" she asked in a surprised voice. "Why he was here just a minute ago. Where can he be? Is he behind the radio?" She went over there and looked. "No, he's not there. Is he behind the door? No." Then she went over to the chair where Joe was and lifted up the cushion. "Why *here* he is."

But before she could say anything else Joe slid out of the chair and ran upstairs.

"I guess he's going to hide in the bathroom," I told Sarah Blevins. "Sometimes he does that when ladies bother him because they can't go in there after him."

Sarah went to the foot of the stairs. "Joe's sleepy," she said in a loud voice. "I guess he wants to go to bed. He will tell us a story tomorrow. Good night, Joe."

Then she came back and sat down in the living room. She looked sort of mad. "Helen," she said, "you must keep quiet when I'm talking to Joe. What's wrong with him now is that he's heard people say he's shy so much that he thinks he is shy. So he acts shy. He isn't really shy, he only thinks he is. When he withdraws like this you must pretend it's just a game he's playing, or you must explain it to him like I did just now and make it reasonable. Have I made it clear to you? Do you understand?"

"I don't know if I do or not," I said.

"Well it doesn't matter. Just so you keep quiet and let me manage your little brother my own way. By the time your mother comes back I'll have him adjusted. But you must co-operate."

"All right," I told her. Because it would be nice and my mother would be glad if she got home and Joe was talking to people and not running from them any more, and not being stubborn and singing little songs when they asked him to, and making speeches and things like that. So I would do like Sarah Blevins said, and be quiet and pretend I didn't know why he was hiding.

The next morning we had breakfast and I looked on the paper to see what I was supposed to do. I was supposed to do Household Tasks for

14

a half an hour. Sarah Blevins told me to go upstairs and make up my bed, and then come down and play outdoors until lunch. So I went up and began to clean up the bedroom, and I looked out of the window and saw Joe playing in the front yard. He had some marbles and he was putting them in a row on the grass.

Pretty soon I saw Sarah Blevins coming out there and she had some papers in her hands. "Hello, Joe," she said. She sat down on the grass beside him.

"May I play with you?" she asked, stretching her mouth into a smile at him.

Joe looked down at the ground and began to pick up the marbles one at a time. He would not look at Sarah Blevins.

"Would you like to play a game that I have here?" Sarah Blevins said. She put one of the papers down on the grass. "It's a game with pictures. Look. It's fun. Do you want to play it with me?"

Joe began to shake his head. He began to slide away from her a little toward the bush.

"See the little girl in the picture," Sarah Blevins told him, holding it up. "She is rolling a hoop. But something is missing. Can you take the red pencil and put in what is missing?"

Joe kept shaking his head and Sarah kept holding out the pencil to him. Finally Joe got up and ran to the bush and hid behind it. But Sarah went over there too and sat down. "It's nicer over here, isn't it, Joe?" she said. "Let's don't play that game then, let's play another one. Listen."

She took another piece of paper and began to read off of it.

"The sun was shining on the sea, shining with all its might. Can you say that, Joe? Listen. The sun was shining on the sea, shining with all its might. Now you say it."

But Joe began to look more nervous than ever, and he went around to the other side of the bush, and Sarah followed him around there. She kept on talking. "This is fun, isn't it, Joe?" she said. "It's like a game I know called follow the leader. Did you ever play that game?"

Joe began to look kind of wild. He looked for another place to hide. There wasn't any. He ran toward the front porch, but I guess he thought that wouldn't be any good, and all of a sudden he started climbing up the rose trellis. There weren't many roses on it, and it was just like a ladder. He went half way up and then he turned his head around to see if Sarah was coming.

15

This time she did not follow him. But anyway he climbed on higher until he got to the porch roof, and then he crawled up on it and sat there and looked down at Sarah.

I spread up the bed in a hurry and went on downstairs and out into the yard to where they were. I wanted to see what Sarah was going to do next to adjust Joe.

Sarah was standing there on the ground looking up at the roof. Her face was red and she looked sort of mad, but she laughed and said to me, "Did you see Joe go up the trellis? He's playing that he's a little squirrel, I guess. Did you see him climb?"

"Yes," I said. I was not going to say anything else, because I was supposed to co-operate with her and keep quiet.

"I wonder how a little squirrel comes down off a roof," Sarah Blevins said. "Can you show us, Joe?"

We waited about ten minutes, but Joe did not come down. He went over and sat down behind the chimney. We could just see his legs and a piece of his blouse.

Then I forgot. "We could get the step-ladder and get him down that way," I told Sarah Blevins. She gave me an awful mad look.

"Be quiet," she said under her breath. Then she said in a loud voice, "Why, we don't want to get a little squirrel down with a ladder. He will come down himself in a little while to get some nuts."

"Or maybe he thinks he's a bird," I said.

But Sarah Blevins didn't pay any attention to me. "I'm going to fix your lunch now, and when I get back I wouldn't be surprised if Joe is on the ground playing with you, Helen," she said. "Being a squirrel is fun, but after all it's nicer to be a little boy, isn't it?" And she took the papers and things and went into the house.

I sat down on the ground and looked up at Joe.

16

After awhile I said, "Sarah Blevins has gone inside now, Joe. Why don't you come down off of the roof and surprise her?"

Joe got from behind the chimney. "No," said Joe. After a minute he asked, "When is she going home?"

"Maybe not till next Wednesday," I said. "So come on down and do what she says. We're supposed to."

"I'll come down next Wednesday," Joe said.

I could see that he was going to be stubborn and not come down off of the roof, and then Sarah Blevins couldn't adjust him before mother came back. I didn't know what to do, so I just sat there and tried to think of something.

After a while some children from the next block came skating along the sidewalk. "What are you doing, Helen?" they asked.

"Nothing," I told them. "Only sitting here waiting for my little brother Joe to come down off of the roof."

They came up in the yard and looked up at Joe's face, which was sticking over.

"What is he doing up there?" they asked.

"Just waiting. He's going to sit there until next Wednesday."

They all stood there staring at Joe with their mouths open.

Just then an automobile with two men in it came driving slowly along the street. The men looked out at us and stopped the car. A fat one stuck his head out the window. "Hey, kids," he said. "Having a big time with school out and everything?"

"Yes sir," we said.

"Well sir, how would you like to have your pictures on the Kiddies Vacation page of the *Morning Journal* so all the other kids all over the city can see what fun you are having. Would you like that?"

"Yes sir," we told him.

So they got out of the car and the thin one had a camera. The fat one told us to stand in a line with our hands on each others shoulders and pretend that we were skating. One of the other children said, "Hey, mister, can Joe be in the picture?"

"Sure, sure," the fat man said. "Who is Joe, your dog?"

"No," I told him. "He's my little brother. He's up there." I pointed up at the roof.

"Sure Joe can be in it," the fat man said. "Hold everything Bill," he said to the man with the camera. "Come on down, Joe," he said.

"He can't be in the picture if he has to come down to be in it," I told

17

the man. "He's going to stay up there all the rest of this week and some more too."

"Ha, ha," laughed the fat man. "That's a new one, ain't it. All over town they're sitting in trees, but he's the first roof sitter. Well, I'll tell you what. We wouldn't want Joe to spoil his record, so we'll take a picture of him from the ground. The rest of you can stand around and be looking up at Joe. We'll give him some free publicity."

So we all stood around and pointed up at the roof, and the cameraman clicked the picture so quick that Joe couldn't hide his face or do anything about it. Then the man asked us our names and how old we were, what grades at school we were in, and then they got in their car and drove away. And the children from the next block hurried home to tell their mothers about having their pictures taken. And just then Sarah Blevins came to the door and said lunch was ready. "We have peanut butter sandwiches, Helen," she said. "Maybe Joe will come down and get some."

But he didn't. I went in and sat down at the table.

"A man took our pictures," I told Sarah Blevins.

But she didn't pay any attention. I guess she was thinking what to do next to adjust Joe. When we finished lunch she said we would just let Joe alone until he got hungry, and she put the dishes to soak and sat down and began to look at a magazine.

I went outside and stayed in the front yard. So the afternoon went by and it was beginning to get dark, and after awhile it was really dark, and still Joe was on the roof.

I went in the house to see if supper was ready and to ask Sarah Blevins what she was going to do.

"It's dark," I said, "and Joe is still up on the roof. He still won't come down."

"Go out and tell him that supper is ready," said Sarah Blevins. "But do not tell him to come down. He must decide that for himself. He must make up his own mind what he is going to do. If I make him come down now, everything will be ruined."

So I went out and told Joe supper was ready. "Don't you want any?" I asked him.

His voice sounded very weak and far away. "No," he said.

"Are you going to sleep up there?" I asked him.

"Yes," he said, and he sounded scared and stubborn at the same time.

I went back and told Sarah Blevins. "Very well," she said.

18

So we ate supper and it was bedtime, and I went upstairs. I went to the window of my mother and father's bedroom. The moon was shining and I could look down on the porch roof and see Joe, sitting up close to the chimney.

"Are you awake, Joe?" I asked him.

"Yes," his voice came up.

"Good night, then," I said. I went to bed and I felt awful. I thought well anyway he can't roll off, because the roof is wide and flat, but it would be hard and maybe he would be hungry. So after awhile I got two pillows and a blanket, and I went to the window and dropped them down to Joe. I didn't care if I had promised Sarah to co-operate. I knew my mother wouldn't want Joe to sleep out-of-doors without a blanket. "Do you want something to eat, Joe?" I asked him low so she wouldn't hear.

"Yes," he said. "I want a peanut butter sandwich and some crackers."

So I went into the kitchen and when I went past the living room I told Sarah Blevins I was going for a drink of water, and I got some peanut butter sandwiches and a whole box of crackers, and I went back up to the window and let them down to Joe by a string.

"But you oughtn't to be so stubborn, Joe," I told him while he was eating them. "You ought to do more what people say and mind them better, or something awful might happen to you."

"I don't care," Joe said. He was fixing the blanket and the pillow. He lay down on them and went to sleep.

The next morning Joe was still on the roof. We talked to him from the upstairs window, but he turned his back because Sarah was there and he wouldn't say anything to her. "Your little brother is a very strange case," Sarah Blevins said to me. She told me to get a bottle of milk and let it down to him, because we couldn't have him starving. And she would think what to do next.

About ten o'clock people began to drive past the house and they would drive slow and point up to our roof. A few of them stopped their cars and came up on the sidewalk and looked. "Little girl," they said to me, "is this where the little boy lives that's sitting on the roof, that his picture was in the *Journal* this morning?"

I went and got the paper and there we all were on the vacation page, and under it it said "Out to establish new record," and "Little Joe Marsden, 7, has joined the ranks of marathon sitters and declares that he will stay on his roof until next Wednesday afternoon."

19

You couldn't see much of Joe in the picture, only his head. But the rest of us were plain. I ran and showed the paper to Sarah Blevins. "Look!" I said. "Joe got his picture in the paper and look out in the street at the people."

Sarah looked and she turned sort of pale. She asked me some questions, but she didn't listen to what I said. She straightened out her mouth and looked mad. "I'm going out there and try one more time," she said to herself. "And this is the last straw."

"You mean you're not going to try to adjust him any more?" I asked her, following her out into the yard, but she didn't answer me.

She looked up at him from the sidewalk. She changed her voice from mad to sweet. "Helen, do you believe in magic?" she said to me. "I do. I'm going to close my eyes and count to ten, and when I open them I believe Joe will be down off of the roof, standing right here on the grass." Then she shut her eyes and began to count.

By now there were two cars parked in front of the house and a fat man and a woman was in one of them and his face was red and he acted funny. He made funny motions at Joe and he yelled, "Don't you do it, sonny. You stay there. She's just trying to get you down." But he didn't talk plain, and he smelled funny. "Shhhh," the woman in the car said, "Shhhh." But she was giggling herself and she acted nearly as funny as her husband.

"Six, seven, eight," Sarah was saying very slow.

But just then something funny seemed to happen to Joe. He looked down and saw the people looking up at him and he heard the fat man yelling, "Don't you do it, sonny." Then all of a sudden instead of hiding from them he began to jump up and down on the roof and yell at Sarah, "This is my house. Let me alone." And then he called her a bad name. "Go home, old jackass," he said.

Sarah opened her mouth and looked surprised. I guess she was surprised that Joe could talk. He had not said anything before her until now.

The fat man began to laugh as loud as he could. "That's telling her!" he said and he drove the car away, and he was sort of whooping as he went and so was his wife. "That's telling her," they said.

The people in the other car stayed though. Twice Sarah started to climb the trellis so she could talk to Joe better, but both times he said, "Let me alone," and looked like he was going to jump. So Sarah had to get down, and she went over and talked to a woman. She told her

20

that in all the time she had worked with children she had never in her life seen one as stubborn as Joe. But she said if everyone had just let him alone she could have had him adjusted, but now everything was spoiled.

But nobody paid much attention to her, because now Joe had turned out to be famous, because he was the only roof sitter in town, and nobody cared what Sarah thought.

The more people stopped and looked up at Joe, the more I got proud of him, and I would tell everybody I was his sister and that he had stayed up there all day and all night and was going to stay on until Wednesday, and everybody asked me questions about him and laughed, and about three o'clock some newsreel cameramen that were in town for something else took some pictures of Joe for the movies.

It was just after this that my father and mother came home. When they got out of the taxi my mother saw the people standing there and began to looked scared. "What is it?" she said. "What's happened?"

"Look, Mother. Look, Daddy," I yelled, pointing up to the roof. "Joe's up there. He's been up there nearly two days. He had his picture in the paper, and the people have been coming to see him all day. He's famous now."

Then Sarah Blevins ran over and began talking fast, and she was really crying. She kept saying things about how she had tried to adjust Joe, and then these people began to come and notice him and encourage him, and everything was spoiled.

"And he called her a jackass," I said. "And this is the stubbornest he ever was in his life. But now he's not shy any more. He didn't hide from the people. Aren't you glad Joe's going to be in the movies, and everybody will get to see him?"

But my father and mother didn't seem to be glad. And my father climbed up the trellis to get Joe, and Joe started to jump off, but when he saw that Sarah was leaving he said he would come down now. And Sarah went away with her little black bag, and she said she was so nervous she didn't know what she was doing. All the people went away, and that was the end of Joe being a roof sitter. He had to eat his supper and go to bed, even if it wasn't dark, and he couldn't have any of the box of candy they had brought from Nashville where they had left and come home because my father's Aunt Sadie had turned out not to be so sick after all.

But Joe was famous for several days and all over town children began

21

sitting on roofs, trying to break the record. One of them, a little girl named Gladys Potts, sat on her garage roof for ninety-three hours, but a storm came up, and she had to come down.

And another thing, it seemed that all the attention he had got had adjusted Joe, because he was hardly at all shy after that, and not so stubborn. He stopped hiding from people, and he would be in plays and things if he could have some bananas afterward. And at school the next year he let them dress him up in a long-tailed coat and long trousers and be an usher in a Tom Thumb wedding. So I guess it was a good thing after all.

"Now I know who Hedy Lamarr reminds me of—it's YOU!"

THE FIREFLY

OGDEN NASH

The firefly's flame
Is something for which science has no name.
I can think of nothing eerier
Than flying around with an unidentified glow on a
     person's posteerier.

22

BEWARE THE BRAZILIAN NAVY

RUTH MC KENNEY

I ONCE had a perfectly frightful experience with the Brazilian Navy which has made me very shy of navies, especially South American navies. It was just an example of the kind of thing that often happened to me while I earned my living as a newspaper reporter, but *l'affaire Brazil* (which is the term by which Eileen always grumpily refers to the frightful incident) was rather more spectacular than most of my professional troubles.

My relations with the Brazilian Navy began under the worst possible circumstances. The gallant boys from our neighbor land on the equator came whooping into New York during one of those heat waves when people were keeling over right and left in subways. On the third day of it, when everybody in town simply began to go to pieces, the Brazilian Navy arrived in Brooklyn, expecting to be greeted by little children throwing flowers, by mayors, men in silk hats, and bevies of flashing-eyed American peacherinos. The little children, of course, were home with the heat rash, the Mayor was in Washington, the Deputy Consul got lost in Brooklyn and was four hours even finding his countrymen. To cap the dismal climax, all available American peacherinos, like admirals' daughters and such, refused point-blank to abandon Newport and Southampton for Brooklyn to do any welcoming of the flower of Brazilian manhood.

23

You can imagine, then, the distress and disappointment of the brave lads of the Brazilian Navy when it got to be eleven o'clock on their first morning in New York and no mayors, no little tots with bouquets, and especially no beautiful girls who were heiresses to rubber-goods fortunes, had turned up to gladden their South American hearts.

Just as annoyance was beginning to develop into definite pique, a taxicab drove up on the pier and I clambered out, panting like a dog in the heat.

"Whee!" shouted a manly little ensign, in what I was just able to recognize as rich Portuguese. "A dame!"

Instantly a throaty cheer went up from more than half a hundred sturdy South American throats. Scores of brand-clean white hats went sailing recklessly in the air. A dense crowd gathered at the side rail of the boat, the better to see the approaching lady. Merry cries went up from the thick clusters of brave Navy lads.

My first move was to dig a crumpled piece of paper from my pocket-book and, standing sullenly in the blazing sun, read it carefully through. This baffled the gentlemen hanging over the rail. The piece of paper was a City News "Note to all City Editors," giving the glad tidings that a Brazilian training ship had come to Brooklyn on a world tour. "The crew," said City News enthusiastically, "is entirely composed of Brazil's future admirals and many of the young men now scrubbing decks on this sailing ship are heirs to great coffee fortunes."

Just as I finished reading this interesting document, four gorgeous future admirals marched down the gangplank to the pier, right-faced, removed their glistening white hats, and bowed in solemn unison. The leader of this little band then began a long speech in that lovely romantic language of the coffee country. At intervals during the speech, the

24

men on the rail of the ship cheered and threw their hats in the air. I began to wish vaguely that I were clad in one of those long, fluttery dresses the girls always wear in the newsreels for Daisy Day at Annapolis. Finally the man who was making the speech rose to a terrific climax, all hands cheered again, and a pregnant silence fell.

I dug my battered press card from my pocketbook, took a deep breath, and handed it to the orator, saying nervously, "I'm afraid you've got me wrong. I'm only a newspaper reporter." The orator examined the press card with great interest; then he handed it to the resplendent future admiral beside him, who also examined it with careful eye, and finally all four of the boys were crowded around it, shaking their heads with anxious curiosity. At last they handed it back, smiled in happy unison, and bowed.

The orator then made another speech, and the boys at the rail cheered again. At the end of this speech two future admirals drew up on my left flank, two on my right, and we all began to march smartly toward the gangplank. I kept looking over my shoulder for somebody from another newspaper or even from the A.P. to show up, but nobody did, of course.

"No speakee Portugee," I said desperately to the orator, who was piloting me up the gangplank by careful pressure on my perspiring left elbow. It was certainly hot that day.

"*Je ne parle pas français ou portugee,*" I said to the handsome creature on my right. He winked, odiously. There seemed to be nothing further to add; so I marched onto the ship in dreary silence.

Upstairs, or above decks, as they say in the Navy, the boys were all waiting for our little party. Cheers broke out as I clambered up the stairs, wiping my perspiring face with a limp handkerchief. Quite a lot of coffee heirs tried to horn in on the orator, and several succeeded. The press was terrific.

"Hot!" I barked desperately, making gestures of fanning myself. Instantly great activity broke out. I was led to a patch of shade under an awning. I was lowered into a chair. Three handsome lads turned up with tall glasses of some liquid with ice in it. In front of my chair several score Brazilians lined up, natty as anything in their fresh white uniforms, and stared at me. Several score more stood in back of my chair and fanned me with their white hats. They made quite a little wind.

Just as I was getting ready to enjoy the breeze, the orator began to talk to me, softly and earnestly, with a gleam in his eyes.

"No understando," I kept saying. "*Nicht verstehe, ne parle pas français.*" The orator kept talking. The men standing in front of me stared with lustrous black eyes, and several of them grinned—wickedly, I thought.

I could feel a blush getting up under my sunburn. Finally the orator took my pocketbook.

"Hey!" I said earnestly.

He opened the pocketbook, extracted the press card, bowed, took out a little silver pencil and a neat little notebook, and began to copy the information on the card. Hordes of other future admirals crowded around him, but he beat them back with angry gestures. At this point I decided to leave.

"Go!" I said earnestly. "Leave, good-by!" They got the good-by. All hands began to shout, "Goot bee, goot bee," or something like that, and I was marched off in great style.

I was sitting at my desk in the newspaper office, quietly drinking a chocolate soda and waiting for it to be five-thirty, when the lad who prevents process-servers and people who have a plan to end war from entering the city room approached me with what is called a worried mien.

"Say," the lad asked earnestly, "where did you meet the Navy?"

A chill spread through my heart. At that very moment there was a

stir in the city room, for five strong, in perfect order, dressed in gleaming, spotless white, the Brazilian Navy was marching down the city-room aisle.

"Cheese it! The cops!" cried the political reporter, an Irishman of ready wit.

While men stood on chairs to get a better view and printers rushed in from the composing room to see what was up, the five future admirals marched to my desk, removed their caps, held them over their hearts, and bowed from the waist. A man in the financial section, far off, whistled between his teeth. Otherwise there was breathless silence.

"Hello," I said.

All five future admirals bowed again and grinned. Their black eyes sparkled and the man in the middle winked.

"No speakee Portugee," I said firmly.

The Brazilian Navy smiled pleasantly.

The night city editor came over and said, "Wow!"

The situation had now grown intolerable. Even the moving-picture critic had been summoned from his office on the third floor to get a load of the Brazilian Navy paying ardent court to the lady reporter. Whistles were rife all over the city room, and I thought them in very poor taste. I would have to get rid of the Navy even if I took them out myself.

I seized my hat, said "Go!" to the Brazilians, and started for the door. A Brazilian immediately seized each of my arms, and three more Brazilians marched proudly and happily behind.

"Have a nice time," the copy editor shrieked in a horrid falsetto.

"Whee!" screamed the moving-picture critic.

Outside the office, I said "Good-by" firmly, and started for home. But the Navy didn't get the idea. We progressed, my Brazilians and I, majestically up to Sheridan Square, creating a sensation of the first water on the West Side Seventh Avenue local, not to mention the excitement

we caused strolling along Christopher Street. Grocery-store keepers kept running to their doors crying, "Parade!"

Finally we reached the door of the modest apartment where my sister and I lived. "Goot bee," I said desperately. The Navy bowed, smiled, lifted their white hats. I unlocked the door and they followed me in, stepping briskly.

My sister, who is a very, very pretty girl, was lying on a daybed, her arms stretched out, her hat on the pillow beside her. Her eyes were closed, but as she heard my familiar step, she said, "Boy, the heat's got me! I'm too done-in to stagger into a shower."

"Hey!" I said.

She opened her eyes to see the five future admirals regarding her with open admiration. Her jaw dropped and she sat up.

"They're Brazilians," I said, waving my arm at the Navy.

"Brazilians?" Eileen repeated blankly. The five gentlemen, holding their hats over their hearts, bowed and smiled at my sister.

"They don't speak a word of English," I said, dropping into a chair and pushing back my hat wearily. The five Brazilians now sat down in a happy row on the other daybed, staring with five pairs of gleaming black eyes at my pretty sister.

There was a long silence. Finally Eileen said, "They're winking at me."

"I know," I murmured. "They do that a lot. They think it is the universal language."

"Hmm," my sister replied.

"I'm so hot I could die," I said faintly. "I've had a terrible day. I had to go to Brooklyn, and Brooklyn is the hottest place in the world."

"Listen," my sister said in a very grim voice, "don't sit there full of idle chatter about the weather. Get rid of the Navy."

"Go away, boys," I said without much conviction. The Brazilians smiled.

Eileen stormed into the bathroom muttering.

When she emerged, all fresh from her shower and with her second-best dress on, she said, firmly, "I'm starving. Let's go to the nearest air-cooled eatery, with or without the Navy."

"Eat!" I said to the Navy, grinding my teeth ferociously. The future admirals looked startled.

"You're scaring them," Eileen objected. In the end, we drew a picture of what we felt looked like a restaurant.

28

"Be careful," Eileen said anxiously as I sketched. "For God's sake, don't let them get any wrong ideas."

We waltzed along Eighth Street, white uniforms to the right and left of us, until we came to a large sign that said "Village Barn. Air-Cooled."

The Brazilian Navy never quite got over the overpowering effects of the Village Barn, and neither did we, for that matter. For one thing, twenty large, fat, oldish women were having a paper-hat birthday dinner as we came in, and their pretty screams of joy and laughter nearly drowned out the orchestra. Then, all the waiters were dressed in overalls and large straw hats, and there was a real stream of water and a real Old Mill quite near our table.

Our little party got off to a sullen start. Eileen kept saying that she never thought she would end up at a place like the Village Barn with a good section of a South American navy. My sister is an anti-militarist. As for the Navy, they were very cold and miserable. They kept making piteous gestures indicating that their necks were getting stiff. I guess you have to build up resistance to modern air-cooling.

Finally, however, the Navy began on their fourth round of rum punches and the orchestra played a rumba. I suppose you might say this was the high point of the Brazilian shore expedition. The little admirals from the far southland were, to our surprise, copiously supplied with American dollar bills, which they kept giving to the waiter, who put them in the pants pocket of his overalls, and to the orchestra, so they would play more rumbas.

Once I retired behind what was labeled a haymow to repair the ravages of several rumbas with Number Three, and when I returned a hideous sight struck my eye. All the jolly patrons of the Village Barn, which apparently gets a lot of out-of-town trade besides Brazilians, were lined up around the dance floor, three deep, jaws agape. In the center of the floor, in lonely magnificence, my sister and the Number One boy from Brazil were prowling around each other while the orchestra played a sneaky, sinister rumba. I was struck dumb by the horrid sight of my only sister doubling for the floor show.

The final blow came when Brazilian Number Two, watching from from the sidelines, tossed Number One his natty white hat. Number One caught the hat with practiced gesture, threw it on the floor, and the next thing I knew Eileen and the future hero of Brazil were snake-hipping around that hat, forehead to forehead. It was spectacular.

29

When the music stopped, **even** the orchestra cheered.

Everybody in our little party brightened up after that except me.

What seemed to me hours later, Eileen and I conferred on how to draw a picture of the fact that we wanted to go home because we had to work the next morning. If you will reflect on this a moment, you will see that it was a delicate situation. Pictures of home and the like can lead to fearful misunderstandings.

In the end, we just marched smartly home, the five brave sea dogs singing some little Portuguese sea chanty in tango time and trotting along beside us.

At the door of the apartment Eileen stopped, stretched out her arm, as Isolde does in the first act, and shouted, "Go!" The Brazilians all looked in the direction to which she was pointing, and, seeing nothing, giggled fatuously. Eileen said grimly, "They can't be that dumb."

"They aren't," I replied bitterly. "This is what comes of dancing around hats. They have got the wrong idea."

There was a long pause, Eileen nervously played with the front-door key. The five Brazilians wore eager, alert expressions.

"They're watching me like a rat in a trap," Eileen snapped.

"You open the door," I whispered, "and I'll slip in and hold it for you."

"You open the door," Eileen countered, "and *I'll* slip in."

So I did. Eileen slipped in successfully but left me outside with the Navy. The Brazilians did not look downcast, only determined.

It was four minutes before the Navy lads fell for the "Oh, look!" gag, where you point in one direction and run like hell in the other. After we were both inside, the Brazilians got mad and rattled the door and carried on generally. Several people stuck their heads out their doors and roared "Quiet!" and "Stop the noise!"

Eileen finally went to bed with her shoes on, and the eggbeater beside her pillow. We slept but fitfully, however, for the Brazilians resorted to serenades about 4 A.M. and there seemed to be a fight in the hall about 4:30. Things quieted down after that.

When we finally woke up in the heat of the bright morning sun, we opened the door a crack and looked out. The Brazilian Navy were gone—forever, as it turned out. I guess they were pretty disappointed in American girls.

THOSE TWO BOYS

FRANKLIN P. ADAMS

When Bill was a lad he was terribly bad.
    He worried his parents a lot;
He'd lie and he'd swear and pull little girls' hair;
    His boyhood was naught but a blot.

At play and in school he would fracture each rule—
    In mischief from autumn to spring;
And the villagers knew when to manhood he grew
    He would never amount to a thing.

When Jim was a child he was not very wild;
    He was known as a good little boy;
He was honest and bright and the teacher's delight—
    To his mother and father a joy.

All the neighbors were sure that his virtue'd endure,
    That his life would be free of a spot;
They were certain that Jim had a great head on him
    And that Jim would amount to a lot.

And Jim grew to manhood and honor and fame
    And bears a good name;
While Bill is shut up in a dark prison cell—
    You never can tell.

THE ALIENIST

KEITH PRESTON

An alienist is not a joke;
He finds you cracked and leaves you broke.

FIGHTING WORDS

DOROTHY PARKER

Say my love is easy had,
  Say I'm bitten raw with pride,
Say I am too often sad,—
  Still behold me at your side.

Say I'm neither brave nor young,
  Say I woo and coddle care,
Say the devil touched my tongue,—
  Still you have my heart to wear.

But say my verses do not scan,
And I get me another man!

"Attractive leg of lamb, hasn't she?"

HI, ROVER,

or,

OLIVER AMES WANTS A DOG

PHYLLIS MC GINLEY

"We ought to have a dog," said Oliver to me.
"Don't you think we ought to get a dog?" said he.
"For calling closer
    In alarms and dangers;
To greet the grocer
    And to bark at strangers,
To fight our battles
    With the raiding mouse,
To guard our chattels
    And to watch our house;
A dog with dignity, a dog with pride,
A fine great brute I can walk beside,
Who won't go wandering in other people's grounds
Or running after motor cars with predatory sounds;
Who knows his station and his master's voice,
One to make a gentleman's heart rejoice—
A Doberman, say, with a pedigree.
Let's get a dog,"
Said Oliver to me.

I said to Oliver, "Oh, yes, indeed,
A dog is positively what we need.
But a quaint small pup
    Is my whole intent,
And one brought up
    As an ornament,
Obedient whatever
    Be our demands—
A little dog, clever
    At shaking hands;

34

A dog with decorum, a calm-voiced dog
To slumber on a cushion by the warm gas log,
That won't tear curtains and won't chew chairs
Or decorate the sofa with his cast-off hairs.
Or disarrange the rugs in his antics hearty,
Or leap on a lady when she's ready for a party.
Say, a spaniel carefully from proud sires bred.
Let's have a dog,"
I think is what I said.

So we have a dog, have Oliver and I,
A roving Orphan Andy who just strayed by.
He's never quite certain
    Of our demands,
He chews the curtain
    And he won't shake hands.
He flees like most men
    From trumped-up dangers;
He barks at postmen
    And he fawns on strangers.
When motorists elude him, he takes it hard.
He loves to go exploring in the neighbor's yard.
He leaps on a lady with enthusiastic paws,
And he fancies Oliver is Santa Claus.
For poise and decorum he doesn't care a fig,
And he's not very little and he's not very big
And he isn't so brave as Hercules or Daniel
And he's not a Doberman and not a spaniel,
And we aren't quite sure about *what* he is.
But our sofa and our house and our hearts are his.
And we wouldn't give him up
For anybody's pup.

TACT IN ENTERTAINING

FRANKLIN P. ADAMS

IN LITERALNESS, as those who have made a study of me know, I am a Casabianca under whose charred remains a dozen decks might burn. I am like George Ade's Ernest, who had been Kicked in the Head by a Mule when Young and Believed Everything he Read in the Sunday Papers. I believe what I read in the dailies, too.

"The ancient theory," wrote Julia Hoyt in the *Evening World*, "that if a guest upsets a cup of coffee or a glass of wine on the tablecloth the perfect hostess will follow suit is, of course, slightly extravagant and such a procedure is decidedly unnecessary. But the idea in back of it is an admirable one—that at all costs the guest must be placed at ease. So, if the pie is burnt or the meat cooked to a crisp, do not force your guests into the false position of extolling the ruined food, but make a joke of it yourself or do not notice it at all."

The day I read Mrs. Hoyt's evening article—Julia's Night Piece, one might call it—we had, by rare good fortune, dinner guests.

They arrived ten minutes late. "Sorry," said Selina, for that was not her name, "to be late." I could see she actually was sorry, so I knew the hostly thing to do was to fall in with her mood.

"You ought to be sorry," I said. "There isn't any excuse for it. You knew you were to be here at seven-thirty, and you probably haven't had a thing to do since three. Besides—"

At this point my wife, a hostess in herself, suggested that maybe somebody would like a cocktail. "I don't care one way or another," said Freddie.

Well, I could sense that he really didn't want anything, so I decided to put him at his ease. "Let's not have any," I said. "Our stock is way down." So we went into the dining-room. First we had some fruit. I noticed that there were no soup spoons at our places. I thought our guests observed it, too, and that a wave of chagrin and disappointment passed over them. "Hell," said I to my wife, kindly, "why couldn't we have had soup instead of this junk?" "Or both?" suggested Freddie. "Do you think we are made of money?" I asked him, smoothing things over.

Next we had veal and lima beans. I don't like them, and I was sure our guests didn't, either. "Why don't you have this some night when I'm not home?" I asked. "I do," said my wife, ever so gently; but I knew what she meant.

The talk then went to less worldly matters. "Do you think the Army will beat the Navy?" asked Freddie. "They might," I said, "and they might not. At any rate, I shall enjoy seeing Service Men in Annual Grid Tilt as Thousands Cheer."

Next came the salad. It was too vinegary. Selina made a face. "Put her at her ease," I said to myself. With me, as my admirers know, to think is to act. "Ain't the salad dressing something terrible?" I said, merrily. "Some people like it that way," said Selina. "Name me one," I said. I had her there. "You would think," I went on, "that after all these years we could get salad dressing the way we wanted it. But it's always too sour." That isn't true, for we often have the dressing just right, but my first duty, I said to myself, was to make the guests feel comfortable.

The dessert was all right. I never tasted better prune whip in my life. I tasted it. "Oh," I said, "prune whip again." And there I did the most tactful thing of the whole evening. That's all I said about it, and the guests—it takes all kinds to make a world of thought—appeared to like it.

"Coffee?" asked my wife. I rushed in there. "Not for me," I said. "It keeps me awake." "Then we certainly won't have any," said Freddie, who, of course, didn't want any anyway.

"Shall we go into one of the other eight rooms?" I said. As Freddie and Selina have a three-room apartment, I thought it would make them feel pretty good to realize that they didn't have the trouble and expense of keeping up such a large establishment.

"It isn't worth while," said Selina. "We have tickets for the theatre, so we must be going." I knew they didn't have, and they were just going because they thought I wanted to read, and that they would be in the way.

"That's lucky," I said. "I haven't finished 'Young Felix' yet, and if I get right at it I can finish it by eleven. Goodnight."

And so passed a perfect evening. I never can thank Mrs. Hoyt adequately.

MY NEXT GIRL

MAX SHULMAN

My next girl is going to be honest. I don't care if she looks like a door-knob. Just so she's honest.

This determination arises from a late unhappy attachment to one Clothilde Ellingboe. Now, don't misunderstand; I'm not calling Clothilde a crook. Let's say she was irresponsible. Or unethical. Or unprincipled. Or amoral. Let's not go around calling ladies crooks. Watch that stuff.

I met Clothilde at the University of Minnesota's annual Freshman Prom. I was standing in the stag line and I saw her dancing with a fellow halfway across the floor. They were doing the Airborne Samba, the latest dance craze at the University. In the Airborne Samba the girl locks her hands behind the fellow's neck and he carries her all through the dance. She never touches the floor; she just lashes out rhythmically with her feet.

I cut in on them, laughing lightly at the resultant abrasions. I transported Clothilde through the rest of the medley, and then we went out on the terrace for some air. There, in a very short time, I knew I was hers. How vivacious she was! How socially aware she was! You would never believe she was only a freshman, the way she had been everywhere and had done everything and knew everyone. In a very short time I was, as I say, hers. Then began a social whirl that I would not have thought possible. We were out every night—dancing, movies, sleigh rides, hay rides, wiener roasts, bridge games, community sings. Not a night did we miss.

At first I was a little worried. "Clothilde," I would say, "I'd love to

39

go out tonight, but I've got homework. I've got to translate ten pages of Virgil for Latin tomorrow."

"Henry, you oaf," she would laugh, "don't you know *anything?*" Then she would produce a Virgil pony—a Latin textbook with English translations set in smaller type beneath each line of Latin.

When I'd say I had to do some work in political science, she would hand me a syllabus that condensed the whole course into an hour's easy reading. If I was concerned about an English-history quiz, she would come up with a card the size of a bookmark on which were printed the dates of all the kings in the British dynasty, plus thumbnail sketches of all significant events.

"This is all very well," I said one night, "but I don't feel that I'm learning anything."

"To the contrary, Henry," she replied, taking my hands in hers. "Without all this social life, you could never become a well-rounded-out personality. What's more important, Henry, to know a lot of old facts and figures or to become a well-rounded-out personality?"

"To become a well-rounded-out personality," I said. "Clearly."

"There you are," she said, spreading her palms. "C'mon, Henry, let's go down to the Kozy Kampus Kave and hear E-String Eddie and his T.N.T. Trio."

"Roger," I said. That's Air Force talk.

And so it went, night after night. I'll confess I was a stranger to the Phi Beta Kappa selection board, but nonetheless, my grades were adequate. I got by, and whatever happened in my classes, I had the comfort of knowing that I was becoming a well-rounded-out personality.

But occasionally a doubt would dart through my mind like a lizard across a rock. Then I would say to myself, "This can't go on forever." I found out I was right one morning, in my English class.

On that morning at the end of the class hour, our instructor, Mr. Hambrick, announced: "There will be a fifteen-hundred-word theme due Friday. Write about any subject you want to. No excuses will be accepted for late themes."

The heart within me sank. I had long been worried about Mr. Hambrick. Mr. Hambrick was one of those English instructors who had taken teaching jobs thirty years before so they could have an income while they worked on their novels. Now they were still teaching English and they were still on the first chapters of their novels. They vented their frustration on their students.

40

Up to this assignment I had managed to get along in Mr. Hambrick's class. Before this I had had to turn in three or four book reports, all of which Clothilde supplied from the *Book Review Digest*. But a theme was different. You can't go about clipping original themes from other sources.

"Clothilde," I said that evening, "I'm afraid the movies are out for tonight. I've got to turn in a theme for English on Friday, and here it is Tuesday, and I'd better get to work."

"But, Henry," wailed Clothilde, "it's Van Johnson. He knocks me out. Doesn't he knock you out?"

"No," I said truthfully. "Listen, Clothilde, I'd better do this theme. This isn't the kind of thing I can chisel **on.**"

"How long does it have to be?"

"Fifteen hundred words."

"What's the topic?"

"Anything I want."

"Well, then, what's your hurry? It's only Tuesday. You've got Wednesday and Thursday to work on it."

"No, I'd better start it right away. I don't know whether I can finish it all in one night. Don't forget, Clothilde, I'm not very bright."

"Yes, I know," she said, "but even you should be able to do a fifteen-hundred-word theme in one night. Especially if you can pick your own subject."

"Look, Clothilde, I don't want to seem stubborn, but I've made up my mind. I'm going to start that theme tonight, and that's final."

"Lana Turner is in the picture, too."

"Let's hurry so we can get good seats," I said.

The next night, Wednesday, I was positively going to work on the theme. *Positively*. But Benny Goodman was playing a one-night stand at the Auditorium, and, as Clothilde said: "You can't just not go to hear Benny Goodman. How will you explain it to people?"

And Thursday afternoon there was a Sunlite Dance in the Union with a jitterbug contest, for which Clothilde and I had been rehearsing for weeks. Unfortunately, Clothilde threw a shoe and pulled up lame at the end of the second lap and we had to drop out.

Not until six o'clock Thursday evening did I get to the theme. I set two fountain pens, a bottle of ink, an eraser, three pencils, a dictionary, a thesaurus, and a ream of fresh white paper on my desk. I adjusted the gooseneck lamp for minimum eyestrain. I pulled up a straightback

41

chair. I opened the window. I filled a pitcher with water. I took my phone off the hook. Then I sat down and drew isosceles triangles for two hours.

Not an idea came to me. Not a fragment of an idea. Not a teensy-weensy glimmer of an idea. I had just about decided to drop out of the University and enroll in a manual-training school when I heard Clothilde calling me outside my window. I stuck my head out.

"How ya doin', Henry?" she asked.

I grimaced.

"I thought so," she said. "Well, don't worry. I've got it all figured out. Look." She held up two white cards.

"What's that?" I asked.

"Stack permits," she replied.

"What?"

"Come on out and I'll explain the whole thing."

"Listen, Clothilde, I don't know what you're up to, but I don't want any part of it. I'm going to sit here all night if I have to, but I'm going to finish that theme. I don't care what you say; there's no other way to do it."

"Come on out, you jerk. I've never failed you yet, have I? Listen, you'll not only have your theme written tonight, but we'll be able to catch the last feature at the Bijou."

"No."

"You don't really believe you're going to get that theme written, do you?"

She had me there.

"Come on out."

"What's a stack permit?" I asked.

"Come on out."

I came out.

She took my arm. "We'd better hurry, Henry. It's after eight o'clock and the library closes at nine."

"What's that got to do with anything?"

She was pulling me along, toward the library. "Henry, you've been to the library, haven't you?"

"I used to go occasionally," I said, "before I met you."

"All right. You know how the library works?"

"Sure," I said. "You go in and look up the book you want in the card catalogue and then you write your name and the card number of

42

the book on a request slip and you give the slip to the librarian and she sends a pageboy after your book."

"Ah," said Clothilde, "but do you know where the books come from?"

"They keep them on shelves in the back of the library."

"Stacks," said Clothilde. "Those are called stacks."

"So?"

"Ordinarily," Clothilde continued, "they don't let students go back in the stacks. They're afraid we might get the books mixed up or steal them or something."

"This is all very informative, Clothilde, but I wish you had picked another time to tell it to me. I've got a theme to write."

Clothilde's big blue eyes narrowed craftily into little blue eyes. "Some students, Henry, *are* allowed to go back in the stacks. Some graduate students and a few seniors get stack permits. These—" she waved the two white cards—"are permits."

"I still don't see—"

"I borrowed them," said Clothilde, "from a couple of graduate students I know. One is doing a Ph.D thesis on the calcium content of beeswax and the other on forerunners to the hydraulic jack. With these cards we can get into the stacks."

"But how is all this going to get my theme written?"

"Henry Ladd, you dope. I swear if you didn't have freckles and a crew haircut, I'd quit going with you in a minute. Don't you understand? We're going to find some old books of essays that nobody has ever heard of, and you'll copy one of the essays, and that will be your theme."

I stopped dead. "Clothilde," I whispered, "you can't mean it."

"Why not? It's foolproof. There won't be any record of your ever having seen the book. You won't turn in a request slip for it. We're going into the stacks on somebody else's permit, so you can't be checked that way. You're not going to take the book out, so there won't be a withdrawal record on your library card. I've got pencil and paper in my purse. You'll copy the essay while you're in the stacks. Then you'll put the book back exactly where you found it. Then we'll leave and nobody will ever be the wiser."

I sat down beside a tree in front of the library and pulled her down beside me. "Clothilde," I said, "why don't we just get a couple of revolvers and go hold up a filling station?"

Her ruby-red lips drew tight against her pearly teeth. "Henry," she said coldly, "I won't be talked to that way."

"For heaven's sake, Clothilde," I cried, "this is the most dishonest thing I ever heard of. What's the difference between this and highway robbery? There might be some justification for all the other stuff I've been doing in Latin and political science and history—although I fail to see it at the moment—but this is plain larceny."

"Henry, are you calling me a crook?"

"Perish the thought, Clothilde. It's just that I think you're making a little mistake. Anyway," I protested, "it's not safe. How can we be sure that Mr. Hambrick, my English instructor, hasn't read the book that I'm going to copy the essay out of?"

Clothilde smiled. "I was hoping you'd ask that question. Come along, I'll show you."

She dragged me into the library, up the stairs, and to the main desk. "Stop perspiring, Henry," she whispered. "We don't want anybody to remember us." She showed the two stack permits to the librarian. The librarian nodded us back into the stacks.

The stacks filled me with awe. They consisted of metal bookshelves arranged in banks. Each bank was seven tiers high, and each tier was six feet tall. At the head of each bank was a metal spiral staircase, wide enough for only one person. Narrow catwalks ran along each tier, and the various banks were joined by other catwalks. The whole thing, I thought, looked like the cell blocks you see in prison movies. I shuddered at the significance of the comparison.

"Come along," said Clothilde. "The essay collections are in the seventh tier of the fourth bank. Hurry. We haven't much time. The library closes at nine."

We raced along the catwalks. Our footsteps echoed metallically, and I expected to hear sirens and see spotlights at any moment. I felt like James Cagney in *Each Dawn I Die*.

When we got to the essay shelves, Clothilde said: "Now, quickly, look for a book with a lot of dust on it. Don't take any clean ones."

We looked for a few seconds, and I found a volume gray with dust. I pulled it off the shelf. "This all right, Clothilde?"

She took it. She opened the book and looked at the record card in the envelope pasted inside the cover—the card that the library files when you take out a book. "This one is no good," said Clothilde. "The card shows that this book was last taken out in 1942. It's not very

44

likely, but there's just a chance that your English instructor was the one who took it out. That was only four years ago, and he might still remember the essays. We don't have to take chances; we can find a book that hasn't been taken out for at least ten years. Then, even if your instructor was the one who checked out the book, there's not much chance that he'll remember it."

"You thought any about becoming a gun moll?" I asked.

"Hurry, Henry, it's half past eight."

We found a couple more dusty volumes, but their cards showed that they had been out of the library within the past ten years. At twenty minutes to nine, we found the right one.

"This is perfect," said Clothilde, holding up the book, a slim collection called *Thoughts of My Tranquil Hours* by one Elmo Goodhue Pipgrass. Mr. Pipgrass' picture appeared as the frontispiece—a venerable gentleman with side whiskers and a white string tie. The record card was almost lily white. The book had been taken out only once, and that was in 1926—twenty years before.

"This is perfect," Clothilde repeated. "It was published—" she looked at the title page—"in 1919. The picture of Pipgrass shows that he was a man of at least seventy at that time. He's certainly dead now, so you don't even have to worry about plagiarism."

"Plagiarism!" I exclaimed. "You didn't say anything about that before."

"No use to alarm you, Henry," she said. "Hurry up, now. Here's pencil and paper."

"Plagiarism," I muttered.

"Hurry, Henry. For Pete's sake, hurry."

With the greatest reluctance, I took pencil and paper and began to

45

copy the first essay in *Thoughts of My Tranquil Hours*. The first essay started like this:

"Who has not sat in the arbor of his country seat, his limbs composed, a basin of cheery russet apples at his side, his meerschaum filled with good shag; and listened to the wholesome bucolic sounds around him; the twitter of chimney swifts, the sweet piping of children at their games, the hale cries of the countryman to his oxen, the comfortable cackling of chickens, the braying of honest asses; and felt his nostrils deliciously assailed with aromas from the kitchen: the nourishing saddles of beef, the beneficent gruels, the succulent tarts; and basked in the warmth of sun and earth, full bounty of abundant nature; and thought, 'Of what moment is man's travail for gain, his mad impetus toward wealth, his great unsettled yearning for he knows not what, when all about him if he would but perceive are the treasures of the globe, more precious far than any jewel which lies deep beneath virgin earth across unplumbed and perilous seas?' "

That was the first sentence, and the shortest one. I scribbled furiously until I had the whole thing down, and we left. We got out of the library at five seconds before nine.

Outside, I turned on Clothilde. "Why did I ever listen to you?" I cried. "Not only do I run the risk of getting kicked out of school in disgrace, but I've got to worry about getting arrested for plagiarism, too. And to top it all off, the essay stinks. He'll probably flunk me on it anyway."

"Could you have done better?" she asked.

"That's not the point."

"Oh, Henry, you're hopeless," she said. "Sometimes I think your personality will never get rounded out. Come on, we'll miss the last show at the Bijou."

I didn't enjoy the show one bit. I enjoyed even less handing in my theme Friday morning. As I laid the sheets on Mr. Hambrick's desk, visions of policemen and hanging judges and prison gates sped through my head. My forehead was a Niagara of perspiration.

"You feel all right, Mr. Ladd?" asked Mr. Hambrick.

"Yes, sir," I said. "I feel fine, thank you."

"I was just asking," he said. "I don't really care."

The gaiety of the weekend failed to cheer me up. Dressed as a buccaneer on Saturday night, I swashbuckled listlessly through a masquerade party, and on Sunday I sat like a lump all through a hay ride, never once joining in the four hundred verses of *Sweet Violets*.

In my English class Monday morning I was resigned. I was prepared for the worst. I wasn't even surprised when Mr. Hambrick told me to stay behind at the end of the class. "Never mind the handcuffs," I thought. "I'll go quietly."

"I want to talk to you about the theme you turned in Friday, Mr. Ladd," said Mr. Hambrick when we were alone in the room.

"Yes, sir," I said, my voice hitting high C above middle E.

"Frankly," he continued, "I was amazed at that theme. Until Friday, Mr. Ladd, I had merely thought of you as dull."

"Yes, sir."

"But now I know I was wrong. The trouble with you is that you're archaic."

"Huh?"

"You're archaic. You're way behind the times. You were born one century too late. And," he added, "so was I. I tell you, Mr. Ladd, I have no regard for modern writing. It all seems like gibberish to me— all that clipped prose, that breakneck pacing, that lean objectivity. I don't like it. I think writing should be leisurely and rich. Sentences should be long and graceful, filled with meaning and sensitive perception. Your theme, Mr. Ladd, is a perfect example of the kind of writing I most admire."

"Call me Henry," I said genially.

"I'm going to give you an 'A' on that theme, and I hope in the future you will write some more like it."

"You bet," I said. "I know just where to get them."

"And if you're ever free on a Sunday afternoon, I'd be pleased if you'd stop at my place for a cup of tea. I'd like to talk to you about a novel I've been toying with. It's a great deal like your stuff."

"Sure, sir. Now, if you'll give me my theme, I've got to get on to my next class."

"Ah," he smiled, his neutral-colored eyes twinkling behind tortoise-shell glasses, "I'm afraid I can't do that. I've got a little surprise for you, Mr. Ladd. I've entered your theme in the Minnesota Colleges Essay Contest."

I just made it to a chair. "Again," I rasped. "Say that again."

"I've entered your theme in the Minnesota Colleges Essay Contest," he repeated. "It's a competition sponsored once a year by the State Board of Education for all the colleges in Minnesota. The contest is judged by the four members of the Board of Education, and the winner gets a free cruise on the Great Lakes."

"Please!" I screamed. "I don't want to be in any contest. I don't want to win a Great Lakes' cruise. I get seasick."

"Come, come, Mr. Ladd. You mustn't be so modest. Let me give you a bit of advice, my boy. I was just like you. I hid my light beneath a bushel, too. Now look at me—teaching English to a bunch of little morons. No, Mr. Ladd, you've got to assert yourself, and I'm going to see that you do."

"Please, Mr. Hambrick," I begged tearfully.

"It's too late, anyhow. After I read your theme last Friday, I put it in the mail immediately. It's already in the hands of the Board of Education. The results of the contest will be announced Thursday. Well, good-bye, Mr. Ladd. I must rush to my next class."

I sat there alone in that classroom for two hours. Just twitching. I couldn't even think. Then, skulking behind trees, I walked to my room, crawled into bed, and moaned until sundown.

In the evening I found Clothilde and, with a great deal of bitterness, told her the whole story.

"That's not good," said Clothilde. Sharp, that girl.

"I wish," I said honestly, "that I had never set eyes on you."

"Don't be vile, Henry. Let's figure something out."

"How *do* you figure all your things out?" I asked.

"Oh, I just stretch out on my chaise, in the raw, and I read a magazine. I figure out *everything* that way."

"Well," I said, "don't do any more figuring for me. I'm through listening to you. Tomorrow I'm going to Mr. Hambrick and confess everything. There's nothing else to be done, no matter what *you* say."

"Henry, that's the silliest thing I ever heard. Really, I don't see what you have to worry about. If Mr. Hambrick, a professional English instructor, didn't suspect anything, what makes you think that the members of the State Board of Education are going to get wise?"

"Now you listen to me, Clothilde. Every minute I delay my confession just makes it worse for me. It stands to reason that at least one of those Board of Education members has read Elmo Goodhue Pipgrass' *Thoughts of My Tranquil Hours*."

"Fat chance," sneered Clothilde.

"No, Clothilde. I won't do it. I know I'm going to get caught, and I might just as well get it over with."

48

"Honestly, I've never met such a yuck. You'll never get caught, you poor goof. They'll read the theme and reject it, and the whole business will be over with. The things you find to worry about."

"What if I win the contest?"

"With that corn?" she asked. "Ha. Honestly, Henry."

Then she started with that routine about a well-rounded-out personality. But I was firm as a rock. It took her more than twenty minutes to talk me into it.

For the next few days I was numb with fear. Then came Tuesday, and Mr. Hambrick said to me: "Good news, Mr. Ladd. Your essay has advanced into the quarter-finals."

I nodded mutely.

Wednesday Mr. Hambrick said to me: "Great news, Mr. Ladd. Your essay is now in the semifinals."

I tried to confess everything to him then, but all that came out of my throat was hoarse croaks.

And Thursday the walls came tumbling down.

"Mr. Ladd," said Mr. Hambrick, "something very curious has happened. Your essay won out in the semifinals and was entered in the finals. Your competition in the finals was an essay by a young man named Walter Bradbury from Macalester College. Mr. Bradbury's essay is a description of iron mining in northern Minnesota. Now, it happens that of the four members of the Board of Education, two are from the Iron Range district. Those two insist on awarding the prize to Mr. Bradbury. But the other two members want to give you the prize. Neither side will yield."

"I'll withdraw," I said hastily.

"That's noble of you," said Mr. Hambrick, "but it won't be necessary. The Board of Education has agreed to call in an impartial judge to pick the winner. You and Mr. Bradbury are to go to the Board of Education office in the state capital this afternoon for the final judging. I've arranged transportation for you."

"Mr. Hambrick," I pleaded desperately, "let them give the prize to Bradbury. The sea air will do him good."

"Nonsense," laughed Mr. Hambrick. "You're sure to win. I know the judge they picked is going to favor you. He's a distinguished essayist himself, who used to write much as you do. He's been in retirement for many years at a cottage near Lake Minnetonka. He's very old. Possibly you may have heard of him. His name is Elmo

Goodhue Pipgrass."

Click. I heard a distinct click in my head. Then a terrifying calm came over me. I felt drained of emotion, no longer capable of fear or worry. I felt as a man must feel who is finally strapped into the electric chair.

"There will be a car in front of the Administration Building in thirty minutes to take you to the state capital," said Mr. Hambrick.

"Yes, sir," I said. My voice seemed to be coming from far away.

"Good luck—Henry."

I found Clothilde and told her everything—told it to her evenly, cooly, without rancor.

"I'm going to the state capital with you," she said. "I'll think of something."

I patted her shoulder. "Thank you, Clothilde, but no. It will be better if we break clean—now. I don't want you to be known as the consort of a criminal. Your whole life is ahead of you, Clothilde. I don't want to be a burden to you. Try to forget me, Clothilde, if you can. Find somebody new."

"You're awfully sweet, Henry."

"And so are you, Clothilde, in an oblique way."

"Then this—this is it, Henry?"

"Yes, Clothilde. This," I said, the little muscles in my jaw rippling, "is it."

"What are you going to do with those two tickets to Tommy Dorsey tonight?"

"They're yours, Clothilde." I handed them to her and added with a wry smile, "I won't be needing them."

We shook hands silently, and I went off to the Administration Building and got into the car and was driven to the state capital.

I went into the Board of Education office and was directed to the conference room. This room contained a long mahogany table with five empty chairs behind it. There were two chairs in front of the table, and in one of them sat a young man wearing a sweater with "Macalester" emblazoned across the front.

"You must be Walter Bradbury," I said. "I'm Henry Ladd."

"Hi," he said. "Sit down. They'll be here in a minute."

I sat down. We heard footsteps in the hall.

"Here they come," said Bradbury. "Good luck, Henry."

"Oh, no, no, no," I cried. "Good luck to you. I want you to win.

50

With all my heart I do. Nothing would make me happier."

They came in, and the pit of my stomach was a roaring vastness. The four members of the Board of Education were dressed alike in dark business suits and looked alike—all plumpish, all bespectacled, all balding. With them, carrying a gnarled walking stick, was Elmo Goodhue Pipgrass, the littlest, oldest man I had ever seen. His side whiskers were white and wispy, the top of his head egg-bald. His eyes looked like a pair of bright shoe buttons. He wore a high collar with a white string tie, a vest with white piping, and congress gaiters. He was ninety-five if he was a day.

One of the Board members took Pipgrass' arm to assist him. "Take your big fat hand off my arm," roared Pipgrass. "Think I'm a baby? Chopped half a cord of wood this morning, which is more than you ever chopped in your whole life. Weaklings. The government is full of weaklings. No wonder the country's gone to rack and ruin. Where are the boys?"

"Right over here, Mr. Pipgrass," said a Board member, pointing at Bradbury and me. "See them?"

"Of course I see them. Think I'm blind? Impudence from public servants. What's the world come to? Howdy, boys." He nodded vigorously at a hall tree. "Sit down."

"They are sitting down, Mr. Pipgrass," said a Board member. "Over here."

"Whippersnapper," muttered Pipgrass. "I remember when they built this capitol. Used to come and watch 'em every day. If I'd known they were going to fill it with whippersnappers, I'd have dynamited it."

"Mr. Pipgrass," said a member gently, "let's get to the essays. The boys have to get back to school."

"Essays? What you talking about? I haven't written an essay since 1919."

Suddenly hope was reborn within me. The man was senile. Maybe I'd get away with it. Maybe. . . .

"The boys' essays, Mr. Pipgrass. You're to pick the best one, remember?"

"Certainly, I remember. Think I'm an idiot? Who's Bradbury?"

"I, sir," said Bradbury.

"Ah. You're the fool who wrote an essay on iron mining. Iron mining! Why didn't you write one on plumbing? Or garbage disposal?"

51

I felt a sinking sensation.

"Or roofing?" continued Pipgrass. "Or piano tuning? Iron mining! What kind of subject is that for an essay? And furthermore you split four infinitives. Great Jehoshaphat, boy, where'd you ever get the idea you could write?"

Bradbury and I trembled, each for his own reason.

"Ladd," said Pipgrass. "Ladd, you pompous, mealy-mouthed little hack. Who told you that you were a writer?" He picked up my essay, held it a half-inch before his face, and read, " 'Who has not sat in the arbor of his country seat.' " He threw down the essay. "I'll tell you who has not sat in the arbor of his country seat. You haven't. Bradbury hasn't. All of these four fat fellows haven't. Who the devil has got a country seat? What the devil *is* a country seat? Who talks about country seats these days? What kind of writer are you? Who said you were a writer? Can't anybody write in this confounded state?"

"It's a sorry choice," said Pipgrass, "that I have to make between these two wights. Neither of 'em can write worth a nickle. But if I must choose, give the prize to Bradbury."

A great weight rolled off my back. A film dropped from my eyes. I smiled a real smile.

Now they were all around Bradbury shaking his hand, but none so heartily as I. I waited until they all left the room, and then I got down on my knees and sent off six quick prayers. I mopped my forehead, my cheeks, my chin, my neck, my palms, and then I went into the hall.

Pipgrass was waiting for me. "You Ladd?" he asked.

I nodded, holding the doorjamb for support.

He took my arm. "I was tempted to give you the prize, boy. Mighty flattering to know that people are still reading *Thoughts of My Tranquil Hours* after all these years."

Then he was gone down the corridor, chuckling and running his walking stick across the radiators.

EXPERIENCE

DOROTHY PARKER

Some men break your heart in two,
Some men fawn and flatter,
Some men never look at you;
And that cleans up the matter.

CONSTABLE SAM AND THE
UGLY TYKE

ERIC KNIGHT

"Here we are at war," Sam said, "and here Ah am, trying to do ma bit, and what happens?"

"T'Germans tremble and ask for peace," Mully suggested.

"Sarcasm," Sam sniffed. "Let me tell thee, if it weren't for us Auxiliary Policemen, ye'd be murdered in your bed by spies, Ah don't doubt."

"Once Ah read a book about thutty-nine steps," Mully said, going on knitting the khaki sweater. "A reight champion story it were. And t'lad in that one—eigh, how he could cop spies."

"Books," Sam snorted. "Heh, there's no fiction to marching fifteen miles a neight ovver t'moor. Ah don't see why Ah ca'nt hevt' Spread Eagle beat and then . . ."

"Then they'd know right wheer to find thee. They want thee to patrol a beat—not drink it dry. Ah tell thee, yon young bobby's a bright lad. T'schoolmaster's t'only teetotaler in t'village, and he puts him on t'pub beat."

"It's a waste of opportunity," Sam said, pulling on his arm badge. "At least, they might let me hev headquarters duty. Ah can write reports as well as John Willie Braithwaite can."

"What's wrong wi' walking a beat like a man?" Mully asked.

"Oh, it's—er—it's lonesome—and besides, Ah got bunions and they hurt that cruel!"

"Bunions!" Mully snorted. "Tha's nivver had no bunions. Off wi' thee—tha'll be late."

"How can Ah goa? Wheer's ma tin hat?"

"Tha's a policeman, soa do a bit o' detective work and hunt for it," Mully suggested.

"No respect nor comfort a chap gets for serving his King and Country," Sam grumbled, taking the helmet down from behind the door where Mully put it neatly every morning when she tidied up.

He gave a bit of a polish to the helmet with his sleeve, put it on his head at what he hoped was a dare-devil angle, heaved a big sigh, and went out into the evening for his night's patrol.

Mully looked at the door over the top of her spectacles.

"Now what," she mused, "is bothering yon?"

It wasn't really the Spread Eagle beat that worried Sam. Nor was it any such things as bunions. Sam would have liked the headquarters trick, true—but merely because he wanted to be boss of any job he tackled and he felt his dignity was affronted. But his feet—why Sam was a tough old Yorkshireman who could walk fifteen miles before breakfast and never turn a hair.

What worried Sam, the keen-eyed old dog fancier of Polkingthorpe Brig, was nothing more or less than—a dog! And what a dog it was!

Undoubtedly all of you have seen such a dog in your lives. You know the kind. Someone buys it as a puppy because it's furry and cuddly and lovable—and six months later its ancestral past catches up with its present to ruin everyone's future. It generally looks something like an over-size polo pony wearing someone's caracul coat. Usually it has the brains of an idiot, the soul of a springbok, and the dexterity of a rhinoceros.

That's what this dog was like. At first Sam hadn't minded it. He knew the dog and forgave its existence. For it was owned by the old Widow Cathingham. She was Yorkshire only by marriage and so couldn't be expected to have that inborn omniscience on matters canine that true Tykes have. She always left it outside at nights in the fond belief that it was guarding her door. Instead, the great ugly tyke went lolloping foolishly round the whole Riding. And of late it had taken to following Sam on his night patrol.

Sam had shrugged the matter off at first. Although such a misshapen brute could inculcate no affection in the heart of a dog fancier, in his lonesomeness he had accepted it.

"It'll be a bit o' company, like, as Ah stroll along, happen," he said to himself.

But the dog had got on his nerves. Its horrible slip-sloppy way of walking, its ebullient over-friendliness, its refusal to leave him in peace—those things had all been enough. But finally Sam had become obsessed with one more feature. The dog destroyed his dignity.

How, I ask you, could a man walk along his beat with that tremendous dignity so necessary to service as a British constable—even an auxiliary one—with a great ape of an ugly dog pacing behind him, imitating him, mocking his every effort to go with stern, law-defending tread.

For it is hard enough for a little, aging man, not much more than five feet, to achieve the dignity compatible with the role of bobby. Sam had worked hard at it. Every once in a while he would pull in his tummy, turn his mustache up, set his jaw in a way that brooked no good for evil-doers, and say: "Remember, Sam! Tha's a constable now."

That was hard enough to do. But what on earth chance had a man when, in addition, there was a great, fool, lumbering dog slolloping along after him, keeping step with him, stopping when he stopped, going when he went, mocking his every movement?

Sam had become right put out about that dog.

Sam Small shut his eyes and shuddered. Through the darkness he could hear the dog coming. It was always at this time, and this place. He steeled himself, helplessly. In the murky light of a half-moon he waited, his eyes closed. Then the thing hit him. Sam had given up even defending himself.

The beast rose, planted its paws on his chest, sent him bowling over, and slobbered in hobbledehoy joy over his face.

Sam fought himself free, struggled to his feet, and aimed a kick at the thing. It retreated beyond range, sat down, and looked at him adoringly, with its huge tongue lolling out.

"One prick ear," Sam said, "and one over the starboard bow! A coat like a coconut doormat! A face like a lion! A gait like a kangaroo! One hand higher and tha's a hunter! Ten pounds heavier and they'd have thee hitched to a plow! Yer misgotten, ugly, nasty insult to all dogs—go home!"

The dog jumped up and there, in the moonlight, danced an eerie conga.

"Ooooh, ma gum," Sam moaned. "And it wants to play!"

He put his hand before his eyes to shut out the sight, and staggered away on the Wuxley patrol. But if he could shut it from sight, he could not from hearing. Behind him, on the hard path, he could hear the ghastly slip-sloppering of those shapeless paws. He plugged his fingers in his ears and ran. The dog ran after him.

Sam turned round and charged at the dog. The dog retreated hurriedly. Sam stopped. The dog stopped. Sam took up his patrol. The dog stalked behind him.

With hate in his eye Sam went on. At last he came to where the moor path joined the hard-topped Wuxley road. A gleam came in his eye. Stealthily he hunted along the edge of the road. The dog sat down, watching him. At last Sam found what he wanted—a fine, big rock. A sturdy rock. About the size of a cricket ball and the weight of a sledge hammer.

The dog moved politely away.

"Nice doggie, coom here," Sam said, advancing.

With a happy laugh in his eye, the dog moved just as far away.

"All reight, then. A long shot," Sam said.

He spat on the rock, twirled his arm and then . . .

From the shadow under a roadside oak tree came a voice.

"Mr. Small!"

Sam halted, his arm bent. A quick beam of light shot out. From under the tree came a uniformed figure, pushing a bicycle. It was Constable Hurst—a real constable—the young chap sent down from West Riding headquarters to supervise, train, encourage, and abet the wartime volunteers.

"Mr. Small. Auxiliary Constable Small," the young chap said, patiently, sadly. For he had experienced many things in his recent duty that gave him cause for weary bewilderment.

"Ah were jooost—just off to chuck this here rock," Sam said, as if this would free him from the charge of canicide he had contemplated.

"So I see," said Constable Hurst, sadly. He clicked his tongue. "Throwing stones for a dog to chase! Playing games while on patrol. Mr. Small, a constable—even an auxiliary constable—doesn't play games with a dog while he's on duty. Because when he's on duty, Mr. Small—he's ON DUTY!"

This last was given in a military shout—in a manner that told Sam Small that Constable Hurst was standing for no monkey business.

"Aye," said Sam.

Without another word he strode off on his beat.

And still, from behind him, came the flip-floppering of the paws of that horrible tyke.

It was the duty of the man on the Wuxley patrol to inspect the old Wuxley quarry. Why, no one was quite sure. You just sort of—well, inspected it.

So Sam was strictly in the line of duty when he crouched in the lee of a tumble-down hut deep in the quarry. But what he was doing—that wasn't exactly duty.

"Nice doggie," he was saying—and nearer and nearer came the horrible, but affectionate, dog. Sam patted its head, deceitfully, lovingly. He scratched behind its ears until it almost crooned in ecstasy. He whispered loving words to it as he tickled its back. And then, over its head he slipped a noose of old, one-inch rope. And the other end of the rope was fastened to a steel rod. The steel rod was set in a concrete base for some departed and forgotten piece of quarry machinery.

Sam jumped up, contemplating the scene with happiness.

"Now, ye ugly, joogling, bluggy blooger," he said. "Tow that after thee. Ta-ta!"

And with a heart carefree for the first time in many nights, Sam went on his way. Steadily, majestically, he swung along with his feet going in the stately rhythm which for ages has told the good British burghers

that all was well and the watchful police were afoot in the night.

He chuckled to himself happily, and set his mind to the duties that lay before him.

"Now," he said. "Swing round the Wuxley football field, trying all doors o' t' clubhouse to see they're locked. Then heading home along the Allerby road, trying the gate at Colonel Polliwell's villa. Thence..."

And there he stopped. A shudder ran through him. It could not be true. And yet it was! Behind him was the sound of paws. They were falling in rhythm to his own feet. It was the dog. It was behind him. It was parading in mocking imitation of him!

Sam, without losing pace, looked slowly behind him. There was the dog, going in a beautiful burlesque of his own imitation of a policeman's stride. Its huge maw was lolling open in what was undoubtedly a derisive grin. Behind it it was towing two yards of stout hemp rope.

"Oooh," Sam moaned in agony. "Why do all these things have to happen to me? Ah give up! Lord knows Ah've tried and tried!"

Miserable, resigned to his fate, he bowed his head and started down the dark road to the Wuxley football field.

At the gate to Colonel Polliwell's villa Sam halted, alert.

Something, his senses told him, was wrong. As he phrased it in his own mind—summat foony was up!

He looked again at the padlocked chain on the colonel's iron gate. Surely it was fastened. And all else was well. The doors of the football clubhouse had all been locked. He hadn't forgotten anything.

Sam started on his way again. But his mind wouldn't be quieted. There was something. . . .

"T'ugly tyke!" he said, suddenly.

That was it. The dog was no longer following him. From behind came no slip-sloppering of paws. He was free, alone, at peace.

He almost capered for joy, but then he halted again. And his mind refused to soar, untrammeled. For Sam Small, above all else, was a dog man. He knew dogs. He had raised them, trained them, coped them. He knew dogs from the inside out, and this knowledge was gnawing away at his content.

"Eigh, now," he counseled himself. "It's left thee, so be happy for unexpected blessings and go on thy way."

But he shook his head.

"That isn't good enough," another voice seemed to say in the back of his head. "You couldn't get rid of that dog for love nor money. But now it's gone. Why? Why isn't it following you any more?"

"That's it!" Sam said aloud. "Why?"

"Don't worry why. Just be thankful," another part of him advised.

"It ain't good enough," Sam answered himself aloud. "Why has that dog left thee? It wouldn't leave thee for nowt—there must be summat interesting . . ."

But he had passed no one. No one was abroad at that night hour. There had been no sounds of anyone moving in the night. And yet . . .

"Steady, Sam lad," Sam advised himself. "Now what tha has to do is just go back over thy trail until tha comes to where t'dog is. And, since this is police wark, tha might as well go quietlike."

Silently, he stole back along his own tracks. As he came to the football field, instead of going in the main gate he tiptoed to a gap in the fence, and then went quietly over the turf toward the rear of the clubhouse. And then, his heart leaped. For there, sitting in the murk, looking up at the back door, his tail sweeping over an already well-swept arc, was the ugly tyke.

"So, there's somebody in there, and he wants 'em to come out and play," he thought. "Get ready, Sam!"

He pulled his chinstrap all the way under his chin, and then pulled from under his clothing a ten-inch length of lead pipe. Sam had never let anyone know about that lead pipe—not even Mully. It was a secret all his own, a secret between him and his dream that some night there might come a glorious moment when he, Sam Small, did battle with some burly evil-doer—and won.

He spat on his right hand and gripped the pipe. He tiptoed forward. With his left hand he reached down and tickled the ugly tyke between the ears. The animal gave a fatuous sound of contentment. Sam looked around for another hand to try the door. He solved it by putting the pipe between his teeth. With his right hand he tried the door. It was quite firm.

Sam pondered on this problem. Then he nodded his head. He had no knowledge of the ways of criminals beyond that gained in occasional and somewhat despairing lectures given to the handful of village men by Constable Hurst. And from one of these drifted back words he had not thought he remembered at the time:

"The ordinary burglar effects entrance by a rear door, then sets wedges under that door, and makes his exit later by another route—

usually the front door, leaving casually as if he were an ordinary resident in the place."

"All right. The front door, then," Sam said. "He'll not have that one wedged. So we'll crash in, rush him, and take him by surprise. Aye—that's the ticket!"

Quietly he tiptoed around to the front of the clubhouse.

He went up the steps, hunched his shoulders, drew a breath, and charged. Sam got his first surprise. Even while in the air, he half saw the doorknob turn, half glimpsed a man opening the door. Then he caromed off the loose door, went through space and landed in a heap on the floor. His tin hat went bumping away in the darkness. He sat up, with his teeth aching so badly that he could taste a brassy sort of taste in his mouth. But he was not deterred.

"So there is a burglar," he told himself. "And he was just trying to leave by the front. Probably he heard thee at the back. So up and after him."

He could still hear, like a memory of a thing gone by, the scurry of feet down the hall.

"Come, come, Sam lad," he said.

He got up and started down the hall in pursuit—or that was what he meant to do. Unfortunately, he happened to tread on his own tin hat, and so went into his second one-point landing.

"Nasty, slippery things, tin 'ats," Sam said.

He was sitting up, fingering a great, dull area on the point of his chin. He could feel it swelling like a balloon, even in the short space of time that had passed since he landed on it.

62

"Aye, Sam," he said, sadly, "tha doesn't seem to be going about this the right way. Now don't be so bloomin' impetuous, ma lad."

He groped around for his helmet—but it was gone again. He got up.

"Now, go easy and don't tread on it no more. Tha's certainly spoiled any chance o' taking him by surprise. So tha'll have to use tactics—aye, that's it. Tactics. He's down the hall somewhere, and probably playing bobbies and thieves wi' thee. So go get him. But tha'd better go quiet-like."

Sam sat down and unlaced his boots. He set them side by side, neatly, in the middle of the floor. He stole, silently, in his stockinged feet, down the corridor. Halfway down he stopped. The office door at the right, his groping hands told him, was locked. The one at the left swung ajar.

That was it. He'd heard no door slam after the feet scurried away. The man was hiding in this office!

He listened. There came the faintest, minute sounds—and there was a curious, faint, warm smell in the air. The man was in there!

And at that point, for the first time, Sam Small felt the very human emotion of fear. There was a man in there—a criminal—one who might kill him if cornered. And here was he, aging Sam Small, with not even the activity and strength of middle age left to him, to pit against it.

"Ooooh, I wish I'd turned down this job before I started it," he moaned to himself.

But even as this passed through his mind, and the perspiration of panic rolled down his forehead, his brain began reciting words—words that one could almost hear again—spoken in the crisp, young voice of the bobby chap:

"Remember, that when a British constable has nothing else left, he

63

always has the important weapon of authority. That is why we carry no firearms. For this weapon of authority, if used with promptness, confidence, and boldness, will overcome superior numbers and often cow the most dangerous criminal type."

Sam steeled himself.

"Ba gum," he said, silently. "I hope tha's right, lad. Because there's liable to be an awful bloomin' splash if tha's been kidding us. But here goes!"

And, trembling and afraid in every fiber of his body, Sam gripped his lead pipe, reached around the door, found the electric switch, snapped it on, and stepped into the room.

"All right. I've got yer," he said.

Then he stood in surprise. For there wasn't one man. There were two. One was seated, quietly, behind a desk. The other stood, his shoulders hunched, in the corner, staring toward the door.

"Ooooh, ma gum," Sam groaned mentally. "Two of 'em."

But he took another step into the room, planted his feet apart as though barring any escape, put his thumbs in his belt and smiled on them, pityingly.

"Now," he said, sternly. "Will ye come quietly—or shall I come and take yer? And—remember. Anything ye say may be used in evidence against yer."

The last part he had read in detective stories, and it sounded very policemanlike, he thought.

Then, as he waited, with the men unmoving, Sam began to perspire, and he forgot about the weapon of authority. For, somehow, he saw himself as the two men must see him—a little fattening man, past middle age, standing there in his stockinged feet, his blue serge suit crumpled and covered with dust, his helmet gone, his chin bleeding and swollen from his tumble.

He wished he knew what to do next.

"Oooh, ba gum," he thought. "Mully was right. I shouldn't have gone sticking myself forward to help out the bobbies. I wonder if I can just walk out and pretend I never saw them. They'll run away—sort of a mutual armistice, in a manner o' speaking."

But, as he thought this, and the bigger man in the corner bent forward and took a step forward, Sam, much to even his own surprise, spread his arms to barricade the door and clenched the lead pipe.

"Ah, no, ye don't," he snarled. "No, ye don't."

64

At that moment the man behind the desk waved his companion back, and spoke, pleasantly. "Why, good evening," he said, in a pleasant voice. "What can we do for you?"

"For me?" Sam said. "Well—I'm an auxiliary constable. Look!"

Almost indignantly he held up his arm for the man to see the brassard.

"Why, so you are," the man said. His voice was calm and with what Sam would have called a very swanky accent.

"But just what, exactly, can we do for you, my good man?"

"Well, look here," Sam said. "I thought ye were burglars."

The man smiled, forgivingly. "Now, constable," he said, "do we look like burglars?"

Sam examined them. They certainly did not look like burglars. Both were dressed in expensive tweeds. They wore colored ties—what the toffs called regimental ties. The big chap by the corner had a smart Tattersall waistcoat. Sam had never seen two more British-gentlemen-looking chaps. The week-end, country type.

"No, sir," he said, respectfully. "Ye don't. But what are ye doing here?"

The man smiled. "We're friends of Mr. Black," he said. "You know Mr. Black, don't you—the vice-president of the club?"

"Oh, aye," Sam said. "Of course." He didn't know any Mr. Black, but then he didn't want to appear too ignorant, either.

"Well, he gave us permission to sit here—we're doing a little business—going over records and so on."

Sam scratched his head. "That's all right then, sir. But still and all, I don't know exactly what I ought to do. I'm afraid I'll have to ask you to come along with me and explain to the bloody bo—to headquarters."

"Why, we'd be delighted," the man said.

He rose, brushing his short, guardee mustache. Sam saw a quick glance he gave toward his companion. And then his heart sank.

These two gentlemen—suppose, now, they were up to any nasty business—get him outside in the dark, cosh him on the blooming head, and get away.

He looked around wildly, as if seeking help. Then his eye lit on a neat suitcase on the table beside the wall. It was standing, open-hinged. But it wasn't a suitcase. Inside there was a panel, and dials. That was what he had smelled—the warm, curious odor. A wireless set!

He stepped back and gripped the lead pipe. "Hold on," he said. "A wireless. What yer doing with that there?"

The man leaned back against the desk and laughed. He turned to his companion. "You see, Derek, old chap," he said, "there's no eluding the eye of our ever alert volunteer constables."

He turned back to Sam: "Good for you, my man. I suppose I'll have to tell you the truth. Do you ever play the football pools?"

"Ah, who doesn't?" Sam said, guardedly.

"And I suppose you know that they're swindles—cleverly rigged-up schemes to sweat the hard-earned money from the working classes—oh, a few small prizes once in a while—but do you think those people really exist that they say win immense fortunes?"

"Well," Sam agreed, nervously, "I often did think there might be some fishy business in it——"

"It's crooked, I tell you. Now me and my partner, Mr. Derek Forsythe, here, have a plan. We're putting in a wireless at every soccer field in the land. We'll send secret information of the games to a central headquarters in time to post entries. We'll break the crooked ring of corrupt financial interests that are grinding you."

Now Sam Small was little, he was grubby, he was insignificant. He was slow-thinking. He was even, if you wish, an ignorant little rural Englishman. But he was marked also by the saving quality of all his kind—he had a superabundance of native common sense. And he knew the man was lying.

First, he knew that all football-pool entries had to be postmarked long before any game started. Depend upon it, Sam had dwelt long enough on some private system of beating the football pools not to have stubbed his mental toe on this elementary fact. That made the man a plain liar.

Second, the man had spoken as if this were a soccer field. While the rest of the world might think of all Britain as being an immense green field where men played and watched soccer, in Sam's bleak section a round ball was considered something for little lassies and Englishmen to play with. The football played in that part of the country—played and watched and bet on and cheered about by thousands—was of the type known as Northern Union. It was played with an oval ball which a man dribbled, carried, punted, drop-kicked or passed—a jolly sort of mass mayhem in which if a man was "laid out," as they called it, no substitution could be made—leading to the simple conclusion that if you could kick the other team right off its feet you had the field all to yourselves and could then proceed to score at will. And mistaking the place for a soccer field meant that the man was a very poorly informed stranger to Yorkshire.

These things Sam had stored away. But when he heard the last speech, the light broke on him. He had heard too many loudmouthed arguers in pubs and on the election platforms and read his paper too well, and listened too long on the wireless not to have developed a critical faculty where such speeches were concerned. And as he heard it, he said, mentally, "Sounds like a speech by that bloody Hitler!"

And then he knew it. The wireless!

"Why," he said, in childish awe, "ye're Gairman spies!"

As he breathed it he knew it sounded fantastic. The men looked so— so British.

"Of course they do, gormless," he counseled himself. "D'ye expect they'd sneak in with a Gairman sossidge in one hand and a dachshund in t'other?"

The man before the desk was smiling. "So?" he said.

"Aye—so," Sam said back.

"And if we were German spies, what would you do, constable?"

"I'd—I'd have to arrest ye," Sam said.

The man stroked his chin. Then his voice came swift and hard: "And if I were to offer you five thousand pounds—now! What then?"

"Five thousand pounds," breathed Sam. "Nay—I'd have to arrest ye."

The man stood erect. He lifted his hand in signal to the man in the corner. Sam looked over. The man was holding a metal thing—by gum! It was a pistol! Sam started back in horror. All he could see was that small blue circle of steel, and the hole in the middle of it.

Sam felt his whole body break out in a perspiration. "Here, here, now," he said. "Don't point that bloody thing at me!"

"Ah, that changes your mind," the man by the desk said, smiling.

Sam looked from the gun to the man at the desk and then back again. He felt a burning in his throat. "No," he said, firmly. "I've got to arrest ye! Don't ye see? I've got to arrest ye!"

He reached around for his handcuffs, in a futile gesture. He held them out and took a step forward. "Come on, now," he said. "Come quietly—or—I'll have to come and take you!"

The slim man made a sound of impatience. Then he motioned to the other with his hand.

The man with the gun nodded and began walking forward. Sam

67

leaped back to the door and stood with arms outstretched across it.

The man with the gun spoke for the first time. "If you move," he said, "I'll shoot."

Step by step he came forward. Sam waited. And then all three froze into silence, and stood listening.

"There, ye see," Sam cried, with soul-felt hope. "Our chaps has the house surrounded." He had got that from detective novels, too.

"Quiet," the man with the gun said.

Quickly he jabbed Sam in the side with the gun, pushing him away from the door. He stood, watching Sam, but listening to the darkened corridor. Sam's heart leaped with joy as he heard sounds. And then, as rapidly, it sank.

For the sound he heard was the gangling, slipperty-slop of the ugly tyke.

"Oh, ma gum," groaned Sam, inwardly. "As though I haven't enough on ma hands now."

As he thought it he saw the ungainly, awful shape come through the door. With a sort of moan of slobbery affection the lop-eared hound leaped at the man with the gun. Under the rush of such enthusiasm, he went over backward, firing the gun as he did so.

68

Now Sam had been in many a Yorkshire rough-and-tumble in his younger days, and what he did then was due to no process of thought. It was more a matter of instinct. He dove at the man, and smacked him across the knuckles with the lead pipe. He managed to skin his own knuckles doing so. Quickly he snapped one end of the handcuffs over the wrist.

Then he pushed away the great, wriggling dog, which was trying to slobber over both their faces in a sort of adolescent delight. He rapped the man on the skull with his homemade blackjack. He wondered where the gun had gone. He wondered where the other man was. He looked up. He saw the other man in the corner. At that moment, the dog saw him, too. It opened its huge mouth in a grin of delight at the prospect of even more playmates. It drew back, putting its forelegs and head close to the floor, as in a puppyish position preliminary to a frolicking leap. Sam heard the man shouting:

"Hold your dog! Hold your dog!"

For the first time the truth flashed through Sam's mind. They were afraid of the dog. That was it. The man on the floor had rolled over and was covering his neck with his interlaced hands. The man in the corner was pressed back in terror. They thought this great shambling dog was dangerous. But if they ever found out it merely wanted to play . . .

Sam dove forward and just managed to grab the terrible tyke by the tail. It let out an outraged wail. He clawed himself, in a sort of hand-over-hand fashion, up the dog's back until he had its mane.

"Now then," he said. "Come over here—holding out yer arm—for I can't hold him much longer." And, to give Sam credit, he was speaking the truth when he said that. The hound was as strong as a bull rhinoceros.

His eyes staring at the dog's great, dripping jaws, the slim man edged forward. Sam pulled his wrist down to the floor, and snapped the other end of the handcuffs tight. Then he blew out a breath of relief.

"There," he said. "I told ye I'd have to arrest ye. Get up and march."

The only difficulty that Sam had after that was due to the fact that he'd snapped the handcuffs on the right wrist of each prisoner, which left them facing in opposite directions.

"Well, I can't help that now," he thought. "Ye can't do everything right the first time ye try it—especially when ye're sort of hurried. And, besides, I don't have the key with me."

It was solved by having the prisoners march closely one behind the other.

"It's quite an invention," Sam thought proudly. "Certainly stops 'em from running away—happen I've invented summat in police procedure."

With his prisoners going before him in clumsy chain-gang march, Sam started back, grimly gripping his piece of lead pipe.

The gentleman from London sat back in the great leather chair in constabulary headquarters in the smoky northern city, and shook his head.

"I still can't believe it, Colonel," he said. "The first really important spy arrest—made by an unarmed auxiliary constable. Two men, armed—taken by one unarmed man in his fifties—I mean—glad as I am, of course, and no offense—it almost sounds fishy."

Colonel Hartingale, head of the South Riding Constabulary, coughed proudly. "It sounded so to me," he said, "but Constable Hurst, here . . ."

The gentleman from London looked at Constable Hurst, who stood at attention, his eyes straight ahead. The colonel made a sign.

"After taking care of detention of the prisoners," he recited, "I investigated the story of Auxiliary Constable Small, sir. Although I could elicit next to nothing from him, most obviously he had been forced to put up a tremendous struggle."

"What makes you think that, Constable?"

"Well, sir, his clothes were—were considerably disarranged and soiled. The knuckles of his right hand were badly skinned. There was a contusion on his jaw that was—er—quite noticeable. His steel helmet, found in the clubhouse, was dented by what must have been a tremendous blow of some sort. The gun he had spoken of was found under the desk in the club house office. I had doubted that myself—but it was there."

"But how in the devil—your men are unarmed—and a man with a gun. He's lying somewhere. How can an unarmed man . . ."

The colonel coughed.

"Well, as a matter of fact, the—er—the men insist—privately, of course—in carrying an—er—er . . ."

"A conker, sir," Constable Hurst prompted.

"Exactly. A conker."

70

"A what?" the gentleman said.

"A—a conker," the colonel explained. "A sort of—er—a little lead pipe, y'know, and a little wrapping of adhesive tape, and a little of this and that. Sort of a—a cosh-stick, you might say."

"Oh, a cosh-stick! Exactly," the man from London said.

"Yes, sir. Of course, quite illegal and we warn them . . ."

"Of course. Quite. Quite," the gentleman from London said.

"And then, too, they—er—they wear quite heavy boots, y'know. Kicking is considered quite a—a fair weapon of offense and defense here, y'know. Not as in London . . ."

The gentleman from London laughed and shook his head.

"Some day, when this war's over, we ought to send a mission up here to Yorkshire to get to know you better. However, I don't need to say that—ah—the government is quite cognizant and pleased by the way you have taken over this important work of training auxiliary protective forces."

The colonel beamed, happily.

"Thank you," he said. "This particular unit has been under the supervision of Constable Hurst, here."

"Ah, Constable Hurst. Quite."

"I am quite pleased with him," the colonel said.

The gentleman from London looked pleased. Colonel Hartingale looked pleased. Constable Hurst stared straight ahead, but he was pleased, too. The room was full of pleasure.

"Well," the gentleman from London said. "Let's take a look at this raw-meat eater. He's here?"

71

"Oh, yes. Constable Hurst drove him down. I'll buzz for him."

Thus Sam Small came into the presence of the mighty. He felt no pleasure in it. His eye lit gladly on Constable Hurst. At least "the bloody bobby" was a familiar face.

"Now, lad," he greeted cheerfully, and then was a bit hurt, for Constable Hurst stared straight ahead. Sam waited. The toff in the chair was speaking, in a clipped sort of English that was quite hard for Sam to understand. But he understood he was being asked if he was the man who made the arrest.

"Aye," he said, with a flat intonation.

The toff was shaking his head, sadly, and then asking if he knew he'd done quite a brave thing.

"Aye," Sam said, with a falling intonation. And he supposed he knew that there'd be a mark of recognition?

"Aye?" he said, with a rising inflection.

Was there anything particular that Mr. Small wished?

Sam didn't hesitate. "Aye," he said, with finality. "Transfer me to the Spread Eagle beat."

The gentleman looked at the colonel, smiling. The colonel looked at Constable Hurst, smiling. The constable shook his head without smiling.

"Well, all right," Sam said. "Happen ye're right. Then give me the headquarters do. There's John Willie Braithwaite, he sits there reading the newspapers all night, and I have bunions that hurt me something horrid. Give him my beat, and let me sit down for a change."

The gentleman behind the desk nodded his head, and waved his hand. The colonel signaled to Constable Hurst. Constable Hurst said, "I'll make the change in duty immediately, sir."

"Nay, hold on," Sam said. "Don't rush me. Make it beginning tomorrow night. I've got summat special on ma beat tonight."

That night, as Sam Small made his farewell tour over the long beat, he carried a package. When the great dog came bounding through the darkness, he unwrapped the package, and took out chunks of liver. He flung them down the gaping, slobbering jaws. Then he looked at the dog and shook his head.

"Heavens knows, I like dogs," he said. "Heavens knows tha saved ma life. Heavens knows tha's made a hero o' me. But Heavens knows— I *still* don't like thee."

And he went away in the darkness.

72

A VISION FOR WILLY

MARION STURGES-JONES

DURING the summer of 1917 the girls in Dr. Witherspoon's office went to work with positive frenzy on their hope chests. Engagements and hasty marriages were flourishing, as is usual in wartime, and every girl gave her all to the accumulation of lunch sets and initialed pillowcases against the happy day when she would be led to the altar. It seemed to be the prevailing opinion in the group that no marriage would be quite legitimate unless the bride had a couple of tons of household linens ready, and the girls felt so righteous about their efforts that they didn't even mind chiseling a little extra lunch-hour time to crochet and hemstitch. Dr. Witherspoon himself seemed to condone this, and if he surprised a group of females doing needlework during office hours he did no more than raise his brows warningly while he made some jocose remark about the lucky gentlemen who would get his fine-fingered girls. The girls would blush and giggle happily at this, feeling a delicious sense of popularity plus virtue.

Being a complete stranger to all womanly accomplishments, I naturally despised the sewing circle at first, but to my own astonishment I soon found myself yearning to put French knots on guest towels with the rest of them.

The desire to conform has always hit me at erratic intervals. Most of the time I can get along sunnily without joining in the activities of the people around me, but every once in a while I am seized with an irresistible impulse to participate in some curious occupation of my fellow-men. The sewing urge of that summer could be traced, I think, to a Williams College boy who goes down rather bleakly in memory as my first beau.

I had met Willy Lane when I was visiting in Rhode Island the previous summer, and we had corresponded ever since. Willy was an immature boy of nineteen who had been kept away from girls by his widowed mother, and who moreover suffered lamentably from hay fever. He so often stressed the fact that I was the most "sympathetic" girl he had ever met that I was forced to the unflattering conclusion that my interest in *him* was the most attractive thing about me. This was a fairly discouraging thought, but at sixteen one is humble. I realized that Willy was no ball of fire, but he wore white flannels nicely and he was sweet when he wasn't sneezing. He took me canoeing and to dances and at the end of my visit he *almost* gave me his fraternity pin. I also knew that he wanted to kiss me good-by when I left but that he didn't dare because his mother thought I was badly brought up and frivolous.

Mrs. Lane was a wonderful housekeeper of the New England type, prim but exquisitely proper. Her house was filled with the art needlework creations to which she had devoted a lifetime, and I felt sure that only a girl who could embroider would find favor in her eyes. I didn't really want to marry Willy, or even get engaged to him, but I grew to have a dreamy ambition to hemstitch my way into Mrs. Lane's good graces and then lightly give Willy the brush-off.

I was careful, of course, not to give Mother any hint as to why I was suddenly interested in sitting on a cushion and sewing a fine seam. She had never met the Lanes and would have thought them both colossal bores if she had. My sudden passion for needlework amazed her, but she put it down to delayed adolescence and let it go at that.

"How fascinating, dear!" she exclaimed when I showed her a bread-tray cover I was embroidering. "We must get a bread-tray some day—I am sure we could find some use for it!"

Meantime, Willy threw all my plans askew by offering his services to the army.

The War was in the foreground of everyone's thoughts at that time, and Willy assumed a new and imposing stature by his act. He became

74

not only a hero, but *my* hero—he wrote me that he expected to be in the army by the end of August, and that he was coming to Philadelphia to say good-by to me before he reported to Camp Devens.

His letter was couched in such solemn terms that I felt like weeping. I didn't even resent his saying that he was glad he had such a "sympathetic" girl to leave behind. I glowed with pride and patriotism and wondered what I could do to show Willy that I was worthy of him.

Somewhere along the line of this thought I began to picture myself stepping out on Chestnut Street with Willy when he came to say good-by. The picture satisfied me only when I saw myself wearing a pink organdy dress. Pink organdy, and nothing else, would leave in Willy's mind the vision I wanted him to carry away with him. I could see poor Willy in the mud, in the grime—yes, in the *hell* of No Man's Land, being sustained only because a girl in pink organdy was waiting at home for him . . . a girl in a pink organdy dress *that she had made herself!*

At last I had thought of a way in which I could be worthy of Willy. I would be the kind of a girl that each of his New England grandmothers had been—a girl who made her own dresses. This was even better than doing art needlework!

Across the hall from Mother and me in Mrs. Wright's boardinghouse on Spruce Street was a plump, middle-aged spinster named Miss Hinckley who sewed on a little portable hand machine. I consulted with Miss Hinckley, who gave excited shrieks when she heard about Willy and who agreed joyfully to help create the vision that would accompany him into battle. Miss Hinckley regretted that she was soon going to Ocean City for a month, but she promised to help me cut out the dress and to lend me her machine when she went away.

After considerable study of current issues of *Pictorial Review*, the *Delineator*, and the *Ladies' Home Journal*, I settled on a pattern that was described in this lyrical prose:

"She walks down the garden path in her cool dress and hat of lilac mull. The bertha is outlined in rows of mull cording, and over the long clinging skirt, shirred at the top, frivols a loose cascade of the material. The hat, which Gainsborough would have loved, has a band of mull that slides down the crown and cuddles at one side into a soft bow."

A lady who looked like a combination of Hazel Dawn and Mrs. Vernon Castle was pictured wearing this enchanting costume, and I knew at once that it, and it alone, was the thing for me. I hadn't counted on making a hat—but why not? One of the girls in the office had whipped up a creation that summer by crocheting a red crown on a brim of black tuile and we all thought it very tricky. With Miss Hinckley's machine to do all the actual work, I saw no reason for being illiberal with my creative instinct. The dress called for 7¾ yards of 40-inch material, so I got another two yards for the hat that Gainsborough would have loved.

I was a trifle overwhelmed the first evening when I tried to find space in our bedroom for all the pink organdy, the patterns, the machine, Miss Hinckley, Mother and myself. Mother was nothing but an innocent bystander as far as the project was concerned, since she had never sewed in her life and admittedly knew nothing about it. When she was confronted with the material and the pattern, however, she scanned them anxiously and then inquired in a weak voice whether I expected to lease Rittenhouse Square for the evening when Willy arrived. Coming from anyone else, I would have thought this a catty remark, but I knew that Mother was merely bewildered. Next, she studied the pattern for a few minutes and asked if I was quite sure organdy was a good substitute for mull, it being so much *stiffer?* This didn't seem to me like constructive criticism, so I suggested kindly that she go to the new Clara Kimball Young picture while Miss Hinckley and I got down to work.

Mother saw quite a few movies after that, as I had more or less to drive her out each evening.

The dress was made over a long *crepe de chine* slip, but when we had cut out both slip and skirt and basted them together for a quick try-on, I got panicky over the possibility of onlookers seeing my legs through the skirt. Nothing appalled a young girl of twenty-five years ago so much as the thought that the shadow of her lower limbs might be apparent when she walked abroad, and two petticoats were the usual thing when thin summer materials were worn.

Before we progressed any further with the dress, therefore, I had to take another lunch-hour to buy more *crepe de chine* for a second underskirt. After that was put together, I heaved a sigh of relief—until the thought of immodesty *above* the waist-line suddenly smote me. It was repellent to contemplate additional sewing, so I decided to wear a camisole under the slip under the dress—just to be sure.

The effect of all these layers of underclothing, plus the shirred organdy dress, seemed to stagger both Miss Hinckley and Mother into speechlessness, but *I* was entirely satisfied. Willy's trip to bid me good-by was a serious matter and I had no intention of appearing in a dress that was indecorous in any way. It seemed probable that Willy would kiss me good-by *this* time, and if he really did get that close to me I wanted to be thoroughly clothed.

The dress was less than half done when Miss Hinckley departed for Ocean City and I was left to finish it alone. I had watched her operate the machine several times and it looked easy as pie, but when I came to work it myself I ran into trouble. I have never been knowledgeable about either machinery or horses, and they both seem to know it. Miss Hinckley's machine became possessed of the devil the moment I set hands upon it, and it either refused to operate at all or else careened so wildly over my precious pink organdy that it left a line suggesting the the blind staggers. After I'd spent several agonizing evenings sewing and ripping, I abandoned the machine entirely and set to work to finish the dress by hand.

As it happened, I had plenty of time. The army seemed in no great rush to accept Willy, and his mother shipped him up to Maine for a vacation before he entered the service. This delay was good news at first, but, as the summer wore on, I began to get anxious. What if Willy didn't get to town until it was too late in the season to wear an organdy dress?

Both the dress and hat were finished and wrapped in tissue paper in the closet. I had had considerable trouble with the placket on the skirt, and I still felt rather worried about it. Mother, however, cheered me up.

"It's such a *very* full skirt, darling, that the puckers will never be noticed at all. I mean, the placket looks just like the rest of it, don't you think?"

When I came to finish the hat, the band that was to "slide down the crown and cuddle at one side into a soft little bow" turned perversely into an effect that seemed designed for Miss Mabel Normand in one of her pie throwing moods. I was reluctant to deviate from the pattern, but I felt sure that Gainsborough would *not* have loved my hat, even in his most indulgent mood. Something else had to be tried, so I covered the brim with grosgrain ribbon, moss rosebuds and forget-me-nots. This not only looked mighty cute to me, but served to hide the stitching.

Mother was very sweet about my sewing, but I had a curious feeling that she thought Willy wouldn't get to Philadelphia at all. She had

77

never met him, and could, therefore, have had no reason for objecting to him, so her attitude was all the more puzzling.

In August I had two weeks' vacation, and Mother and I went up to the Delaware Water Gap for part of the time. I hated to be far from Philadelphia, but Willy's visit seemed still to be indefinite, so I finally agreed to go. I wouldn't take the organdy dress and hat, however, as I wanted to wear them for the first time when I went out with Willy. Fortunately, Mother was very understanding about this, and never once all summer did she suggest that I put them on.

It was nearly mid-September when I got a telegram from Willy saying that he would arrive the next day. He had a cousin in Overbrook with whom he would stay, but he asked permission to take me out after dinner that evening. The "after dinner" was slightly disappointing, but it was not entirely a surprise to me. I knew I was as much a "best girl" as Willy had, but even when seeing me for what might be the last time, he was too much the cautious New Englander to be a spendthrift.

Willy's wire arrived on a broiling hot day, and I prayed that the weather would not change. Girls were beginning to wear black velvet hats in town, but both Mother and I thought it poor taste to rush the season that way, and as long as it stayed warm I intended to wear the organdy outfit.

I rushed home from the office that afternoon and washed my hair before dinner. My hair always curled up after a shampoo, and the humid atmosphere would help to make it look its best. A storm seemed to be brewing, but with any luck it would be over before Willy arrived.

While my hair was drying, I consulted *Theatre*, Mother's favorite magazine, for advice on the new movies. *Rasputin, the Black Monk*, with Montagu Love, had been my tentative choice, but fortunately I found out about it in time.

"Rasputin," said *Theatre*, "is a series of salacious and lewd incidents in the life of the Monk, titled in such a manner as to leave nothing to the imagination." What a narrow escape! I decided to play safe and take my hero to see Mary Pickford in *Rebecca of Sunnybrook Farm*. After the movie, I thought I could steer Willy to Page & Shaw's for ice cream without appearing to be a golddigger.

I had intended to wear the organdy dress down to our boardinghouse dining room that evening, but Mother persuaded me not to put it on until later. She thoughtfully pointed out that I would crush the skirt. I was a trifle reluctant to miss the sensation such a gala costume would

78

cause among the boarders, but on second thought I realized that **Willy** was entitled to the first sight of it.

After dinner I hurried upstairs and got into the camisole, the petticoat, the slip, and finally the frock itself. I couldn't see the whole effect in the mirror of our bureau, but I knew it must be simply tremendous. After that I tried on the hat. I had the knot of my hair a little too high and the hat sat up oddly at first, but after I'd fixed my hair a couple of times, and bent the hat a trifle, it came down over my ears in the mode of the day. The crown became disengaged from the brim during the process, but I pinned it so that it scarcely showed.

Mother worked herself up into a nervous state while I was dressing because she said she felt sure there was going to be a heavy rain that would ruin the organdy costume. I had been too excited to notice the weather, but I kept telling her not to worry. She seemed overcome by pessimism, however, and peered out of the window every few seconds, like Sister Anne in the story of Bluebeard.

And, sure enough, thunder did begin to roar in the distance just a few minutes before Willy was announced. It wasn't much of a roar, but to Mother it seemed to herald the deluge and she made the most unaccustomed fuss over it.

Nothing that I could say or do would calm her sudden fears over the storm, and when one of the boarders came up to tell me that a gentleman was waiting for me in the parlor, Mother was right behind me with my old raincoat over her arm.

"It's been so hot all day, I *know* the storm will be a bad one, dear, and you mustn't go out in that lovely, lovely hat. You don't really need any hat at all, so leave it at home, and slip into this raincoat—" She pulled the hatpins out in a twinkling and tossed the organdy hat back on the bureau before she pushed me out into the hall.

This was so unlike Mother that I was still in a daze when I greeted Willy, but I felt wretchedly sure that the sight of me in an olive-drab mackinaw that reached my ankles must be anything but a vision. It appeared, however, that Willy had been waiting nearly half an hour before anyone announced his arrival, and in Mrs. Wright's parlor was a vast Japanese bowl filled with goldenrod. Poor Willy was so overcome by sniffles and sneezes that he could barely get through the introduction to Mother, and it was plain that his one idea was to get the hell out of that room as fast as he could.

The storm blew all sorts of further pollen into Willy's sensitive nose as we made our way to the movies, and his hay fever took on the semblance of a tornado that made nature's own little thunderstorm seem nothing in comparison.

"I thingg we bedder ged oud of here—I'm spoiling other people's fud," Willy whispered in my ear after I'd said the fifth "*Gesundheit!*" to him in five minutes of Mary Pickford.

We went to Page & Shaw's after that, but it was so early that the store was empty, and we ate college ices in self-conscious silence. I took off the raincoat when we got there and waited for Willy to comment on my dress, but he just stared at it moodily between sneezes.

Finally I said, "Willy, I made this dress myself."

Willy nodded. "I thoudd you must of," he said. He had another bout of sneezing and then added, "Bedder lug next dime."

I concluded that he was hoping I'd have better luck the next time I went out with a boy, and I was unhappily willing to drink any kind of toast to that one.

Willy was called up by the army for his physical examination soon after that, but they rejected him before they'd even reached him in the line of enlistees—said he was making so much noise sniffling that they couldn't hear the heartbeat of the man ahead of him. He seemed quite relieved that his attempt to be a hero was over, and in his next letter to me he made a joke of the whole thing. It didn't seem funny to me, however, and when I finally answered I was so careful *not* to be sympathetic that I never heard from Willy Lane again.

A NEW YEAR WISH

LAURA LEE RANDALL

To those, my friends, who hold me dear
I wish great joy throughout the year.

To other friends, who like me less,
A full ten months of happiness.

For such as like me not at all,
I hope they'll have good luck till Fall.

FILLING THAT HIATUS

ROBERT BENCHLEY

THERE has already been enough advice written for hostesses and guests so that there should be no danger of toppling over forward into the wrong soup or getting into arguments as to which elbow belongs on which arm. The etiquette books have taken care of all that.

There is just one little detail of behavior at dinner parties which I have never seen touched upon, and which has given me personally some little embarrassment. I refer to the question of what to do during those little intervals when you find that both your right-hand and your left-hand partner are busily engaged in conversation with somebody else.

You have perhaps turned from what you felt to be a fascinating conversation (on your part) with your right-hand partner, turned only to snap away a rose bug which was charging on your butter from the table decorations or to refuse a helping of salad descending on you from the left, and when you turn back to your partner to continue your monologue, you find that she is already vivaciously engaged on the other side, a shift made with suspicious alacrity, when you come to think it over. So you wheel about to your left, only to find yourself confronted by the clasp of a necklace and an expanse of sun-browned back. This leaves you looking more or less straight in front of you, with a

81

roll in your hand and not very much to do with your face. Should you sit and cry softly to yourself, with your underlip stuck out and tears coursing unnoticed down your cheeks, or should you launch forth into a bawdy solo, beating time with your knife and fork?

Of course, the main thing is not to let your hostess notice that you are disengaged, for, if she spots you dawdling or looking into space, she will either think that you have insulted both your partners or else will feel responsible for you herself and start a long-distance conversation which has no real basis except that of emergency. So above all things you must spend the hiatus acting as if you really were doing something.

You can always make believe that you are talking to the person opposite, making little conversational faces and sounds into thin air, nodding your head "Yes" or "No," and laughing politely every now and again, perhaps even continuing the talk from which you had been cut off, just as if someone were listening to you. This may fool your hostess in case her glance happens to fall your way (and sometime we must take up the difficulty of talking to hostesses whose glances must, of necessity, be roving up and down the board while you are trying to be funny) but it is going to confuse the person sitting opposite you in case he or she happens to catch your act. If one looks across the table and sees the man opposite laughing and talking straight ahead with nobody on the other end, one is naturally going to think that he had better not take any more to drink, or perhaps even that he had better not go out

to any more parties until some good specialist has gone over him thoroughly. It is this danger of being misjudged which makes the imitation conversation inadvisable.

You can always get busily at work on the nuts in front of your plate, arranging them on the tablecloth in fancy patterns with simulated intensity which will make it look as if you were performing for somebody's benefit, especially if you keep looking up at an imaginary audience and smiling "See?" Even if you are caught at this, there is no way of checking up, for anyone of the dinner guests might possibly be looking at you while talking to somebody else. It isn't much fun, however, after the first five minutes.

If you have thought to bring along a bit of charcoal, you can draw little pictures on the back on either side of you, or lacking charcoal and the ability to draw, you might start smothering the nicer-looking back with kisses. This would, at least, get one of your partners to turn around—unless she happened to like it. As time wears on, and you still find yourself without anyone to talk to, you can start juggling your cutlery, beginning with a knife, fork, and spoon and working up to two of each, with perhaps a flower thrown in to make it harder. This ought to attract *some* attention.

Of course, there is always one last resort, and that is to slide quietly out of your chair and under the table, where you can either crawl about collecting slippers which have been kicked off, growling like a dog and frightening the more timid guests, or crawl out from the other side and go home. Perhaps this last would be best.

THE TREASURE HUNT

MARY ROBERTS RINEHART

HAD we not been so anxious about our dear Tish last summer, I dare
say it would never have happened. But even Charlie Sands noticed
when he came to our cottage at Lake Penzance for the week-end that
she was distinctly not her old self.

"I don't like it," he said. "She's lost her pep, or something. I've been
here two days and she hasn't even had a row with Hannah, and I must
say that fuss with old Carpenter yesterday really wasn't up to her
standard at all."

Old Carpenter is a fisherman, and Tish having discovered that our
motor-boat went better in reverse than forward, had miscalculated
our direction and we had upset him.

As it happened, that very evening Tish herself confirmed Charlie's
fears by asking about Aggie's Cousin Sarah Brown's Chelsea teapot.

"I think," she said, "that a woman of my age should have a hobby—
one that will arouse interest at the minimum of physical exertion. And
the collection of old china——"

"Oh, Tish!" Aggie wailed, and burst into tears.

"I mean it," said Tish. "I have reached that period of my life which
comes to every woman, when adventure no longer lurks around the
next corner. By this I do not refer necessarily to amorous affairs, but
to dramatic incidents. I think more than I did of what I eat. I take a
nap every day. I am getting old."

"Never!" said Aggie valiantly.

"No? When I need my glasses nowadays to see the telephone direct-ory!"

"But they're printing the names smaller, Tish."

"Yes, and I dare say my arm is getting shorter also," she returned with a sad smile. She pursued the subject no further, however, but went on knitting the bedroom slippers which are her yearly contribution to the Old Ladies' Home, leaving Charlie Sands to gaze at her thoughtfully as he sipped his blackberry cordial.

But the fact is that Tish had outgrown the cottage life at Penzance, and we all knew it. Save for an occasional golf ball from the links breaking a window now and then, and the golfers themselves who brought extra shoes done up in paper for us to keep for them, paying Hannah something to put them on the ice, there was nothing to rouse or interest her.

Her mind was as active as ever; it was her suggestion that a clothes-pin on Aggie's nose might relieve the paroxysms of her hay fever, and she was still filled with sentiment. It was her own idea on the anniversary of Mr. Wiggins' demise to paint the cottage roof a fresh and verdant green as a memorial to him, since he had been a master roofer by pro-fession.

But these had been the small and simple annals of her days. To all outward seeming, until the night of the treasure hunt, our Tish was no longer the Tish who with our feeble assistance had captured the enemy town of X—— during the war, or held up the band of cut-throats on Thundercloud, or led us through the wilderness of the Far West. An aeroplane in the sky or the sound of the Smith boys racing along in their stripped flivver may have reminded her of brighter days, but she said nothing.

Once, indeed, she had hired a horse from the local livery stable and taken a brief ride, but while making a short cut across the Cummings estate the animal overturned a beehive. Although Tish, with her cus-tomary presence of mind, at once headed the terrified creature for the swimming-pool, where a number of persons were bathing and sunning themselves in scanty apparel about the edge, the insects forsook the beast the moment horse and rider plunged beneath the surface, and a great many people were severely stung. Indeed, the consequences threatened to be serious, for Tish was unable to get the horse out again and it was later necessary to bring a derrick from Penzance to rescue him. But her protests over the enormous bills rendered by the livery man were feeble, indeed, compared to the old days.

"Twenty dollars!" she said. "Are you claiming that that animal, which should have been able to jump over a beehive without upsetting it, was out ten hours?"

"That's my charge," he said. "Walk, trot, and canter is regular rates, but swimming is double, and cheap at that. The next time you want to go out riding, go to the fish pier and I reckon they'll oblige you. You don't need a horse, lady. What you want is a blooming porpoise."

Which, of course, is preposterous. There are no porpoises in Lake Penzance.

She even made the blackberry cordial that year, a domestic task usually left to Aggie and myself, but I will say with excellent results. For just as it was ready for that slight fermentation which gives it its medicinal quality, a very pleasant young man came to see us, having for sale a fluid to be added to home-made cordials and so on which greatly increased their bulk without weakening them.

"But how can one dilute without weakening?" Tish demanded suspiciously.

"I would not call it dilution, madam. It is really expansion."

It was a clear, colourless liquid with a faintly aromatic odour, which he said was due to juniper in it, and he left us a small bottle for experimental purposes.

With her customary caution, our dear Tish would not allow us to try it until it had been proved, and some days later, Hannah reporting a tramp at the back door, she diluted—or rather expanded—a half-glass of cordial, gave him some cookies with it, and we all waited breathlessly.

It had no ill effect, however. The last we saw of the person he was quite cheery; and, indeed, we heard later that he went into Penzance, and, getting one of the town policemen into an alley, forced him to change trousers with him. As a matter of record, whether it was Tish's efforts with the cordial itself, or the addition of the expansion matter which we later purchased in bulk and added, I cannot say. But I do know that on one occasion, having run out of petrol, we poured a bottle of our blackberry cordial into the tank of the motor-boat and got home very nicely indeed. I believe that this use of fruit juices has not heretofore been generally known.

Tish, I know, told it to Mr. Stubbs, the farmer who brought us our poultry, advising him to try cider in his car instead of feeding his apples to his hogs. But he only stared at her.

"Feed apples to hogs these days!" he said. "Why, lady, my hogs ain't seen an apple for four years! They don't know there is such a thing."

Occupied with these small and homely duties, then, we went on along the even tenor of our way through July and August, and even into September. In August, Charlie Sands sent us a radio, and thereafter it was our custom at 7:20 a.m. to carry our comforters into Tish's bed-room and do divers exercises in loose undergarments.

It is to this training that I lay Tish's ability to go through the terrible evening which followed with nothing more serious than a crack in a floating rib.

And in September, Charlie Sands himself week-ended with us, as I have said; with the result of a definite break in our monotony and a revival of Tish's interest in life, which has not yet begun to fade.

Yet his visit itself was uneventful enough. It was not until Mrs. Ostermaier's call on Saturday evening that anything began to develop. I remember the evening most distinctly. Our dear Tish was still in her dressing-gown, after a very unpleasant incident of the morning, when she had inflated a pair of water-wings and gone swimming. Unluckily, when some distance out she had endeavored to fasten the water-wings with a safety-pin to her bathing-garments and the air at once began to escape. When Charlie Sands reached the spot only a few bubbles showed where our unfortunate Tish had been engulfed. She had swallowed a great deal of water, and he at once suggested bailing her out.

"By and large," he said, "I've been bailing you out for the last ten years. Why not now?"

But she made no response save to say that she had swallowed a fish. "Get me a doctor," she said thickly. "I can feel the thing wriggling."

"Doctor, nothing!" he told her. "What you need is a fisherman, if that's the case."

But she refused to listen to him, saying that if she was meant to be an aquarium she would be one; and seeing she was firm, he agreed.

"Very well," he said cheerfully. "But why not do the thing right while you're about it? How about some pebbles and a tadpole or two?"

The result of all this was that Tish, although later convinced there was no fish, was in an uncertain mood that evening as we sat about the radio. She had, I remember, got Chicago, where a lady at some hotel was singing "By the Waters of Minnetonka". Turning away from

87

Chicago, she then got Detroit, Michigan, and a woman there was singing the same thing.

Somewhat impatiently, she next picked up Atlanta, Georgia, where a soprano was also singing it, and the same thing happened with Montreal, Canada. With a strained look, our dear Tish then turned to the national capital, and I shall never forget her expression when once more the strains of "Minnetonka" rang out on the evening air.

With an impatient gesture she shoved the box away from her, and the various batteries and so on fell to the floor. And at that moment Mrs. Ostermaier came in breathless, and said that she and Mr. Ostermaier had just got Denver, and heard it quite distinctly.

"A woman was singing," she said. "Really, Miss Carberry, we could hear every word! She was singing——"

"'The Waters of Minnetonka'?" asked Tish.

"Why, however did you guess it?"

It was probably an accident, but as Tish got up suddenly, her elbow struck the box itself, and the box fell with a horrible crash. Tish never even looked at it, but picked up her knitting and fell to work on a bedroom slipper, leaving Mrs. Ostermaier free to broach her plan.

For, as it turned out, she had come on an errand. She and Mr. Ostermaier wished to know if we could think of any way to raise money and put a radio in the State penitentiary, which was some miles away along the lake front.

"Think," she said, "of the terrible monotony of their lives there! Think of the effect of the sweetness disseminated by 'Silver Threads Among the Gold' or 'By the Waters of——'"

"Mr. Wiggins always said that music had power to soothe the savage breast," Aggie put in hastily. "Have you thought of any plan?"

"Mr. Ostermaier suggested that Miss Tish might think of something. She is so fertile."

But Tish's reactions at first were unfavorable.

"Why?" she said. "We've made our gaols so pleasant now that there's a crime wave so people can get into them." But she added: "I'm in favour of putting one in every prison if they'd hire a woman to sing 'The Waters of Minnetonka' all day and all night. If that wouldn't stop this rush to the penitentiaries, nothing will."

On the other hand, Charlie Sands regarded the idea favourably. He sat sipping a glass of cordial and thinking, and at last said:

"Why not? Think of an entire penitentiary doing the morning daily

88

dozen! Or laying out bridge hands according to radio instructions! Broaden 'em. Make 'em better citizens. Send 'em out fit to meet the world again. Darned good idea—'Silver Threads Among the Gold' for the burglars and 'Little Brown Jug' for the bootleggers. Think of 'Still as the Night' for the moonshiners, too, and the bedtime stories for the cradle-snatchers. Why, it's got all sorts of possibilities!"

He then said to leave it to him and he would think up something, and, falling to work on the radio, soon had it in operation again. His speech had evidently had a quieting effect on Tish, and when the beautiful strains of "The Waters of Minnetonka" rang out once more she merely placed her hands over her ears and said nothing.

It was after his departure on Monday that he wrote us the following note, and succeeded in rousing our dear Tish:

Beloved Maiden Ladies,

I have been considering the problem of the radio for our unfortunate convicts. How about a treasure hunt—à la Prince of Wales—to raise the necessary lucre? I'll write the clues and bury a bag of pennies —each entrant to pay five dollars, and the profits to go to the cause.

Oil up the old car and get out the knickerbockers, for it's going to be a tough job. And don't forget, I'm betting on you. Read the "Murders in the rue Morgue" for clues and deductive reasoning. And pass me the word when you're ready.

Devotedly,

C.S.

P.S. My usual terms are twenty per cent, but will take two bottles of cordial instead. Please mark "Preserves" on box.

C.

II

We saw an immediate change in Tish from that moment. The very next morning we put on our bathing-suits and, armed with soap and sponges, drove the car into the lake for a washing. Unluckily a wasp stung Tish on the bare knee as we advanced and she stepped on the gas with great violence, sending us out a considerable distance, and, indeed, rendering it necessary to crawl out and hold to the top to avoid drowning.

Here we were marooned for some time, until Hannah spied us and rowed out to us. It was finally necessary to secure three horses and a long rope to retrieve the car, and it was some days in drying out.

But aside from these minor matters, things went very well. Mr. Oster-maier, who was not to search, took charge of the hunt from our end and reported numerous entrants from among the summer colony, and to each entrant the following was issued:

1. The cars of the treasure hunters will meet at the Rectory on Saturday evening at eight o'clock.

2. Each hunter will receive a password or sentence and a sealed envelope containing the first clue.

3. This clue found, another password and fresh sealed envelope will be discovered. And so on.

4. There are six clues.

5. Participants are requested to use care in driving about the country, as the local police force has given notice that it will be stationed at various points to prevent reckless driving.

6. After the treasure is discovered, the hunt will please meet at the Rectory, where light refreshments will be served. It is requested that if possible the search be over before midnight in order not to infringe on the Sabbath day.

In view of the fact that certain persons, especially Mrs. Cummings—who should be the last to complain—have accused Tish of certain unethical acts during that terrible night, I wish to call attention to certain facts:

(a) We obeyed the above rules to the letter, save possibly number five.

(b) There was no actual identification of the scissors.

(c) If there was a box of carpet-tacks in our car, neither Aggie nor I saw them.

(d) The fish pier had been notoriously rotten for years.

(e) We have paid for the repairs to the motor-cycle, and so on.

(f) Dr. Parkinson is not permanently lamed, and we have replaced his lamps.

(g) Personally, knowing Tish's detestation of crossword puzzles, I believe the false clues were a joke on the part of others concerned.

(h) We did that night what the local police and the sheriff from Edgewater had entirely failed to do, and risked our lives in so doing.

Most of the attack is purely jealousy of Letitia Carberry's astute brain and dauntless physical courage.

I need say no more. As Tish observed to Charlie Sands the next day, when he came to see her, lifting herself painfully in her bed:

"I take no credit for following the clues; they were simplicity itself. And I shall pay all damages incurred. But who is to pay for this cracked rib and divers minor injuries, or replace poor Aggie's teeth? Tell me that, and then get out and let me sleep. I'm an old woman."

"Old!" said Charlie Sands. "Old! If you want to see an aged and a broken man, look at me! I shall have to put on a false moustache to get out of town."

But to return to the treasure-hunt.

On the eventful day we worked hard. By arrangement with Mr. Stubbs, our poultry-man, he exchanged the licence plates from his lorry for ours in the morning, and these we put on, it being Tish's idea that in case our number was taken by the local motor policeman, Mr. Stubbs could prove that he was in bed and asleep at the time. We also took out our tail-light, as Tish said that very probably the people who could not unravel their clues would follow us if possible, and late in the afternoon, our arrangements being completed, Tish herself retired to her chamber with a number of envelopes in her hand.

Lest it be construed that she then arranged the cross-word puzzles which were later substituted for the real clues, I hasten to add that I believe, if I do not actually know, that she wrote letters concerning the missionary society at that time. She is an active member.

At 5:30 we had an early supper and one glass of cordial each.

"I think better on an empty stomach," Tish said. "And I shall need my brains tonight."

"If that's what you think of Aggie and myself, we'd better stay at home," I said sharply.

"I have not stated what I think of your brain, Lizzie, nor of Aggie's either. Until I do, you have no reason for resentment."

Peace thus restored, we ate lightly of tea, toast, and lettuce sandwiches; and, having donned our knickerbockers and soft hats, were ready for the fray. Aggie carrying a small flask of cordial for emergencies and I a flashlight and an angel-food cake to be left at the Rectory, we started out on what was to prove one of the most eventful evenings in our experience.

91

Tish was thoughtful on the way over, speaking occasionally of Poe and his system of deductive reasoning in solving clues, and also of Conan Doyle, but mostly remaining silent.

Aggie, however, was sneezing badly, due to the dust, and this annoying Tish, she stopped where some washing was hanging out and sent her in for a clothes-pin. She procured the pin, but was discovered and chased, and undoubtedly this is what led later to the story that the bandits—of whom more later—had, before proceeding to the real business of the night, attempted to steal the Whitings' washing.

But the incident had made Aggie very nervous and she took a second small dose of the cordial. Of this also more later on.

There was a large group of cars in front of the Rectory. The Smith boys had brought their flivver, stripped of everything but the engine and one seat for lightness, and the Cummingses, who are very wealthy, had brought their racer. Tish eyed them both with a certain grimness.

"Not speed, but brains will count, Lizzie," she said to me. "What does it matter how fast they can go if they don't know where they're going?"

After some thought, however, she took off the engine-hood and the spare tyre and laid them aside, and stood gazing at Aggie, now fast asleep in the rear seat.

"I could leave her too," she said. "She will be of no help whatever. But, on the other hand, she helps to hold the rear springs down when passing over bumps."

Mrs. Ostermaier then passed around glasses of lemonade, saying that every hunt drank a stirrup-cup before it started, and Mr. Ostermaier gave us our envelopes and the first password, which was "Ichthyosaurus."

It was some time before everyone had memorized it, and Tish utilized the moments to open her envelope and study the clue. The password, as she said, was easy; merely a prehistoric animal. The clue was longer:

Water, water everywhere, nor any drop to drink.
Two twos are four, though some say more, and i-n-k spells ink.

"Water?" I said. "That must be somewhere by the lake, Tish."

"Nonsense! What's to prevent your drinking the lake dry if you want to? I-n-k! It may be the stationer's shop; but if it ever saw water,

I don't believe it. 'Two twos are four, though some say more!' Well, if they do, they're fools, and so is Charlie Sands for writing such gibberish."

What made matters worse was that the Smith boys were already starting off laughing, and two or three other people were getting ready to move. Suddenly Tish set her mouth and got into the car, and it was as much as I could do to crawl in before she had cut straight through the canna bed and out on to the road.

The Smith boys were well ahead, but we could still see their tail-light, and we turned after them. Tish held the wheel tightly, and as we flew along she repeated the clue, which with her wonderful memory she had already learned by heart. But no light came to either of us, and at the cross-roads we lost the Smith boys and were obliged to come to a stop. This we did rather suddenly, and Mr. Gilbert, who is a vestryman in our church, bumped into us and swore in a most unbefitting manner.

"Where the hell is your tail-light?" he called furiously.

"You ought to know," said Tish calmly. "Somewhere in your engine, I imagine."

Well, it seemed that everyone had been following us, and no one except the Smith boys apparently knew where to go from there. And just then a policeman came out of the bushes and asked what the trouble was.

"Ichthyosaurus," said Tish absently. " 'Water, water everywhere, nor any drop to drink. Two twos are four, though some say more, and——' "

"Don't try to be funny with me," he said. "For a cent I'd take the whole lot of you into town for obstructing traffic. You've been drinking, that's what!"

And just then Aggie sat up in the back seat and said: "Drinking

93

yourself! Go on, Tish, and run over him. He'sh a nuishance."

Well, I will say her voice was somewhat thick, and the constable got on the running-board and struck a match. But Tish was in her seat by that time, and she started the car so suddenly that he fell off into the road. As the other cars had to drive round him, this gave us a certain advantage; and we had soon left them behind us, but we still had no idea where to go. Matters were complicated also by the fact that Tish had now extinguished our headlights for fear of again being molested, and we were as often off the road as on it.

Indeed, once we brought up inside a barn and were only saved from going entirely through it by our dear Tish's quick work with the brakes; and we then had the agony of hearing the other cars pass by on the main road while we were backing away from the ruins of a feed-cutter we had smashed.

We had also aroused a number of chickens, and as we could hear the farmer running out and yelling, there was nothing to do but to back out again. Just as we reached the main road a load of buckshot tore through the top of the car, but injured nobody.

"Luckily he was shooting high," said Tish as we drove on. "Lower, and he might have cut our tyres."

"Luckily!" said Aggie, from the rear seat. "He'sh taken the crown out of my hat, Tish Carberry! It was nish hat too. I loved my little hat. I——"

"Oh, keep still and go to sleep again," said Tish. " 'Water, water everywhere, nor any drop to drink. Two twos are four, though some say more, and i-n-k spells ink.' "

"So it did when I went to school," said Aggie, still drowsily. "I-n-k, ink; p-i-n-k, pink; s——"

Suddenly Tish put her foot on the gas and we shot ahead once more.

"School-house of course," she said. "The school-house by the water-tower. I knew my sub-conscious mind would work it out eventually."

III

Unfortunately, we were the last to get to the school-house, and we had to witness the other cars streaming triumphantly down the road as we went up, shouting and blowing their horns. All but the Simmonses' sedan, which had turned over in a ditch and which we passed hastily, having no time to render assistance.

94

Miss Watkins, the school-teacher, was on the porch, and as we drew up Tish leaped out.

"Pterodactyl!" she said.

"Warm, but not hot," said Miss Watkins.

"Plesiosaurus!"

"The end's all right."

"Ichthyosaurus!" said Tish triumphantly, and received the envelope. Aggie, however, who had not heard the password given at the Ostermaiers', had listened to this strange conversation dazedly and now burst into tears.

"There'sh something wrong with me, Lizzie!" she wailed. "I've felt queer ever since we started, and now they are talking and it doesn't sound like sensh to me."

It was some time before I was able to quiet her, but Tish had already received the second password, or sentence, which was "Prevention is better than cure, ting-a-ling", and was poring over the next clue.

> Always first in danger, always last to go,
> Look inside the fire-box and then you'll know.

I still think that had she taken sufficient time she could have located this second clue easily and without the trouble that ensued. But finding herself last when she is so generally first had irritated her, and she was also annoyed at Miss Watkins, it having been arranged that the last car was to take her back into town.

"Mr. Ostermaier said the clue's in town anyway. And he didn't think the last car would have much chance, either," she said.

"Who laughs last laughs best," said Tish grimly, and started off at a frightful speed. Miss Watkins lost her hat within the first mile or two, but we could not pause, as a motor-cycle policeman was now following close behind us. Owing to Tish's strategy, however, for when he attempted to come up on the right of us she swerved in that direction and vice versa, we finally escaped him, an unusually sharp swerve of hers having caught him off guard, so to speak, and upset him.

Just when or where we lost Miss Watkins I have no idea. Aggie had again dozed off, and when we reached the town and slowed up, Miss Watkins was gone. She herself does not know, as she seems to have wandered for some time in a dazed condition before reaching home.

But to the hunt.

95

I still think our mistake was a natural one. One would think that the pass sentence, "Prevention is better than cure, ting-a-ling", certainly indicated either a pharmacy or a medical man and a door-bell, and as Tish said, a fire-box was most likely a wood-box. There being only two doctors in the town, we went first to Dr. Burt's; but he had already retired, and spoke to us from an upper window.

"We want to examine your wood-box," Tish called.

"Wood-box?" he said, in a stupefied voice. "What do you want wood for? A splint?"

"We're hunting treasure," said Tish sharply. " 'Prevention is better than cure, ting-a-ling.' "

The doctor closed the window violently; and although we rang for some time, he did not appear again.

At Dr. Parkinson's, however, we had better luck, discovering the side entrance to the house open and finding our way inside with the aid of the flashlight. There was only one wood-box on the lower floor, and this we proceeded to search, laying the wood out carefully on to a newspaper. But we found no envelopes, and in the midst of our discouragement came a really dreadful episode.

Dr. Parkinson himself appeared at the door in his nightclothes, and, not recognizing us because of our attire and goggles, pointed a revolver at us.

"Hands up!" he cried in a furious tone. "Hands up, you dirty devils! And be quick about it!"

" 'Prevention is better than cure, ting-a-ling'," said Tish.

"Ting-a-ling your own self! Of all the shameless proceedings I've ever——"

"Shame on you!" Tish reproved him. "If ting-a-ling means nothing to you, we will leave you."

"Oh no, you don't!" he said most unpleasantly. "Put up your hands as I tell you or——"

I do not now and I never did believe the story he has since told over the town—that Tish threw the fire-log she was holding at his legs. I prefer to credit her own version—that as she was trying to raise her hands the wood fell, with most unfortunate results. As a matter of fact, the real risk was run by myself, for when on the impact he dropped the revolver, it exploded and took off the heel of my right shoe.

Nor is it true, as he claims, that having been forced out of his house, we attempted to get back in and attack him again. This error is due

96

to the fact that, once outside, Tish remembered the revolver on the floor, and, thinking it might be useful later, went back to get it. But the door was locked.

However, all is well that ends well. We had but driven a block or two when we perceived a number of the cars down the street at the engine-house, and proceeded to find our next clue in the box of the local fire-engine.

The password this time was "Prohibition", and the clue ran:

Just two blocks from paradise and only one from hell,
Stranger things than truth are found in the bottom of a well.

The Smith boys had already gone on, but we were now at last on equal terms with the others, and as the sleep and the cold night air had by now fully restored Aggie, Tish called a consultation.

"So far," she said, "the Smiths have had the advantage of superior speed. But it is my opinion that this advantage is an unfair one, and that I have a right to nullify it if opportunity arises."

"We'll have to catch them first," I observed.

"We shall catch them," she said firmly, and once more studied the clue.

"Paradise," she said, "should be the Eden Inn. To save time we will circumnavigate it at a distance of two blocks."

This we did, learning later that Hell's Kitchen was the name locally given to the negro quarter, and once more Tish's masterly deciphering of the clue served us well. Before the other cars had much more than started, we espied the Smiths' stripped flivver outside the Gilbert place, and to lose no time drove through the hedge and on to the lawn. Here, as is well known, the Gilberts have an old well, long disused, or so supposed. And here we found the Gilberts' gardener standing and the Smith boys drawing up the well bucket.

"Give the word and get the envelope," Tish whispered to me, and disappeared into the darkness.

I admit this. I admit, too, that, as I have said before, I know nothing of her actions for the next few moments. Personally, I believe that she went to the house, as she has stated, to get the Gilbert cook's recipe for jelly roll; and, as anyone knows, considerable damage may be done to an uncovered engine by flying stones. To say that she cut certain wires while absent is to make a claim not borne out by the evidence.

But I will also say that the Smith boys up to that moment had had an unfair advantage, and that the inducing of a brief delay on their part was not forbidden by the rules, which are on my desk as I write. However . . .

As Mr. Gilbert is not only prominent in the church but is also the local prohibition officer, judge of our surprise when, on the well bucket emerging, we found in it not only the clues but some bottles of beer which had apparently been put there to cool. And Mr. Gilbert, on arriving with the others, seemed greatly upset.

"Hawkins," he said to the gardener, "what do you mean by hiding six bottles of beer in my well?"

"Me?" said Hawkins angrily. "If I had six bottles of beer, they'd be in no well! And there aren't six; there's only four."

"Four!" said Mr. Gilbert in a furious voice. "Four! Then who the dev——" Here, however, he checked himself; and as Tish had now returned we took our clues and departed. Hawkins had given us the next password, which was "Good evening, dearie," and the clue, which read:

98

Down along the lake front, in a pleasant place,
Is a splendid building, full of air and space.
Glance within a closet, where, neatly looped and tagged,
Are the sturdy symbols of the game they've bagged.

Everybody seemed to think it meant the Duck Club, and in a few moments we were all off once more except the Smith boys, who were talking loudly and examining their engine. But Tish was not quite certain.

"These clues are tricky," she said. "They are not obvious, but subtle. It sounds too much like the Duck Club to be the Duck Club. Besides, what symbols of dead ducks would they keep? I've never seen anything left over but the bones."

"The feathers?" Aggie suggested.

"They wouldn't keep feathers in a closet. And besides, there's nothing sturdy about a feather. What other large building is on the lake front?"

"The fish-cannery," I said.

"True. And they might keep boards in a closet with the outlines of very large fish on them. But the less said about the air there the better. However, we might try it."

Having made this decision, as soon as we were outside of Penzance we began once more to travel with extreme rapidity, retracing for some distance the road we had come in on, and thus it happened that we again saw the motor-cycle policeman with his side-car. He was repairing something and shouted angrily at us as we passed, but we did not even hesitate, and soon we arrived at the fish-cannery.

None of the others had apparently thought of this possibility, and when we reached it there was no one in sight but a bearded watchman with a lantern, sitting on a barrel outside. Tish hopefully leaped from the car and gave him the password at once.

" 'Good evening, dearie.' "

But the wretch only took his pipe out of his mouth and, after expectorating into the lake, replied:

"Hello, sweetheart. And what can I do for you?"

"Don't be impertinent," said Tish tartly. "I said 'Good evening, dearie,' as a signal."

"And a darned fine signal I call it," he said, rising. "Let's have a look at you before the old lady comes along with my supper."

"I have given you the signal. If you haven't anything for me, say so."

"Well, what is it you want?" he inquired, grinning at us in a horrible manner. "A kiss?"

As he immediately began to advance towards Tish, to this action on his part may be laid the misfortune which almost at once beset us. For there is no question that had it not discomposed her she would never have attempted to turn by backing on to the fish pier, which has been rotten for years. But in her indignation she did so, and to our horror we felt the thing giving way beneath us. There was one loud sharp crack followed by the slow splintering of wood, and the next moment we were resting gently on some piles above the water, with the shattered framework of the pier overhead and the watchman yelling that the company would sue us for damages.

"Damages!" said Tish, still holding to the steering-wheel, while Aggie wailed in the rear. "You talk of damages to me! I'll put you and your company in the penitentiary if I have to——"

Here she suddenly checked herself and turned to me.

"The penitentiary, of course!" she said. "How stupid of us! And I dare say they keep the ropes they hang people with in a closet. They have to keep them somewhere. Speaking of ropes," she went on, raising her voice, "if that old fool up there will get a rope, I dare say we can scramble out."

"Old fool yourself!" cried the watchman, dancing about. "Coming here and making love to me, and then destroying my pier! You can sit there till those piles rot, far's I'm concerned. There's something queer about this business anyhow; how do I know you ain't escaped from the pen?"

"My dear man," said Tish quietly, "the one thing we want is to get to the penitentiary, and that as soon as possible."

"Well, you won't have any trouble getting there," he retorted. "I'll see to that. Far's you're concerned, you're on your way."

He then disappeared, and one of the piles yielding somewhat, the car fell a foot or two more, while Aggie wailed and sneezed alternately. But Tish remained composed. She struck a match, and leaning over the side inspected the water and so on below us.

"There's a boat down there, Lizzie," she said. "Get the towrope from under Aggie and fasten it to something. If we can get down, we'll be all right. The penitentiary isn't more than a half-mile from here."

100

"I slide down no rope into no boat, Tish Carberry," I said firmly.

But at that moment we heard the engine of a motor-cycle coming along the road and realized that our enemy the policeman had followed us. And as at that same instant the car again slipped with a sickening jar, we were compelled to this heroic attempt after all.

However, it was managed without untoward incident, Aggie even salvaging the flask of blackberry cordial. But the boat was almost filled with water, and thus required frantic bailing with our hats, a matter only just accomplished when the motor-cycle policeman came running on to the pier.

Whether the watchman had failed to tell him of the break or not, I cannot say, but we were no more than under way when we heard a splash followed by strangled oaths, and realized that for a time at least we were safe from pursuit.

Wet as we now were, we each took a small dose of the cordial and then fell to rowing. Tish's watch showed only ten o'clock, and we felt greatly cheered and heartened. Also, as Tish said by way of comforting Aggie, the licence plates on the car belonging to Mr. Stubbs, it was unlikely that we would be further involved for the present at least.

IV

Owing to the fact that the cars still in the hunt had all gone to the Duck Club, the brief delay had not lost us our lead, and we proceeded at once, after landing near the penitentiary, to the gate. Our halt there was brief. Tish merely said to the sentry at the entrance, " 'Good evening, dearie.' "

"The same to you and many of them," he replied cheerfully, and unlocked the gate. We then found ourselves in a large courtyard, with the looming walls of the building before us, and on ringing the bell and repeating the phrase were at once admitted.

There were a number of men in uniform, who locked the grating behind us and showed us into an office where a young man was sitting at a desk.

I had an uneasy feeling the moment I saw him, and Aggie has since acknowledged the same thing. Instead of smiling as had the others, he simply pushed a large book towards us and asked us to sign our names.

"Register here, please," was what he said.

101

"Register?" said Tish. "What for?"

"Like to have our guests' names," he said solemnly. "You'll find your cells all ready for you. Very nice ones—view of the lake and everything. Front, show these ladies to their cells."

Aggie gave a low moan, but Tish motioned her to be silent.

"Am I to understand you are holding us here?"

"That's what we're here for. We specialize in holding, if you know what I mean."

"If it's that fish pier——"

"Is it the fish pier?" the young man asked of two or three men around; but nobody seemed to know.

Tish cast a desperate glance about her.

"I may have made a mistake," she said, "but would it mean anything to you if I said: 'Good evening, dearie'?"

"Why, it would mean a lot," he said politely. "Any term of—er—affection, you know. I'm a soft-hearted man in spite of my business."

But Tish was eyeing him, and now she leaned over the desk and asked very clearly:

"Have you got a closet where, neatly looped and tagged,
  You keep the sturdy symbols of the game you've bagged?"

Suddenly all the guards laughed, and so did the young man.

"Well, well!" he said. "So that's what brought you here, Miss Carberry? And all of us hoping you'd come for a nice little stay! Jim, take the ladies to the closet."

Well, what with the accident and the hard rowing, as well as this recent fright, neither Aggie nor I was able to accompany Tish. I cannot therefore speak with authority; but knowing Tish as I do, I do not believe that Mrs. Cummings' accusation as to what happened at this closet is based at all on facts.

Briefly, Mrs. Cummings insists that having taken out her own clue, Tish then placed on top of the others, a number of similar envelopes containing cross-word puzzles, which caused a considerable delay, especially over the Arabic name for whirling dervishes. This not, indeed, being solved at all, somebody finally telephoned to Mr. Ostermaier to look it up in the encyclopaedia, and he then stated that no cross-word puzzles had been included among the clues. Whereupon the mistake was rectified and the hunt proceeded.

102

As I say, we did not go with Tish to the closet and so cannot be certain, but I do know that the clue she brought us was perfectly correct, as follows:

Password: "All is discovered."

"Where are you going, my pretty maid?"
" 'Most anywhere else," said she.
"Behind the grille is a sweet young man,
"And he'll give my clue to me."

We had no more than read it when we heard a great honking of horns outside, and those who had survived trooped in. But alas, what a pitiful remnant was left! Only ten cars now remained out of twenty. The Smith boys had not been heard of, and the Phillipses had been arrested for speeding. Also Mr. Gilbert had gone into a ditch and was having a cut on his chin sewed up, the Jenningses' car had had a flat tyre and was somewhere behind in the road, and the Johnstons were in Backwater Creek, waiting for a boat to come to their rescue.

And we had only just listened to this tale of woe when Mrs. Cummings sailed up to Tish with an unpleasant smile and something in her hand.

"Your scissors, I believe, dear Miss Carberry," she said.

But Tish only eyed them stonily.

"Why should you think they are my scissors?" she inquired coldly.

"The eldest Smith boy told me to return them to you, with his compliments. He found them in the engine of his car."

"In his car? What were they doing there?"

"That's what I asked him. He said that you would know."

"Two pairs of scissors are as alike as two pairs of pants," Tish said calmly, and prepared to depart.

But our poor Aggie now stepped up and examined the things and began to sneeze with excitement.

"Why, Tish Carberry," she exclaimed, "they are your scissors! There's the broken point and everything. Well, if that isn't the strangest thing!"

"Extraordinary!" said Mrs. Cummings. "Personally, I think it a matter for investigation."

She then swept on, and we left the penitentiary. But once outside the extreme discomfort of our situation soon became apparent. Not only were we wet through, so that Aggie's sneezing was no longer alleviated

103

by the clothes-pin, but Tish's voice had become hardly more than a hoarse croaking. Also, we had no car in which to proceed. Indeed, apparently the treasure hunt was over as far as we were concerned. But once again I had not counted on Tish's resourcefulness. We had no sooner emerged than she stopped in the darkness and held up her hand.

"Listen!" she said.

The motor-cycle was approaching along the lake road, with that peculiar explosive sound so reminiscent of the machine-gun Tish had used in the capture of X—— during the war.

It was clear that we had but two courses of action—one to return to the penitentiary and seek sanctuary, the other to remain outside. And Tish, thinking rapidly, chose the second. She drew us into an embrasure of the great wall and warned us to be silent, especially Aggie.

"One sneeze," she said, "and that wretch will have us. You'll spend the night in jail."

"I'd rather be there than here any day," said Aggie, shivering. However, she tried the clothes-pin once more, and for a wonder it worked.

"He'll hear by teeth chatterig, I'b certaid," she whispered.

"Take them out," Tish ordered her, and she did so.

How strange, looking back, to think of the effect which that one small act was to have on the later events of the evening. How true it is that life is but a series of small deeds and great results! We turn to the left instead of the right and collide with an omnibus, or trip over the tail of an insignificant tea-gown, like my Cousin Sarah Pennell, and fall downstairs and break a priceless bottle of medicinal brandy.

So Aggie took out her teeth and placed them in her ulster pocket, and tied her scarf over her mouth to prevent taking cold without them, and later on . . .

However, at the moment we were concentrated on the policeman. First he discovered and apparently examined the boat on the shore, and then, pushing and grunting, shoved his machine past us and up to the road. There he left it, the engine still going, and went toward the penitentiary, whistling softly and plainly outlined against the lights of the cars outside. A moment later Tish had led us to the motor-cycle and was examining the mechanism by the aid of the flashlight.

"It looks easy enough," she said in her usual composed manner. "Lizzie, get into the side-car and take Aggie on your lap—and hold on to her. I wish no repetition of the Miss Watkins incident."

We watched for a short time, hoping the policeman would go inside;

104

but he was talking to the Cummingses' chauffeur, who seemed to be pointing in our direction. Seeing then that no time was to be lost, Tish hastily adjusted her goggles and pulled down her hat, and being already in knickerbockers, got quickly into the saddle. With the first explosion of the engine the motor-cycle officer looked up, and an instant later began to run in our direction.

But I saw no more. Tish started the machine at full speed, and to a loud cry from Aggie we were off with a terrific jerk.

"By deck's broked!" she cried. "Stop her! By deck's broked!"

Her neck was not broken, however, I am happy to say, and the osteopath who is attending her promises that she will soon be able to turn her head.

How shall I describe the next brief interval of time? To those who have ridden in such fashion, no description is necessary; and to those who have not, words are inadequate. And, in addition, while it was speedily apparent that we were leaving our pursuers behind—for the Cummingses' car followed us for some distance, with the policeman on the runningboard—it was also soon apparent that our dear Tish had entirely lost control of the machine.

Unable to turn her eyes from the road to examine the various controls, an occasional flash of lightning from an approaching storm showed her fumbling blindly with the mechanism. Farmhouses loomed up and were gone in an instant; on several curves the side-car was high in the air, and more than once our poor Aggie almost left us entirely. As the lightning became more frequent we could see frightened animals running across the fields; and finally, by an unfortunate swerve, we struck and went entirely through some unseen obstacle which later proved to be a fence.

However, what might have been a tragedy worked out to the best

possible advantage, for, another flash revealing a large haystack near by, Tish turned the machine toward it with her usual far-sightedness and we struck it fairly in the centre. So great was our impact, indeed, that we penetrated it to a considerable distance and were almost buried, but we got out without difficulty and also extricated the machine. Save for Aggie's neck, we were unhurt; and, the rain coming up just then, we retired once more into the stack and with the aid of the flash again read over the clue:

> "Where are you going, my pretty maid?"
> " 'Most anywhere else," said she.
> "Behind the grille is a nice young man,
> "And he'll give my clue to me."

"Going?" said Tish thoughtfully. " ' 'Most anywhere else'? There's no sense to that." The hay, however, had brought back Aggie's hay-fever, and as sneezing hurt her neck, she was utterly wretched.

"There's a heap of sedse," she said in a petulant voice. "Bost ady-where else would suit be all right. Ad if you're goig to try that dabbed bachide agaid, Tish Carberry, I ab dot."

"If you must swear, Aggie," Tish reproved her, "go outside, and do not pollute the clean and wholesome fragrance of this hay."

"I'd have said worse if I knew andything worse," said Aggie. "And bebbe this hay is wholesobe, but if you had by dose you wouldn't thig so."

"Grille?" said Tish. "A nice young man behind a grille? Is there a grill-room at the Eden Inn?"

But we could not remember any, and we finally hit on the all-night restaurant in town, which had.

" ' 'Most anywhere else' must refer to that," Tish said. "The food is probably extremely poor. And while there we can get a sandwich or so and eat it on the way. I confess to a feeling of weakness."

"Weakness!" said Aggie bitterly. "Thed I dod't ever wadt to see you goig strrog, Tish Carberry!"

It was owing to Aggie's insistence that Tish test out the mechanism of the motor-cycle before any of us mounted again that our next mis-fortune occurred. So far, when one thing failed us, at least we had been lucky enough to find a substitute at hand, but in this instance we were for a time at a loss.

It happened as follows: As soon as the rain ceased, Tish, flashlight in hand, went to the machine and made a few experiments with it. At first all went well, but suddenly something happened, I know not what, and in a second the motor-cycle had darted out of our sight and soon after out of hearing, leaving our dear Tish still with a hand out and me holding a flashlight on the empty air. Pursuit was useless, and, after a few moments, inadvisable, for as it reached the main road it apparently struck something with extreme violence.

"If that's a house it's docked it dowd," Aggie wailed.

But as we were to learn later, it had not struck a house, but something far more significant. Of that also more later on.

Our situation now was extremely unpleasant. Although the storm was over, it was almost eleven o'clock, and at any time we expected to see the other cars dashing past toward victory. To walk back to town was out of the question in the condition of Aggie's neck. Yet what else could we do? However, Tish had not exhausted all her resources.

"We are undoubtedly on a farm," she said. "Where there's a farm there's a horse, and where there's a horse there is a wagon. I am not through yet."

And so, indeed, it turned out to be. We had no particular mischance in the barn, where we found both a horse and a wagon, only finding it necessary to connect the two.

This we accomplished in what I fear was but an eccentric manner, and soon we were on our way once more, Aggie lying flat in the wagon-bed because of her neck. How easy to pen this line, yet to what unforeseen consequences it was to lead!

As we wished to avoid the spot where the motor-cycle had struck something, we took back-lanes by choice, and after travelling some three miles or so had the extraordinary experience of happening on the motor-cycle itself once more, comfortably settled in a small estuary of the lake and with several water-fowl already roosting upon it.

But we reached the town safely, and leaving Aggie, now fast asleep, in the rear of the wagon, entered the all-night restaurant.

v

There was no actual grille to be seen in this place, but a stout individual in a dirty-white apron was frying sausages on a stove at the back end and a thin young man at a table was waiting to eat them.

107

Tish lost no time, but hurried back, and this haste of hers, added to the dirt and so on with which she was covered and the huskiness of her voice, undoubtedly precipitated the climax which immediately followed. Breathless as she was, she leaned to him and said:

" 'All is discovered.' "

"The hell you say!" said the man, dropping the fork.

"I've told you," she repeated. " 'All is discovered.' And now no funny business. Give me what you've got; I'm in a hurry."

"Give you what I've got?" he repeated. "You know damn' well I haven't got anything, and what I'm going to get is twenty years! Where are the others?"

Well, Tish had looked rather blank at first, but at that she brightened up.

"In the penitentiary," she said. "At least——"

"In the pen!" yelped the man. "Here, Jose!" he called to the person at the table. "It's all up! Quick's the word!"

"Not at all," said Tish. "I was to say 'All is discovered', and——"

But he only groaned, and throwing off his apron and grabbing a hat, the next moment he had turned out the light and the two of them ran out the front door. Tish and I remained in the darkness, too astonished to speak, until a sound outside brought us to our senses.

"Good heavens, Lizzie!" she cried. "They have taken the wagon—and Aggie's in it!"

We ran outside, but it was too late to do anything. The horse was galloping wildly up the street, and after following it a block or two, we were obliged to desist. I leaned against a lamp-post and burst into tears, but Tish was made of stronger fibre. While others mourn, Tish acts, and in this case she acted at once.

As it happened, we were once more at Dr. Parkinson's, and even as we stood there the doctor himself brought his car out of the garage, and leaving it at the kerb, limped into his house for something he had forgotten. He was wearing a pair of loose bedroom slippers, and did not see us at first, but when he did he stopped.

"Still at large, are you?" he said in an unpleasant tone.

"Not through any fault of yours," said Tish, glaring at him. "After your dastardly attack on us——"

"Attack!" he shouted. "Who's limping, you or me? I'm going to lose two toenails, and possibly more. I warn you, whoever you are, I've told the police, and they are on your track."

"Then they are certainly travelling some," said Tish coldly.

He then limped into the house, and Tish caught me by the arm.

"Into the car!" she whispered. "He deserves no consideration whatever, and our first duty is to Aggie."

Before I could protest, I was in the car and Tish was starting the engine; but precious time had been lost, and although we searched madly, there was no trace of the wagon.

When at last in despair we drove up to the local police-station it was as a last resort. But like everything else that night, it too failed us. The charge room was empty, and someone was telephoning from the inner room to Edgewater, the next town.

"Say," he was saying, "has the sheriff and his crowd started yet? . . . Have, eh? Well, we need 'em. All the boys are out, but they haven't got 'em yet, so far's I know. . . . Yes, they've done plenty. Attacked Dr. Parkinson first. Then busted down the pier at the fish-house and stole a boat there, and just as Murphy corralled them near the pen, they grabbed his motor-cycle and escaped. They hit a car with it and about killed a man, and a few minutes ago old Jenkins, out the Pike, telephoned they'd lifted a horse and wagon and beat it. And now they've looted the Cummings house and stolen Parkinson's car for a getaway. . . . Crazy? Sure they're crazy! Called the old boy at the fish-cannery 'dearie'! Can you beat it?"

We had just time to withdraw to the street before he came through the door-way, and getting into the car we drove rapidly away. Never have I seen Tish more irritated; the unfairness of the statements galled her, and still more her inability to refute them. She said but little, merely hoping that whoever had robbed the Cummings house had made a complete job of it, and that we would go next to the railway station.

"It is possible," she said, "that the men in that restaurant are implicated in this burglary, and certainly their actions indicate flight. In that case the wagon—and Aggie—may be at the depot."

This thought cheered us both. But, alas, the waiting-room was empty and no wagon stood near the tracks. Only young George Welliver was behind the ticket window, and to him Tish related a portion of the situation.

"Not only is Miss Pilkington in the wagon," she said, "but these men are probably concerned in the Cummings robbery. I merely said to them 'All is discovered', when they rushed out of the place."

109

Suddenly George Welliver threw back his head and laughed.

"Well!" he said. "And me believing you all the time! So you're one of that bunch, are you? All that rigmarole kind of mixed me up. Here's your little clue, and you're the first to get one."

He then passed out an envelope, and Tish, looking bewildered, took it and opened it. It was the next clue, right enough. The password was "Three-toed South American sloth", and the clue as follows:

> Wives of great men all remind us,
> We can make our wives sublime,
> And, departing, leave behind us
> Footprints on the sands of time.

"That ought not to be difficult," said Tish. "If only Aggie hadn't acted like a fool——"

"It's the cemetery," I said, "and I go to no cemetery tonight, Tish Carberry."

"Nonsense!" said Tish briskly. "Time certainly means a clock. I'm just getting the hang of this thing, Lizzie."

" 'Hang' may be right before we're through. And when I think of poor Aggie——"

"Still," she went on, "sands might be an hour-glass. Sands of time, you know."

"And if somebody broke it by stepping on it, it would be footprints on the sands of time!" I retorted. "Go on! All we have to do is to find an hour-glass and step on it. And in the meantime Aggie——"

However, at that instant a train drew in and a posse from Edgewater, heavily armed, got out of it and made for a line of waiting motor-cars. Never have I seen a more ruthless-looking lot of men, and Tish felt as I did, for as they streamed into the waiting-room she pushed me into a telephone-booth and herself took another.

And with her usual competency she took advantage of the fact to telephone Hannah to see if Aggie had returned home; but she had not.

As soon as the posse had passed through we made our escape by the other door and were able to reach the doctor's car unseen, and still free to pursue our search. But I insist that I saw Tish scatter no tacks along the street as we left the depot. If she did, then I must also insist that she had full reason; it was done to prevent an unjustified pursuit by a body of armed men, and not to delay the other treasure hunters.

110

Was it her fault that the other treasure seekers reached the station at that time? No, and again no. Indeed, when the first explosive noises came as the cars drew up she fully believed that the sheriff was firing on us, and it was in turning a corner at that time that she broke the fire-plug.

Certainly to assess her damages for flooded cellars is, under these circumstances, a real injustice.

But to return to the narrative: Quite rightly, once beyond pursuit, Tish headed for the Cummings property, as it was possible that there we could pick up some clue to Aggie, as well as establish our own innocence. But never shall I forget our reception at that once-friendly spot.

As the circumstances were peculiar, Tish decided to reconnoitre first, and entered the property through a hedge with the intention of working past the sundial and so towards the house. But hardly had she emerged into the glow from the windows when a shot was fired at her and she was compelled to retire. As it happened, she took the shortest cut to where she had left me, which was down the drive, and I found myself exposed to a fusillade of bullets, which compelled me to seek cover on the floor of the car. Two of the car windows were broken at once and Letitia Carberry herself escaped by a miracle, as a bullet went entirely through the enevelope she held in her hand.

Yes, with her customary astuteness she had located the fresh clue. The Ostermaier boy had had them by the sundial, and had gone to sleep there. She fell over him in the darkness, as a matter of fact, and it was his yell which had aroused the house afresh.

There was clearly nothing to do but to escape at once, as men were running down the drive and firing as they ran. And as it seemed to

111

make no difference in which direction we went, we drove more or less at random while I examined the new clue. On account of the bullet-holes, it was hard to decipher, but it read much as follows:

The password was "Keep your head down, boy," and the clue was as follows:

> Search where affection ceases,
> By soft and ———— sands.
> The digit it increases,
> On its head it stands.

"After all," Tish said, "we have tried to help Aggie and failed. If that thing made sense I would go on and locate the treasure. But it doesn't. A digit is a finger, and how can it stand on its head?"

"A digit is a number too."

"So I was about to observe," said Tish. "If you wouldn't always break in on my train of thought, I'd get somewhere. And six upside down is nine, so it's six we're after. Six what? Six is half a dozen. Half a dozen eggs; half a dozen rolls; half a dozen children. Who has half a dozen children? That's it probably. I'm sure affection would cease with six children."

"Somebody along the water-front. It says: 'By soft and something-or-other sands.'"

We pondered the matter for some time in a narrow lane near the Country Club, but without result; and might have been there yet had not the sudden passing of a car which sounded like the Smith boys' flivver toward the Country Club gate stimulated Tish's imagination.

"I knew it would come!" she said triumphantly. "The sixth tee, of course, and the sand-box! And those dratted boys are ahead of us!"

Anyone but Tish, I am convinced, would have abandoned hope at that moment. But with her, emergencies are to be met and conquered, and so now. With a "Hold tight, Lizzie!" she swung the car about, and before I knew what was on the tapis she had let in the clutch and we were shooting off the road and across a ditch.

VI

So great was our momentum that we fairly leaped the depression, and the next moment were breaking our way through a small wood

112

which is close to the fourteenth hole of the golf-links, and had struck across the course at that point. Owing to the recent rain, the ground was soft, and at one time we were fairly brought to bay—on, I think, the fairway to the eleventh hole, sinking very deep. But we kept on the more rapidly, as we could now see the lights of the stripped flivver winding along the bridle-path which intersects the links.

I must say that the way the greens committee has acted in this matter has been a surprise to us. The wagon did a part of the damage, and also the course is not ruined. A few days' work with a wheelbarrow and spade will repair all damage; and as to the missing cup at the eighth hole, did we put the horses' foot in it?

Tish's eyes were on the lights of the flivver now winding its way along the road through the course, and it is to that that I lay our next and almost fatal mishap. For near the tenth hole she did not notice a sand-pit just ahead, and a moment later we had leaped the bunker at the top and shot down into it.

So abrupt was the descent that the lamps—and, indeed, the entire fore part of the doctor's car—were buried in the sand, and both of us were thrown entirely out. It was at this time that Tish injured one of her floating ribs, as before mentioned, and sustained the various injuries which laid her up for some time afterward, but at the moment she said nothing at all. Leaping to her feet, she climbed out of the pit and disappeared into the night, leaving me in complete darkness to examine myself for fractures and to sustain the greatest fright of my life. For as I sat up I realized that I had fallen across something, and that the something was a human being. Never shall I forget the sensations of that moment, nor the smothered voice beneath me which said:

"Kill be at odce ad be dode with it," and then sneezed violently.

"Aggie!" I shrieked.

She seemed greatly relieved at my voice, and requested me to move so she could get her head out of the sand. "Ad dod't screab agaid," she said pettishly. "They'll cobe back ad fidish us all if you do."

Well, it appeared that the two men had driven straight to the golf-links with the wagon, and had turned in much as we had done. They had not known that Aggie was in the rear, and at first she had not been worried, thinking that Tish and I were in the seat. But finally she had learned her mistake, and that they were talking about loot from some place or other, and she was greatly alarmed. They were going too fast for her to escape, although once or twice they had struck bunkers which nearly threw her out.

But at last they got into the sand-pit, and as the horse climbed up the steep ascent our poor Aggie had heard her teeth drop out of her pocket and had made a frantic clutch at them. The next moment she had alighted on her head in the sand-pit and the wagon had gone on.

She was greatly shaken by her experience and had taken a heavy cold; but although we felt about for the blackberry cordial, we could not find it, and could only believe it had miraculously remained in the wagon.

As she finished her narrative our dear Tish slipped quietly over the edge of the pit and sat down, panting, in the sand. The storm being definitely over and a faint moon now showing, we perceived that she carried in her hand a canvas sack tied with a strong cord, and from its weight as she dropped it we knew that at last we had the treasure.

It was a great moment, and both Aggie and I then set about searching for the missing teeth. But as Tish learned of Aggie's experience she grew thoughtful.

"Undoubtedly," she said, "those two men are somehow concerned in this robbery tonight, and very probably the rendezvous of the gang is somewhere hereabouts. In which direction did they go, Aggie?"

"They've parked the wagod over id those woods."

"Then," said Tish, "it is our clear duty——"

"To go hobe," said Aggie sharply.

"Home nothing!" said Tish. "Gaol is where we go unless we get them. There are fifteen policemen and a sheriff coming for us at this minute, and——" But here she stopped and listened intently. "It is too late," she said, with the first discouragement she had shown all evening. "Too late, my friends. The police are coming now."

Aggie wailed dismally, but Tish hushed her and we set ourselves to listen. Certainly there were men approaching, and talking in cautious tones. There was a moment when I thought our dear Tish was conquered at last, but only a moment. Then she roused to incisive speech and quick action.

"I do not propose to be dug out of here like a golf-ball," she stated. "I am entitled to defend myself and I shall do so. Lizzie, see if there are any tools in the car there, and get a wrench." She then took a firm hold of the treasure-bag and swung it in her hand. "I am armed," she said quietly, "and prepared for what may come. Aggie, get the clothes-pin, and when I give the word point it like a pistol."

114

"Ab I to say 'bag'?"

But before Tish could reply, the men were fairly on us. We had but time to get behind the car when we could hear their voices. And suddenly Aggie whispered, "It's theb! It's the badits! Ad they've beed at the cordial!"

And Aggie was right; they had indeed, as we could tell by their voices.

"It wash Bill, all righ'," said one man. "I shaw the litsh of hish car."

"Well, wheresh he gone to? No car here, no anything. Black ash hell."

One of them then began to sing a song in which he requested a barman to give him a drink, but was quickly hushed by the others, for there were now three of them. Whether it was this one or not I do not know, but at that instant one of them fell over the bunker at the top of the pit and came rolling down at our feet, and Tish, with her customary readiness, at once struck him on the head with the bag of pennies. He was evidently stunned, for he lay perfectly still, and the men above seemed puzzled.

"Hey, Joe," they called. "Where are you?"

On receiving no reply, one of them lighted a match, and Tish had only time to retire behind the car before it flared up.

"Well, can you beat that? He'sh broken hish neck!"

But the man with the match was sober, and he saw the car and stared at it.

"If that's Bill's car," he said, as the match went out, "we're up against it. Only—where the devil's Bill?"

"He'sh dead too, mosht likely," said the other. "Everybody'sh dead. S'terrible night. Car'sh dead too; buried in a shea of shand. Shinking rapidly. Poor ole car! Women and children first!"

He then burst into tears and sat down apparently, for the other man kicked him and told him to get up, and then came sliding into the pit and bent over Joe, striking another match as he did so. Hardly had he done so when Tish's weapon again descended with full force, and he fell beside his unconscious partner in crime.

We had now only the drunken man to deal with; and as Tish wished no more bloodshed, she managed him in a different manner.

In a word, she secured the towrope from the rear seat of the doctor's car and, leaving Aggie and myself to watch the others, climbed out and approached him from the rear. It was only the work of a moment

115

to pinion his arms to his sides, and as Aggie immediately pointed her impromptu weapon and cried "Hads up!" he surrendered without a struggle. Having securely roped him, we then rolled him into the sand-pit with the others, who showed no signs of coming to.

Fatigued as we were by that time, and no further danger threatening for the moment, we rested for a brief time on the ground and ate a few macaroons which I had carried in a pocket against such an emergency. But by "we" I mean only Tish and myself, as poor Aggie was unable to do so—and, indeed, has been living on soft food ever since. Then retrieving the sack containing the Cummings jewels and silver which the burglars had been carrying, we prepared to carry our double treasure back to the town.

Here, however, I feel that our dear Tish made a tactical error, for after we had found the horse and wagon—in the undergrowth just beyond the seventh hole—instead of heading at once for the police-station she insisted on going first to the Ostermaiers'.

"It is," she said, examining her watch by the aid of the flashlight, "now only half past eleven, and we shall not be late if we hurry. After that I shall report to the police."

"And what is to prevent those wretches from coming to and escaping in the interval?" I asked dryly.

"True," Tish agreed. "Perhaps I would better go back and hit them again. But that would take time also."

In the end we compromised on Tish's original plan and set out once more. The trip back across the links was uneventful, save that on the eighth green the horse got a foot into the hole and was only extricated with the cup still clinging to his foot.

We had no can-opener along, and it is quite possible that the ring of the tin later on on the macadam road led to our undoing. For we had no sooner turned away from the town toward the Ostermaiers' cottage on the beach than a policeman leaped out of the bushes and, catching the animal by the bridle, turned a lantern on us.

"Hey, Murphy!" he called. "Here they are! I've got 'em! Hands up, there!"

"Stand back!" said Tish in a peremptory voice. "We are late enough already."

"Late!" said the policeman, pointing a revolver at us. "Well, time won't make much difference to you from now on—not where you're going. You won't ever need to hurry again."

116

"But I must deliver this treasure. After that I'll explain everything."

"You bet you'll deliver it, and right here and now. And your weapons too."

"Aggie, give up your clothes-pin," said Tish in a resigned voice. "These yokels apparently think us guilty of something or other, but my conscience is clear. If you want the really guilty parties," she told the policeman, "go back to the sand-pit by the tenth hole and you will find them."

"April fool your own self," said the one called Murphy. "I've been following you for two hours and I don't trust you. You're too resourceful. Is the stuff there?" he asked the first man, who had been searching in the wagon.

"All here."

"Then we'll be moving along," he said; and in this fashion did we reach the town once more, and the police-station.

Never shall I forget that moment. Each of us handcuffed and hustled along by the officers, we were shoved into the police-station in a most undignified manner, to confront the sheriff and a great crowd of people. Nor shall I ever forget the sheriff's face when he shouted in an angry voice:

"Women, by heck! When a woman goes wrong she sure goes!"

The place seemed to be crowded with people. The fish-pier man was there, and a farmer who said we had smashed his feed-cutter. And Dr. Parkinson, limping about in his bedroom slippers and demanding to know where we had left his car, and another individual who claimed it was his horse we had taken, and that we'd put a tin can on his off forefoot and ought to be sued for cruelty to animals. And even Mr. Stubbs, because his licence plates were on our car—and of course the old fool had told all about it—and the Cummings butler, who pointed at Tish and said that after the alarm was raised she had tried to get back into the house again, which was, of course, ridiculous.

I must say it looked bad for us, especially when the crowd moved and we saw a man lying in a corner with an overcoat under his head and his eyes shut. Tish, who had not lost an ounce of dignity, gazed at him without expression.

"I dare say," she said, "that you claim that that is our work also."

"Just about killed him, you have," said the sheriff. "Went right through him with that motor-cycle you stole. Murder—that's what it's likely to be—murder. D'you get his name, Doctor?"

117

"Only roused enough to say it was Bill," said Dr. Parkinson. "I wish myself to lodge a complaint for assault and battery against these women. I am per——"

But Tish interrupted him.

"Bill?" she said. "Bill?"

Without a word she pushed the crowd aside, and, bending over Bill, with her poor manacled hands she examined him as best she could. Then she straightened herself and addressed the crowd with composure.

"Under this man's shirt," she said, "you will find what I imagine to be a full set of burglar's tools. If your hands are not paralysed like your brains, examine him and see."

And they found them! The picture of that moment is indelibly impressed on my mind—the sheriff holding up the tools and Tish addressing the mob with majesty and the indignation of outraged womanhood.

"Gentlemen, this is one of the gang which robbed the Cummings house tonight. Through all this eventful evening, during which I regret to say some of you have suffered, my friends and I have been on their track. Had the motor-cycle not wrecked that ruffian's car, they would now have safely escaped. As it is, when we were so unjustly arrested I had but just recovered the Cummings silver and jewels, and alone and unaided had overcome the remainder of the gang. I am exhausted and weary; I have suffered physical injury and mental humiliation; but I am not too weak or too weary to go now to the sand-pit at the tenth hole on the golf-links and complete my evening's work by handing over to the police the three other villains I have captured."

"Three cheers for the old girl!" somebody called in the crowd. "I'm for her! Let's go!"

And this, I think, concludes the narrative of that evening's events. It was almost midnight when, our prisoners safely gaoled, we arrived at the Ostermaiers' to find all the treasure hunters except the Cummingses there and eating supper, and our angel-food cake gracing the centre of the table. Our dear Tish walked in and laid the sack of pennies on the table.

"Here is the treasure," she announced. "It has been an interesting evening, and I hope we shall soon do it again."

Mr. Ostermaier took up the bag and examined it.

"I have the honour of stating," he said, "that this, as Miss Carberry claims, is the treasure, and that Miss Carberry wins the hand-painted candle-sticks which is the prize for the event." He then examined the

118

bag more carefully, and added:

"But this sack seems to be stained. Perhaps our good sister will explain what the stains are."

Tish eyed the bag with an expressionless face.

"Stains?" she said. "Oh yes, of course. I remember now. They are blood."

Then, leaving them staring and speechless with astonishment, she led the way out of the house, and home.

WANTED: ONE CAVE MAN
WITH CLUB

MARGARET FISHBACK

Oh, for a man to take me out
And feed me fowl *or* sauerkraut
Without first asking *where* to dine.
If such there be, would he were mine!

119

ZENOBIA'S INFIDELITY

H. C. BUNNER

DR. TIBBITT stood on the porch of Mrs. Pennypepper's boardinghouse, and looked up and down the deserted Main Street of Sagawaug with a contented smile, the while he buttoned his driving-gloves. The little doctor had good cause to be content with himself and with everything else—with his growing practice, with his comfortable boardinghouse, with his own good looks, with his neat attire, and with the world in general. He could not but be content with Sagawaug, for there never was a prettier country town. The Doctor looked across the street and picked out the very house that he proposed to buy when the one remaining desire of his soul was gratified. It was a house with a hip-roof and with a long garden running down to the river.

There was no one in the house today, but there was no one in any of the houses. Not even a pair of round bare arms was visible among the clothes that waved in the August breeze in every back-yard. It was Circus Day in Sagawaug.

The Doctor was climbing into his gig when a yell startled him. A freckled boy with saucer eyes dashed around the corner.

"Doctor!" he gasped, "come quick! The circus got a-fire an' the trick elephant's most roasted!"

"Don't be silly, Johnny," said the Doctor, reprovingly.

"Hope to die—Honest Injun—cross my breast!" said the boy. The Doctor knew the sacredness of this juvenile oath.

"Get in here with me," he said, "and if I find you're trying to be funny, I'll drop you in the river."

As they drove toward the outskirts of the town, Johnny told his tale.

"Now," he began, "the folks was all out of the tent after the show was over, and one of the circus men, he went to the oil-barrel in the green wagon with Dan'l in the Lion's Den onto the outside of it, an' he took in a candle an' left it there, and fust thing the barrel busted, an' he wasn't hurted a bit, but the trick elephant she was burned awful, an' the ring-tailed baboon, he was so scared he had a fit. Say, did you know baboons had fits?"

When they reached the circus-grounds, they found a crowd around a small side-show tent. A strong odor of burnt leather confirmed Johnny's story. Dr. Tibbitt pushed his way through the throng, and gazed upon the huge beast, lying on her side on the grass, her broad shoulder charred and quivering. Her bulk expanded and contracted with spasms of agony, and from time to time she uttered a moaning sound. On her head was a structure of red cloth, about the size of a bushel-basket, apparently intended to look like a British soldier's forage-cap. This was secured by a strap that went under her chin—if an elephant has a chin. This scarlet cheesebox every now and then slipped down over her eye and the faithful animal patiently, in all her anguish, adjusted it with her prehensile trunk.

By her side stood her keeper and the proprietor of the show, a large man with a dyed moustache, a wrinkled face, and hair oiled and frizzed. These two bewailed their loss alternately.

"The boss elephant in the business!" cried the showman. "Barnum never had no trick elephant like Zenobia. And them lynes and Dan'l was painted in new before I took the road this season. Oh, there's been a hoodoo on me since I showed ag'inst the Sunday-school picnic!"

"That there elephant's been like my own child," groaned the keeper, "or my own wife, I may say. I've slep' alongside of her every night for fourteen damn years."

121

The Doctor had been carefully examining his patient.

"If there is any analogy——" he began.

"Neuralogy!" snorted the indignant showman; "'taint neuralogy, you jay pill-box, she's *cooked!*"

"If there is any analogy," repeated Dr. Tibbitt, flushing a little, "between her case and that of a human being, I think I can save your elephant. Get me a barrel of linseed oil, and drive these people away."

The Doctor's orders were obeyed with eager submission. He took off his coat, and went to work. He had never doctored an elephant, and the job interested him. At the end of an hour, Zenobia's sufferings were somewhat alleviated. She lay on her side, chained tightly to the ground, and swaddled in bandages. Her groans had ceased.

"I'll call to-morrow at noon," said the Doctor—"good gracious, what's that?" Zenobia's trunk was playing around his waistband.

"She wants to shake hands with you," her keeper explained. "She's a lady, she is, and she knows you done her good."

"I'd rather not have anything of the sort," said the Doctor, decisively.

When Dr. Tibbitt called at twelve on the morrow, he found Zenobia's tent neatly roped in, an ampitheatre of circus-benches constructed around her, and this ampitheatre packed with people.

"Got a quarter apiece from them jays," whispered the showman "jest to see you dress them wounds." Subsequently the showman relieved his mind to a casual acquaintance. "He's got a heart like a gun-flint, that doctor," he said; "made me turn out every one of them jays and give 'em their money back before he'd lay a hand to Zenobia."

But if the Doctor suppressed the clinic, neither he nor the showman suffered. From dawn till dusk people came from miles around to stare a quarter's worth at the burnt elephant. Once in a while, as a rare treat, the keeper lifted a corner of her bandages, and revealed the seared flesh. The show went off in a day or two, leaving Zenobia to recover at leisure; and as it wandered westward, it did an increased business simply because it had had a burnt trick elephant. Such, dear friends, is the human mind.

The Doctor fared even better. The fame of his new case spread far and wide. People seemed to think that if he could cure an elephant he could cure anything. He was called into consultation in neighboring towns. Women in robust health imagined ailments, so as to send for him and ask him shuddering questions about "that *wretched* animal." The trustees of the orphan-asylum made him staff-physician—in this

122

case the Doctor thought he could trace a connection of ideas, in which children and a circus were naturally associated. And the local newspaper called him a *savant*.

He called every day upon Zenobia, who greeted him with trumpetings of joyful welcome. She also desired to shake hands with him, and her keeper had to sit on her head and hold her trunk to repress the familiarity. In two weeks she was cured, except for extensive and permanent scars, and she waited only for a favorable opportunity to rejoin the circus.

The Doctor had got his fee in advance.

Upon a sunny afternoon in the last of August, Dr. Tibbitt jogged slowly toward Sagawaug in his neat little gig. He had been to Pelion, the next town, to call upon Miss Minetta Bunker, the young lady whom he desired to install in the house with the garden running down to the river. He had found her starting out for a drive in Tom Matson's dog-cart. Now, the Doctor feared no foe, in medicine or in love; but when a young woman is inscrutable as to the state of her affections, when the richest young man in the county is devoting himself to her, and when the young lady's mother is backing the rich man, a young country doctor may well feel perplexed and anxious over his chance of the prize.

The Doctor was so troubled, indeed, that he paid no heed to a heavy, repeated thud behind him, on the macadamized road. His gentle little mare heard it, though, and began to curvet and prance. The Doctor was pulling her in, and calming her with a "Soo—Soo—down, girl, down!" when he interrupted himself to shout:

"Great Caesar! get off me!"

Something like a yard of rubber hose had come in through the side of the buggy, and was rubbing itself against his face. He looked around, and the cold sweat stood out on him as he saw Zenobia, her chain dragging from her hind-foot, her red cap a-cock on her head, trotting along by the side of his vehicle, snorting with joy, and evidently bent on lavishing her pliant, serpentine, but leathery caresses upon his person.

His fear vanished in a moment. The animal's intentions were certainly pacific, to put it mildly. He reflected that if he could keep his horse ahead of her, he could toll her around the block and back toward her tent. He had hardly guessed, as yet, the depth of the impression which he had made upon Zenobia's heart, which must have been a large

123

organ, if the size of her ears was an indication—according to the popular theory.

He was on the very edge of the town, and his road took him by a house where he had a new and highly valued patient, the young wife of old Deacon Burgee. Her malady being of a nature that permitted it, Mrs. Burgee was in the habit of sitting at her window when the Doctor made his rounds, and indicating the satisfactory state of her health by a bow and a smile. On this occasion she fled from the window with a shriek. Her mother, a formidable old lady under a red false-front, came to the window, shrieked likewise, and slammed down the sash.

The Doctor tolled his elephant around the block without further misadventure, and they started up the road toward Zenobia's tent, Zenobia caressing her benefactor while shudders of antipathy ran over his frame. In a few minutes the keeper hove in sight. Zenobia saw him first, blew a shrill blast on her trumpet, close to the Doctor's ear, bolted through a snake-fence, lumbered across a turnipfield, and disappeared in a patch of woods, leaving the Doctor to quiet his excited horse and to face the keeper, who advanced with rage in his eye.

"What do you mean, you cuss," he began, "weaning a man's elephant's affections away from him? You ain't got no more morals than a Turk, you ain't. That elephant an' me has been side-partners for fourteen years, an' here you come between us."

"I don't want your confounded elephant," roared the Doctor, "why don't you keep it chained up?"

"She busted her chain to git after you," replied the keeper. "Oh, I seen you two lally-gaggin' all along the road. I knowed you wa'n't no good the first time I set eyes on yer, a-sayin' hoodoo words over the poor dumb beast."

The Doctor resolved to banish "analogy" from his vocabulary.

The next morning, about four o'clock, Dr. Tibbitt awoke with a troubled mind. He had driven home after midnight from a late call, and he had had an uneasy fancy that he saw a great shadowy bulk ambling along in the mist-hid fields by the roadside. He jumped out of bed and went to the window. Below him, completely covering Mrs. Pennypepper's nasturtium bed, her prehensile trunk ravaging the early chrysanthemums, stood Zenobia, swaying to and fro, the dew glistening on her seamed sides beneath the early morning sunlight. The Doctor hastily dressed himself and slipped downstairs and out, to meet this Frankenstein's monster of affection.

There was but one thing to do. Zenobia would follow him wherever he went—she rushed madly through Mrs. Pennypepper's roses to greet him—and his only course was to lead her out of the town before people began to get up, and to detain her in some remote meadow until he could get her keeper to come for her and secure her by force or stratagem. He set off by the least frequented streets, and he experienced a pang of horror as he remembered that his way led him past the house of his one professional rival in Sagawaug. Suppose Dr. Pettengill should be coming home or going out as he passed!

He did not meet Dr. Pettengill. He did meet Deacon Burgee, who stared at him with more of rage than of amazement in his wrinkled countenance. The Deacon was carrying a large bundle of embroidered linen and flannel, that must have been tied up in a hurry.

"Good morning, Deacon," the Doctor hailed him, with as much ease of manner as he could assume. "How's Mrs. Burgee?"

"She's doin' fust rate, no thanks to no circus doctors!" snorted the Deacon. "An' if you want to know anything further concernin' her health, you ask Dr. Pettengill. *He's* got more sense than to go trailin' around the streets with a parboiled elephant behind him, a-frightening women-folks a hull month afore th'r time."

"Why, Deacon!" cried the Doctor, "what—what is it?"

"It's a boy," responded the Deacon sternly; "and it's God's own mercy that 'twa'nt born with a trunk and a tail."

The Doctor found a secluded pasture near the woods that encircled the town, and there he sat him down, in the corner of a snake-fence, to wait until some farmer or market-gardener should pass by, to carry his message to the keeper. He had another message to send, too. He had several cases that must be attended to at once. Unless he could get away from his pachydermatous familiar, Pettengill must care for his cases that morning. It was hard—but what was he to do?

Zenobia stood by his side, dividing her attention between the caresses she bestowed on him and the care she was obliged to take of her red cap, which was not tightly strapped on, and slipped in various directions at every movement of her gigantic head. She was unmistakably happy. From time to time she trumpeted cheerily. She plucked up tufts of grass, and offered them to the Doctor. He refused them, and she ate them herself. Once he took a daisy from her, absent-mindedly, and she was so greatly pleased that she smashed his hat in her endeavors to pet him. The Doctor was a kind-hearted man. He had to admit that Zenobia meant well. He patted her trunk, and made matters worse. Her elephantine ecstasy came near being the death of him.

126

Still the farmer came not, nor the market-gardener. Dr. Tibbitt began to believe that he had chosen a meadow that was *too* secluded. At last two boys appeared. After they had stared at him and at Zenobia for half an hour, one of them agreed to produce Dr. Pettengill and Zenobia's keeper for fifty cents. Dr. Pettengill was the first to arrive. He refused to come nearer than the furthest limit of the pasture.

"Hello, Doctor," he called out, "hear you've been seeing elephants. Want me to take your cases? Guess I can. Got a half-hour free. Brought some bromide down for you, if you'd like to try it."

To judge from his face, Zenobia was invisible. But his presence alarmed that sensitive animal. She crowded up close to the fence, and every time she flicked her skin to shake off the flies she endangered the equilibrium of the Doctor, who was sitting on the top rail, for dignity's sake. He shouted his directions to his colleague, who shouted back professional criticisms.

"Salicylate of soda for that old woman? What's the matter with salicylate of cinchonidia? Don't want to kill her before you get out of this swamp, do you?"

Dr. Tibbitt was not a profane man; but at this moment he could not restrain himself.

"*Damn you!*" he said, with such vigor that the elephant gave a convulsive start. The Doctor felt his seat depart from under him—he was going—going into space for a brief moment, and then he scrambled up out of the soft mud of the cow-wallow back of the fence on which he had been sitting. Zenobia had backed against the fence.

The keeper arrived soon after. He had only reached the meadow when Zenobia lifted her trunk in the air, emitted a mirthful toot, and struck out for the woods with the picturesque and cumbersome gallop of a mastodon pup.

"Dern *you*," said the keeper to Dr. Tibbitt, who was trying to fasten his collar, which had broken loose in his fall; "if the boys was here, and I hollered 'Hey Rube!'—there wouldn't be enough left of yer to spread a plaster fer a baby's bile!"

The Doctor made himself look as decent as the situation allowed, and then he marched toward the town with the light of a firm resolve illuminating his face. The literature of his childhood had come to his aid. He remembered the unkind tailor who pricked the elephant's trunk. It seemed to him that the tailor was a rather good fellow.

"If that elephant's disease is gratitude," thought the Doctor, "I'll

127

give her an antidote."

He went to the drug-store, and, as he went, he pulled out a blank pad and wrote down a prescription, from mere force of habit. It read thus:

PESSELS & MORTON,
Druggists,
Commercial Block, Main Street,
Sagawaug
Prescriptions carefully compounded

> ℞ Calcium Sul ℥ ij
> Calcis chl ℥ x2 j
> Capricum pulv ℥ i
> ℔ et ft. Bol.
> Sig Take at once
> Tibbitt

When the druggist looked at it, he was taken short of breath.

"What's this?" he asked—"a bombshell?"

"Put it up," said the Doctor, "and don't talk so much." He lingered nervously on the druggist's steps, looking up and down the street. He had sent a boy to order the stable-man to harness his gig. By-and-by, the druggist put his head out of the door.

"I've got some asafoetida pills," he said, "that are kind o' tired, and half a pound of whale-oil soap that's higher 'n Haman——"

"Put 'em in!" said the Doctor, grimly; as he saw Zenobia coming in sight far down the street.

She came up while the Doctor was waiting for the bolus. Twenty-three boys were watching them, although it was only seven o'clock in the morning.

"Down, Zenobia!" said the Doctor, thoughtlessly, as he might have addressed a dog. He was talking with the druggist, and Zenobia was patting his ear with her trunk. Zenobia sank to her knees. The Doctor did not notice her. She folded her trunk about him, lifted him to her back, rose, with a heave and a sway, to her feet, and started up the road. The boys cheered. The Doctor got off on the end of an elm-

128

branch. His descent was watched from nineteen second-story windows.

His gig came to meet him at last, and he entered it and drove rapidly out of town, with Zenobia trotting contentedly behind him. As soon as he had passed Deacon Burgee's house, he drew rein, and Zenobia approached, while his perspiring mare stood on her hind legs.

"Zenobia—pill!" said the Doctor.

As she had often done in her late illness, Zenobia opened her mouth at the word of command, and swallowed the infernal bolus. Then they started up again, and the Doctor headed for Zenobia's tent.

But Zenobia's pace was sluggish. She had been dodging about woods for two nights, and she was tired. When the Doctor whipped up, she seized the buggy by any convenient projection, and held it back. This damaged the buggy and frightened the horse; but it accomplished Zenobia's end. It was eleven o'clock before Jake Bumgardner's "Half-Way House" loomed up white, afar down the dusty road, and the Doctor knew that his round-about way had at length brought him near to the field where the circus-tent had been pitched.

He drove on with a lighter heart in his bosom. He had not heard Zenobia behind him for some time. He did not know what had become of her, or what she was doing, but he learned later.

The Doctor had compounded a pill well calculated to upset Zenobia's stomach. That it would likewise give her a consuming thirst he had not considered. But chemistry was doing its duty without regard to him. A thirst like a furnace burned within Zenobia. Capsicum and chloride of lime were doing their work. She gasped and groaned. She searched for water. She filled her trunk at a wayside trough and poured the contents into her mouth. Then she sucked up a puddle or two. Then she came to Bumgardner's, where a dozen kegs of lager-beer and a keg of what passed at Bumgardner's for gin stood on the sidewalk. Zenobia's circus experience had taught her what a water-barrel meant. She applied her knowledge. With her forefoot she deftly staved in the head of one keg after another, and with her trunk she drew up the beer and the gin, and delivered them to her stomach. If you think her taste at fault, remember the bolus.

Bumgardner rushed out and assailed her with a bung-starter. She turned upon him and squirted lager-beer over him until he was covered with an iridescent lather of foam from head to foot. Then she finished the kegs and went on her way, to overtake the Doctor.

129

The Doctor was speeding his mare merrily along, grateful for even a momentary relief from Zenobia's attentions, when, at one and the same time, he heard a heavy, uncertain thumping on the road behind him, and the quick patter of a trotter's hoofs on the road ahead of him. He glanced behind him first, and saw Zenobia. She swayed from side to side, more than was her wont. Her red cap was far down over her left eye. Her aspect was rakish, and her gait was unsteady. The Doctor did not know it, but Zenobia was drunk.

Zenobia was sick, but intoxication dominated her sickness. Even sulphide of calcium withdrew courteously before the might of beer and gin. Rocking from side to side, reeling across the road and back, trumpeting in imbecile inexpressive tones, Zenobia advanced.

The Doctor looked forward. Tom Matson sat in his dog-cart, with Miss Bunker by his side. His horse had caught sight of Zenobia and he was rearing high in air, and whinnying in terror. Before Tom could pull him down, he made a sudden break, overturned the dog-cart, and flung Tom and Miss Minetta Bunker on a bank by the side of the road. It was a soft bank, well-grown with mint and stinging-nettles, just above a creek. Tom had scarce landed before he was up and off, running hard across the fields.

Miss Minetta rose and looked at him with fire in her eyes.

"Well!" she said aloud; "I'd like Mother to see you *now!*"

The Doctor had jumped out of his gig and let his little mare go galloping up the road. He had his arm about Miss Minetta's waist when he turned to face his familiar demon—which may have accounted for the pluck in his face.

But Zenobia was a hundred yards down the road, and she was utterly incapable of getting any further. She trumpeted once or twice, then she wavered like a reed in the wind; her legs weakened under her and she sank on her side. Her red cap had slipped down, and she picked it up with her trunk, broke its band in a reckless swing that resembled the wave of jovial farewell, gave one titanic hiccup, and fell asleep by the roadside.

An hour later, Dr. Tibbitt was driving toward Pelion, with Miss Bunker by his side. His horse had been stopped at the toll-gate. He was driving with one hand. Perhaps he needed the other to show how they could have a summer-house in the garden that ran down to the river.

But it was evening when Zenobia awoke to find her keeper sitting on her head. He jabbed a cotton-hook firmly and decisively into her ear, and led her homeward down the road lit by the golden sunset. That was the end of Zenobia's infidelity.

131

TO A YOUNG MAN SELECTING
SIX ORCHIDS

MARGARET FISHBACK

Tell me, brave young man, I pray,
Is she worth the price you pay?

You may think her quite sublime,
But take care while there is time.
Orchids lead to other things—
Satin ribbons, wedding rings,
Leases and refrigerators,
Apron strings, perambulators,
Cereal and safety pins,
Rice, and sometimes, even twins.

Tell me, brave young man, I pray,
Is she worth the price you pay?

132

HOW DOES IT FEEL?

DAVID BURNHAM

JUST before midnight I heard a noise in the corridor and opened my bedroom door the width of my eye. It was Nancy again. She was in evening dress, carrying her slippers in her hand. I watched her tiptoe the length of the hall and start down the stairs.

She disappeared around the bend, and a minute later I heard the front door open, then softly shut. A minute after that I heard a car go into gear a hundred feet up the road. From the noise of it, it was a Fiat. I shrugged my shoulders, went back to bed, and tried to forget the whole thing.

It was none of my business. She was a grown girl, and she had a mother and a father, and it was their affair, not mine, to look after her. My job was the boys. As she had frequently and in no uncertain terms reminded me, how and where and with whom Nancy spent her time was her own funeral.

But it's one thing to tell yourself that, and it's quite another thing to go to sleep.

The morning I arrived, a chauffeur met me at the station in an American station wagon. Don't let that throw you off; last summer in France you could trade a Ford suburban for a Rolls-Royce. It was the last week in June, Cannes; the season was just hitting full stride. The flowers were all out, all the trees were in blossom, the sidewalks were crowded with women out of fashion magazines, men out of the Almanach de Gotha and the Ritz Bar. The color of the Mediterranean was pure Dufy; the back-drop mountains were snow-sprinkled. We drove back toward these, up into the *California* quarter, midway between sea and snow. Mr. Whitman had rented his villa from a Parisian perfume king. It was in the modern style, white, low, cool, clean-cut. Great plate-glass view windows gave onto the sea; outdoor sun decks and terraces were shaded by candy-stripe awnings; the interior was decorated in cool blonds and pastels by a celebrated Finnish architect.

I was shown up to Mr. Whitman's dressing room. The barber from the Carlton was there, trimming Mr. Whitman's hair while he read the financial page of the Paris *Herald*. I introduced myself.

"Graham?"

I reminded him he had hired me in Paris a week ago to tutor his sons.

"Of course. Remembered you at once. You're the man what's-his-name, at the Guaranty Trust, dug up." He shook my hand. "Have you seen Mrs. Whitman yet? She's probably out, unless she broke a leg."

He was a young-looking successful American business man of about forty-five. He said, going back to his paper: "You'll find the boys outside somewhere. Try the swimming pool first."

They weren't at the pool. But from there I heard the *plumping* of tennis balls, and walked down to the next level.

Two boys—or rather, the same boy twice; ten years old, blackhaired, well-built, clean-featured—were playing tennis against their older sister. There seemed to be some question as to whether the last serve was inside or out. One of the boys was good-naturedly shouting across the net:

"You're a dirty stinking liar."

"Who's a liar? Here's the mark. Two feet out."

"You made that mark with your toe. Do you think we didn't see you?"

"I did no such thing!"

"We saw you. Didn't we, Peter?"

"Of course we did. What can you expect from a dopey girl?"

"Who's dopey?"

"I wonder. Who's dopey, Michael? You can have two guesses."

The girl said: "You're impossible. That's what I get for playing with children. I wouldn't if there were anything else to do."

One of the twins said to the other:

"Who's that dope watching us?"

The girl saw me then for the first time. She blushed. Then she scowled to cover it up. She was dark as her brothers, and at least as handsome. Dressed like them in shorts, she might have been anywhere from sixteen to twenty-two. She collected her dignity and came over to greet me.

"I'm Nancy Whitman. You must be the new tutor."

"Right. Jimmy Graham. Princeton '38."

"They're your headaches," she said, pointing across the net. "Heaven

134

help you!" she finished.

Michael and Peter were strolling over, hands in their pockets. "Take your hands out of your pockets," their sister ordered, "and shake hands with Mr. Graham."

Michael, or perhaps it was Peter, held out his hand. When I shook it, I felt something soft and cold and clammy against my palm. When I took my hand away, I was holding a live toad.

"Glad to know you," Michael said. "You know, you shouldn't handle those things. They give you warts."

I dropped the toad on the grass; it hopped indignantly away. There was no toad in Peter's hand. Instead, as soon as our hands met I got a violent electrical shock. Soberly watching me jump, Peter said to Michael: "Seems sort of a nervous type, don't he?"

"Doesn't he," Michael corrected. "You dope."

Nancy said: "Peter! Michael!" To me she said: "I hope father warned you." But she had to hold herself from smiling.

Michael and Peter started after the toad; no telling when he might come in handy again. Nancy asked me what train I came on, and I told her; I asked her whether she liked tennis and she said yes—did I? I did. Neither of us cared much for golf. The twins were back again, watching me light a cigarette. Seeing that my lighter wouldn't work in the wind, Michael handed me a box of matches.

The match exploded in my face.

Nancy said: "If you'd like to use my belt, Mr. Graham." But she was smiling again; looking down my nose, I could see that it was covered with soot.

Maybe, I decided, I didn't want to smoke just now, after all. I put the cigarette back in my case. Peter had given Michael a stick of gum and was unwrapping one for himself. Michael said: "Aren't you going to give him one?"

Peter politely retrieved the package from under the toad in his pocket and offered it to me. When I pulled out a stick, a hidden spring snapped out and nipped my finger.

"Very funny," Michael said witheringly. "Here." He gave me a stick from a genuine package from his own pocket.

There was no spring in Michael's gum. Instead, it was generously flavored with black pepper.

They were watching me, waiting for me to spit it out. I couldn't chew it; my mouth was burning up. So I swallowed it. When it went

135

down, each of their throats gave an involuntary gulp. I said: "Sorry. I swallowed that one. Got another piece?"

A sort of awed admiration widened their eyes as Michael brought out his package again. This stick he pulled from the bottom of the pack. And it was pure, honest peppermint.

They capitulated. Peter, or perhaps it was Michael, said: "Have you got a swimming suit? Last one in the water's a Democrat!"

I met Mrs. Whitman at dinner. I was late. When I came to dress, the sleeves of my dinner jacket had been knotted together, my tie had been decorated with lavender polka dots, and there was a live crab in the toe of each shoe. The twins had dined early. I locked their door before I went down, and my own, and put the two keys in my pocket. This was Nancy's birthday, and as a treat for her Mr. and Mrs. Whitman had invited a dozen of their own friends to dinner. Nancy, in a strapless white evening dress, I scarcely recognized. The nice-looking friendly kid the twins and I had swum and played tennis with had changed into a beautiful young woman, conscious of her new dignity as an adult: she was eighteen.

The guests were just beginning to arrive. Nancy was excited and happy. Each guest had a little present for her: perfume, charms for her bracelet, novelty jewelry. And each guest had a little speech:

"My, such a grown-up girl!"

"What a beauty she's become!"

"What a pretty dress, my dear! Just like a grown-up."

"How does it feel to be a grown-up?"

Their duty discharged, the guests forgot Nancy and settled down to the serious business of Martinis and have you heard the screaming story about Gladys? And *who* do you think we saw Archie with last night? It was a gay and amusing dinner, like the second act of an English comedy. As gay and amusing as that—and as long. I caught Nancy's eye several times. She too seemed to feel that this was a pretty lengthy build-up for ice cream and cake. She was allowed to drink a glass of champagne.

When we adjourned to the drawing room, Mr. Whitman's eye caught the clock set in a slab of moonstone over the fireplace.

"Almost eleven. Suppose we adjourn to the Casino for our brandies. They're saving me a place at the tables."

They looked about for Nancy to say good night. She was in the powder room. When she came out, they had all gone.

136

Hiding her eyes from me, Nancy got out a pack of cards and we played two-handed rummy. Nancy played carelessly at first and I won the first two games, and then she began to get interested and won three games running. She said:

"It's nice having you here. I like this much better than solitaire."

"I'm death," I said, "at Russian bank."

"How about pounce?"

"Nothing doing. A friend of mine lost an arm playing that."

The clock struck twelve. Seeing Nancy's expression, I said:

"Oh, well. Birthdays only come once a year."

Nancy smiled. "I *am* glad you're here."

My bed was pied when I went upstairs; the twins' talents evidently included lock-picking. There was glue in my bedroom slippers. My tooth powder was flavored with Epsom salts. There was a rubber spider on my pillow.

When it came time for lessons next morning, my pencil had a rubber point; my fountain pen contained a live water snake. There was a hot-seat in my chair.

There were three things I could do. Punish them; but that would make me an enemy. Complain to their parents; but they would never forgive that. Or I could meet them on their own ground. That night each of them had a pie bed. When they opened their bathroom door, a bucket of water spilled on them. A hidden alarm clock woke them up at one o'clock; another at three; another at five.

They came back at me with a dozen new tricks. The war was on.

The last tutor—a Harvard man—had left after two days. But I knew the twins weren't malicious—they were just out for fun. They were goodhearted and attractive kids and I liked them, and I didn't think they disliked me. But if I expected any peace this summer, if I wanted to get any work out of them, I had to make them respect me. I must beat them at their own game, think up something they couldn't think up. One afternoon while they were studying I took apart a portable radio and a house-telephone unit and rigged up a system for haunting their bedroom.

My room was next to theirs. I heard them moving around that night when they should have been in bed. I spoke through the microphone:

"Michael, get back into bed."

I heard Michael say: "Who said that?"

"That goes for you too, Peter."

137

"Who said *that*?"

The microphone said: "Look under the bed."

I heard them scrambling about.

"Not that bed; the other one."

More scrambling.

"Try the closet . . . the window seat . . . behind the curtains . . . Jiggers, here comes Mr. Graham!"

I opened their door. "What's all this noise in here? What are you two doing out of bed?"

I kept it up for three days. They tore the whole room apart looking for a clue. Finally, on the fourth day, they gave up and came to me. I unscrewed the head of their shower and showed them how I had run the wire through the pipe and set the microphone in the bend, so that the flare of the spout would act as an amplifier. They took their showers at the bathhouse, so I'd known they wouldn't be using this.

That turned the trick. From now on we were partners. We spent the afternoon transferring the haunter to Nancy's room.

The second night I used it on Nancy, I thought it might be fun to pretend the voice was an unknown admirer who was able to transmit his thoughts through the air. I started out in a sugary voice:

"Hello, darling."

I almost jumped out of bed when a voice said, right beside my ear: "Hello, dear."

I couldn't have really heard it. I went on:

"I'm lying in bed, unable to sleep for thinking about you, wondering if by some happy miracle the air might be able to transmit my thoughts to you . . . "

"Go on," the voice in my ear said. "You interest me strangely."

I said: "You rat! How did you find out? How did you do it?"

"Look under your pillow." There was a microphone there, a duplicate of the one I had made. "Don't disconnect it. I rather like this. You were saying—"

"I was saying you're a smarter girl than I thought you were."

"Don't change the subject."

"If the kids hear of this, my name's Mud."

"That's a useful suggestion. I might blackmail you."

"What would you like me to do?"

"Are you very sleepy?"

"Not particularly. Why?"

138

"How about a swim? There's a full moon."

"Fine. Meet you in five minutes at the pool."

They were good kids, all three of them; we had a good time together. We generally spent the morning doing the twins' lessons. The boys had quick, curious minds, and they learned quickly, once they began to co-operate with me. After lessons there was time for a set of tennis and a swim before lunch. When Mr. Whitman found out I could sail, he rented a boat for the boys, and afternoons I showed them how to handle it. It increased their respect for me that I could play a decent game of tennis and handle a boat. They transferred to me the affection that would ordinarily have gone to their parents, if their parents had cared to claim it.

I don't mean to make out Mr. and Mrs. Whitman as ogres. They were generous and indulgent. The children had all the advantages; they were given everything they asked for. But interest and understanding are something you can't have for the asking. Mr. and Mrs. Whitman had their own interests. The twins, fortunately, had each other. And Nancy—

Nancy, of course, should have been spending the summer at Cape Cod or Nantucket with a crowd of her own friends. I don't say that I wasn't glad she was not. As it was, finding no friends her own age, she spent most of her time with the twins and me. She made a fourth at tennis; she swam with us, sailed with us, went on the drives we took up and down the coast. For myself, it was an ideal arrangement. The days she wasn't with us seemed somehow twice as long. But for Nancy —well, this is what happened;

139

We were sailing one afternoon, and Nancy had the tiller. She was telling us about a man she had met the day before, when she had run into some friends of her mother's on the Croisette. An Italian count: super-handsome, black mustache, monocle. He had kissed Nancy's hand when they were introduced. Nancy had never met a count before. She was very impressed.

"Sounds like a dope," Michael said, bending his fingers in the shape of a monocle.

Peter elaborately kissed Michael's bare foot. "Call me County," he said.

"All right," Nancy said. "Wait until you see him. He promised—" She wasn't watching her course; she was making straight for a bell buoy. I shouted to her. "Come about!"

Nancy's eyes jerked up. She decided she could brush by the buoy by coming closer into the wind. But she obviously couldn't. I ordered again, "Come about."

Nancy set her jaw; she would show me.

She would also wreck the boat. I jumped across and jerked the tiller away from her and came about, and we missed the buoy by the width of a cigarette paper. Nancy was sitting there, her mouth sullen, rubbing her wrist where I had wrenched it.

I said, "Sorry if I hurt you. But when I say come about I mean come about."

Nancy flared up. "Whose boat is this? Yours or ours?"

"I'm skipper. If anything happens, I'm responsible."

"You're also omnipotent, apparently," she said. "It's all very well to order the boys about. But do you think I'm a child too, that I have to do everything you tell me?"

I didn't argue with her. I said: "Michael, you take the tiller. Peter, you take the jib sheets. We'll put back now."

Nancy went up forward and sulked. I was upset. I wanted to apologize; I wouldn't have talked like that if she hadn't frightened me. But I couldn't apologize in front of the boys without undoing everything I had taught them about sailing. Nancy continued to sulk, and I felt worse than there was any reason for. Or perhaps it was suddenly understanding the reason that upset me. We tacked back into the harbor, tied up at our buoy, and rowed ashore. There's a teashop on the quayside where we always stopped for ice cream before we drove home. At first Nancy said she wouldn't have anything, but finally she compromised on a double peach sundae and I began to feel better.

The boys had some sea shells they had picked up earlier. They also had a homemade magnifier—a long cylinder with an arrangement of lenses inside—that they were looking at the shells through, holding one end of the tube against their eye socket, like a telescope. They would look at one of the shells and then exclaim aloud in exaggerated wonderment.

It was pointed, of course, toward Nancy; they were waiting for her to break down and ask to look. She held out for three minutes, and then asked: "Let me look."

Michael gave her the glass. She didn't notice that he turned it about when he handed it to her. She put her eye against the black velvet eyepiece and looked at a shell.

"Is that all? It's just a magnifying glass." When she straightened up, there was a ring of soot around her eye socket. The boys had looked through the other end.

The boys didn't let on. The joke would be when she got home and found out, and wondered how long ago it happened. I called for the check, and we were just leaving when a man came in the door, and Nancy whispered excitedly, "There he is."

"Who?"

"Count Rapallo. The man I was telling you about."

The count recognized her. Nancy was right: he was a handsome party, if you go for that Latin type, and I have no doubt you do. About forty and trying to look thirty; and I'd have bet a month's salary that he wore a corset.

"Ah, Miss Whitman. What a delightful pleasure to see you ag—" He saw her eye and straightened from his hand-kissing stoop. "My dear young lady, whatever happened? *Poverina*. You've had an accident."

Nancy's eyebrows went up.

"Accident?"

"Your eye. So bruised."

Nancy turned to look in the wall mirror. She gingerly touched her eye with her finger. A smear of soot detached itself.

We burst out laughing then, the three of us; we couldn't keep it in any longer. Nancy'd been working so hard to be grown-up and worldly; and the count was so comically bewildered. Nancy took one more horrified look into the mirror, then into the count's handsome agape face, then rushed outside.

141

I followed her. "Nancy."

"I don't want to speak to you!" She kept her back to me and there were tears in her voice.

"Where's your sense of humor?"

"I suppose you think that was funny. Embarrassing me that way in front of—of all those people. What must he think of me?"

"What do you care? You'll never see him again."

"That's just it. He promised yesterday to call. The first attractive man I meet all summer, and you humiliate me in front of him!"

"Why blame me?"

"You probably put them up to it. You encourage them in their idiotic tricks; you teach them new ones. Well," she said, throwing out her chin, "I've had enough of it. I won't take orders from you or anybody else. From now on, you can play your tricks on each other. I refuse to waste my whole summer playing kid games with two children and their hired stooge."

That stopped me, that last phrase; that hit below the belt. There wasn't any answer to that. I stood there watching her get into the station wagon and drive off, leaving the twins and me to walk home.

I was good and mad. And the twins were good and mad, because they knew that Nancy had hurt me. And Nancy was good and mad. She stuck to what she said; our foursome became a threesome. No more tricks were played on Nancy. The twins avoided her like the plague. We went to work seriously on the twins' tennis, their diving, their sailing. In the back of our minds, all that was pointed toward Nancy. We were going to show her how much better things went without her.

The day after the incident at the teashop, the twins' underground grapevine reported that a box of roses had arrived for Nancy.

"From that count. There was a black crown on the card. He's coming this afternoon to call."

It was about a week later that I first heard Nancy sneaking out at night. When I got down to breakfast the next morning, the twins were arguing about whether the count's car that had waited up the road for her was a Bugatti or a Fiat. Her parents wouldn't have objected, probably, if she'd gone out with him openly, but I suppose it was more romantic this way. The car, by the way, the twins found out, was borrowed.

What made me maddest, as Nancy saw more and more of Rapallo,

142

was knowing that if there were anybody else about, people her own age, she never would have looked at him twice; if it hadn't been for that afternoon at the teashop, she probably never would have seen or thought about him again. But a thing can start like that, out of pique, and then grow into something important. He gave her what she wanted. He flattered her, he treated her like a grown-up.

So that night when I saw her go out, and a minute later heard the count's car start up, I told myself it was none of my business and went back to bed. But I didn't go to sleep. I lay there thinking round and round in the same old circle. I would think about it, and the longer I thought the madder I would get. She was a crazy little fool, a spoiled brat, and whatever happened to her would serve her right. But then all at once the madness would be gone, I would feel sorry for her because I felt so sorry for myself. My anger was all for her parents then. Maybe the thing to do was to take it to them, to get them to put a stop to this once and for all. But I knew I couldn't do that, behind her back.

I don't know how long I lay there, turning it over and over, wider awake every minute. Finally I realized I had to do something if I ever wanted to get to sleep, and I pulled on a bathrobe and walked down to the pool for a swim. I swam for half an hour, as hard as I could, until my bones ached, until every muscle was worn out. I rubbed myself down and started up to the house.

I didn't hear her—the first I knew was when I ran smack into Nancy coming up the walk from the front gate.

There wasn't a moon, but it wasn't quite dark either, and I can't tell you how lovely she looked in a fullskirted white evening dress with star sequins on it, and her face relaxed and open to the night.

But that didn't last long. "Well!" She was furious. "This is the last straw. Spying on me."

I was relaxed from my swim—my will as well as my body. An overwhelming impulse came to me to say, very simply: "I love you." But instead I said: "A pretty sight, I must say. Is he afraid to drive you to the door?"

"Have you been waiting here," she said, "hiding in the bushes ever since I left?"

"I've been for a swim," I said, "if you care to know. It's nothing to me if you sneak home from heaven knows where at three o'clock in the morning."

"We were at the Martinez Hotel," she said. "Dancing. Not that it's any of your business."

"You and your phony count."

Nancy snapped: "He's *not* phony. He belongs to one of the oldest families in Europe."

"I don't know about his family tree, but I can tell a phony when I see one."

"You're impossible," she said, and started up the path.

"Wait." I changed my tone. "Nancy, I hadn't meant to bring this up—I'd promised myself not to. But now that it's come up, we may as well have it out. You don't realize what you're doing. You're riding for an awful fall. This isn't one of you friends at home, a nice clean young college boy."

"Are you implying that—"

"I'm not implying anything. But I wonder if you realize what you're implying to your count. This isn't America, you know. In this country, when a young unmarried girl goes out alone at night with a man —much worse, when she sneaks out of the house to do it—that means only one thing to the man. Especially to a man like him."

Nancy drew herself up. "Before you go any further with your insults, you may be interested to know that Count Rapallo has asked me to marry him. He's coming tomorrow to speak to father."

"You little fool," I said, "don't you see he just wants to marry you for your—" Then I saw her eyes, and stopped myself. Slowly, painfully it was coming through. "You mean—you mean you're in love with him?"

"Yes." She set her chin. "Yes. I'm in love with him. And he's in love with me. You wouldn't know about a thing like that."

"Wouldn't I?" I thought. There was nothing to be said except:

"I'm sorry, Nancy. I wouldn't have said all this if I'd realized. You're right; it's none of my business and I should have stayed out of it."

I turned to leave. "Jimmy," she said, "before you go; let's be friends, the way it was at first. Won't you shake my hand and wish me luck? And be nice to Giorgio tomorrow, for my sake?"

I gave the twins a serious talk after lessons the next morning.

"Look, you two. I want to ask you a favor. Nancy's having a guest for lunch today—"

"Sure," they said. "We know. The count."

144

"I want you to promise me: no tricks."

"What's he coming for?"

"That's Nancy's affair, not ours."

"We know, don't we, Michael?"

"Sure. He's coming to ask father can he marry Nancy."

I said: "How did you find that out?"

"How did *you*?"

"She told me last night. But I'll bet my shirt she didn't tell *you*."

"Maybe she didn't exactly tell us."

The other said: "Well, that's one way of getting rid of Nancy."

"That's a nice thing," I said, "to say about your sister."

"We thought you were mad at her."

"I was. But I'm not any more."

"See?" Michael said to Peter. "I told you it was only an act."

"What do you mean, act?" I said.

"Why don't *you* marry her?" Peter said. "Then you could live with us all the time."

"Do you mean," Michael said, "that if she marries the count, then he'll live with us? Kissing hands all the time? Jimmy, you marry her, please!"

"She likes you. After you bawled her out that day in the boat, she cried herself to sleep."

"How do you know?"

"We heard her. And she stole that picture we took of you."

"That's enough of this," I said. "She's in love with Giorgio Rapallo. She told me so herself. And I'm asking you, as a special favor to me, to lay off him today. For once in your life, show a little consideration for your sister."

"Consideration? To let her hook up with that dope?" Peter went through his old gag of kissing Michael's foot.

"All right," I said. "That's enough. Nobody thinks you're funny. Get your swimming suits."

When the twins came down for lunch, their father took one look at them and said, "What's the matter? Are you boys sick?"

They were wearing freshly laundered white suits. Their faces were scrubbed. Their fingernails were spotless. Their hair was slick.

They bowed politely to the count. "How do you do, Count Rapallo?" While we drank our Dubonnets they sat quietly in their chairs, with no fidgeting. Nancy, too, couldn't believe her eyes. She took me

145

aside as we adjourned to the dining room to whisper: "Thank you, Jimmy. I knew you'd help."

Mrs. Whitman sat at one end of the table, Mr. Whitman at the other; the count at Mrs. Whitman's right, Nancy beside him at her father's left; myself between the twins opposite. The count was immaculately dressed in one of those green silk suits they evidently throw in free when you buy a green shirt in Italy. His necktie was a deeper shade of green; his socks were olive; his shoes were green suede.

He ceremoniously bowed Mrs. Whitman into her chair, then Nancy, then took his own. As he squatted, there was an ominous sound of ripping. The count straightened; he lowered himself more carefully. Again the ripping. The count, delicately using the hand away from his hostess, tested the seam of his trousers. They appeared intact; but the noise of ripping continued until he was firmly in his chair. The count wiped a bead of perspiration from his brow with his green-bordered handkerchief. I took a quick look at the twins. Their faces were angelic.

The count, still uncomfortably warm, took a drink of water. A thin stream trickled down his necktie. He apologized to Mrs. Whitman.

"So clumsy of me."

The count began his consommé. All went well until the last sip. He started; the cup slipped from his fingers, smashed itself against the saucer. Mrs. Whitman looked up.

"Fortunately," she said graciously, "it's an open pattern."

The count politely refrained from explaining that he had found a dead fly in the bottom of his cup. He didn't know that it was made of rubber, but I did, and gave the twins a warning glare; and I saw that Nancy was scowling at them too.

The entrées had been passed. The count was glancing strangely at his plate. It was rocking gently to and fro. I reached under the table for the rubber bulb one of the twins must be manipulating, but I couldn't reach it. The count removed his monocle, polished it with his handkerchief, replaced it. He took up his knife to cut his meat. As he pressed down, the knife bent back to a sixty-degree angle.

The count quickly concealed the knife under his napkin, glancing down to see whether Mrs. Whitman had noticed that he was despoiling her silverware. Guiltily he worked to bend it back into shape. Nancy was scowling more deeply; the twins were dead-pan. The count tried his fork. Its prongs squashed together. Mrs. Whitman said:

146

"I must apologize. The silver comes with the house, you know."

The count wiped his brow again. Mr. Whitman said: "Michael, what are you doing under the table?"

Michael came up. "Dropped my napkin, sir."

A minute later the count began to squirm. You might have thought a colony of ants had run up his trouser leg—as no doubt they had.

There were bright spots of anger on Nancy's cheeks as she glared across the table at her brothers.

The count was chewing on a roll. He chewed, and chewed, and chewed. Then he sheepishly set the roll back on his plate, hoping Mrs. Whitman's household pride wouldn't be offended. The roll was a good imitation; any one not knowing the twins would never have suspected it was rubber. Mrs. Whitman was watching the count, more and more puzzled by his strange behavior. Mr. Whitman said, "Peter, now what are *you* doing under the table?"

"Dropped my napkin, sir."

"Seems to me there's a good deal of napkin dropping at this table. Not to mention"—he glanced significantly at Count Napallo—"not to mention other mighty strange goings-on."

The count flushed and reached for his wineglass. This time it was a red stream that ran down his tie.

Mrs. Whitman said, "How unfortunate! Your pretty necktie."

"I'm afraid I've stained your cloth, too." It was her best cloth, and Mrs. Whitman's smile was a bit on the stiff side.

I knew from experience that dribble glasses are only the beginning; under the table, I pinched both the twins. They said together, "Ouch!"

Their mother looked up. "What's the matter?"

"Somebody pinched us. It seemed to come from across the table." Mrs. Whitman glared at the count. His expression was a mixture of embarrassment and bewilderment. He dabbed his forehead with his napkin—it was yellow linen—and a series of bright yellow smudges appeared on his perspiring face. He took another drink from his water glass. Another dribble down his front. Mrs. Whitman was watching him in growing perplexity.

The maids had brought dessert: vanilla ice cream with chocolate sauce. When the count lifted his spoon, it bent back double. Mr. Whitman was grinning now. To cover up, he looked away. Michael's head had disappeared again.

"*Will* you boys stay in your seats?"

147

"Sorry, sir. Napkin again."

Mrs. Whitman said, "I *must* say, this is a very curious luncheon party." She glanced at Nancy as though to ask, "Does your friend always carry on like this at meals?"

The count had found a safe spoon. He beamed with pleasure upon his dessert; it was evidently a favorite of his. He loaded his spoon, raised it to his mouth.

He coughed violently, dropped his spoon, hid his face behind his napkin. Mrs. Whitman, suspecting disaster in the kitchen, sampled her own dessert, then shrugged her shoulders. These foreigners. If she had looked more closely, she might have noticed that the count's chocolate sauce was half a shade darker than ours—pure castoria.

A man's last resource is a cigarette. The count took a cigarette from the crystal container by his place. He lighted it, inhaled deeply. His face lost the better part of its redness, if it couldn't lose its yellow spots. He inhaled again—again, with growing confidence. Now he had recovered himself; a man with a cigarette is beyond embarrassment.

There was a sudden explosion. My eyes, fearing the worst, jumped to the count. He was no longer smoking. A few wisps of blackened tobacco dripped from his lips.

Mr. Whitman had given up. He was doubled up with laughter. The twins let go, too, forgiven by their father's laughter. And even Nancy, at last. You couldn't look at that outraged speckled face without laughing.

The count had had enough. More than enough. He collected the shattered remnants of his dignity and pushed back his chair. "I have always heard that all Americans are insane. Now I know it. I shall never set foot in this house again." He turned his indignant back on us and stalked toward the door. And when I say stalked, I mean stalked.

And then I discovered why the twins had dropped their napkins so often. They had tied a corner of the tablecloth to the count's shoelace. Count Rapallo did not leave alone. The tablecloth followed him. The entire luncheon service crashed to the tile floor.

I found Nancy outside on the terrace.

"Are you angry?"

She wouldn't answer.

"I had nothing to do with it. Honestly."

She didn't answer.

"I made them promise not to. But I'm glad it happened. You weren't

148

really in love with him. It was just growing pains."

No answer; she kept her back to me.

"It *was* funny. Even you thought so, didn't you? You were laughing at the end. It's more fun to laugh than to be grown up, don't you think?"

She turned then. And her eyes weren't angry; they were soft and forgiving and inviting.

Her silence too was an invitation. I came closer to kiss her.

A stream of cold water splashed into my face. The reason she hadn't spoken was because she had filled her mouth with ice water before she left the table.

There were whispered voices in an upstairs window.

Michael: "Two bits he gives her a licking."

Peter: "Two bits he kisses her."

And then, a minute later:

Michael: "See? Pay up."

Another minute.

"Here—give me back that quarter!"

TO A THESAURUS

FRANKLIN P. ADAMS

O precious codex, volume, tome,
    Book, writing, compilation, work,
Attend the while I pen a pome,
    A jest, a jape, a quip, a quirk.

For I would pen, engross, indite,
    Transcribe, set forth, compose, address,
Record, submit—yea, even write
    An ode, an elegy to bless—

To bless, set store by, celebrate,
    Approve, esteem, endow with soul,
Commend, acclaim, appreciate,
    Immortalize, laud, praise, extol

Thy merit, goodness, value, worth,
    Expedience, utility—
O manna, honey, salt of earth,
    I sing, I chant, I worship thee!

How could I manage, live, exist,
    Obtain, produce, be real, prevail,
Be present in the flesh, subsist,
    Have place, become, breathe or inhale

150

Without thy help, recruit, support,
  Opitulation, furtherance,
Assistance, rescue, aid, resort,
  Favour, sustention and advance?

Alas! Alack! and well-a-day!
  My case would then be dour and sad,
Likewise distressing, dismal, grey,
  Pathetic, mournful, dreary, bad.

*   *   *   *

Though I could keep this up all day,
  This lyric, elegiac song,
Meseems hath come the time to say
  Farewell! Adieu! Good-bye! So long!

"Oh, no, it's naturally curly!"

151

THE GREAT PANCAKE RECORD

OWEN JOHNSON

LITTLE SMEED stood apart, in the obscure shelter of the station, waiting to take his place on the stage which would carry him to the great new boarding school. He was frail and undersized, with a long, pointed nose and vacant eyes that stupidly assisted the wide mouth to make up a famished face. The scarred bag in his hand hung from one clasp, the premature trousers were at half-mast, while pink polka-dots blazed from the cuffs of his nervous sleeves.

By the wheels of the stage "Fire Crackers" Glendenning and "Jock" Hasbrouck, veterans of the Kennedy House, sporting the varsity initials on their sweaters and caps, were busily engaged in cross-examining the new boys who clambered timidly to their places on top. Presently, Fire Crackers, perceiving Smeed, hailed him.

"Hello, over there—what's your name?"

"Smeed, sir."

"Smeed what?"

"Johnnie Smeed."

The questioner looked him over with disfavor and said aggressively: "You're not for the Kennedy?"

"No, sir."

"What house?"

"The Dickinson, sir."

"The Dickinson, eh? That's a good one," said Fire Crackers, with a laugh, and, turning to his companion, he added, "Say, Jock, won't Hickey and the old Turkey be wild when they get this one?"

Little Smeed, uncomprehending of the judgment that had been passed, stowed his bag inside and clambered up to a place on the top. Jimmy, at the reins, gave a warning shout. The horses, stirred by the whip, churned obediently through the sideways of Trenton.

Lounging on the stage were half a dozen newcomers, six well-assorted types, from the well-groomed stripling of the city to the aggressive, big-limbed animal from the West, all profoundly under the sway of the two old boys who sat on the box with Jimmy and rattled on with quiet superiority. The coach left the outskirts of the city and rolled into the white highway that leads to Lawrenceville. The known world departed for Smeed. He gazed fearfully ahead, waiting the first glimpse of the new continent.

Suddenly Fire Crackers turned and, scanning the embarrassed group, singled out the strong Westerner with an approving glance.

"You're for the Kennedy?"

The boy, stirring uneasily, blurted out:

"Yes, sir."

"What's your name?"

"Tom Walsh."

"How old are you?"

"Eighteen."

"What do you weigh?"

"One hundred and seventy."

"Stripped?"

"What? Oh, no, sir—regular way."

"You've played a good deal of football?"

"Yes, sir."

153

Hasbrouck took up the questioning with a critical appreciation.

"What position?"

"Guard and tackle."

"You know Bill Stevens?"

"Yes, sir."

"He spoke about you; said you played on the Military Academy. You'll try for the 'varsity?"

"I guess so."

Hasbrouck turned to Fire Crackers in solemn conclave.

"He ought to stand up against Turkey if he knows anything about the game. If we get a good end we ought to give that Dickinson crowd the fight of their lives."

"There's a fellow came from Montclair they say is pretty good," Fire Crackers said, with solicitous gravity. "The line'll be all right if we can get some good halves. That's where the Dickinson has it on us."

Smeed listened in awe to the two statesmen studying out the chances of the Kennedy eleven for the house championship, realizing suddenly that there were new and sacred purposes about his new life of which he had no conception. Then, absorbed by the fantasy of the trip and the strange unfolding world into which he was jogging, he forgot the lords of the Kennedy, forgot his fellows in ignorance, forgot that he didn't play football and was only a stripling, forgot everything but the fascination of the moment when the great school would rise out of the distance and fix itself indelibly in his memory.

"There's the water tower," said Jimmy, extending the whip; "you'll see the school from the top of the hill."

Little Smeed craned forward with a sudden thumping of his heart. In the distance, a mile away, a cluster of brick and tile sprang out of the green, like a herd of red deer surprised in the forest. Groups of boys began to show on the roadside. Strange greetings were flung back and forth.

"Hello-oo, Fire Crackers!"

"How-de-do, Saphead!"

"Oh, there, Jock Hasbrouck!"

"Oh, you Morning Glory!"

"Oh, you Kennedys, we're going to lick you!"

"Yes you are, Dickinson!"

The coach passed down the shaded vault of the village street, turned into the campus, passed the ivy-clad house of the head master and rolled

154

around a circle of well-trimmed lawn, past the long, low Upper House where the Fourth Form gazed at them in senior superiority; past the great brown masses of Memorial Hall and the pointed chapel, around to where the houses were ranged in red, extended bodies. Little Smeed felt an abject sinking of the heart at this sudden exposure to the thousand eyes fastened upon him from the wide esplanade of the Upper, from the steps of Memorial, from house, windows and stoops, from the shade of apple trees and the glistening road.

All at once the stage stopped and Jimmy cried:

"Dickinson!"

At one end of the red-brick building, overrun with cool vines, a group of boys were lolling in flannels and light jerseys. A chorus went up.

"Hello, Fire Crackers!"

"Hello, Jock!"

"Hello, you Hickey boy!"

"Hello, Turkey; see what we've brought you!"

Smeed dropped to the ground amid a sudden hush.

"Fare," said Jimmy aggressively.

Smeed dug into his pocket and tendered the necessary coin. The coach squeaked away, while from the top Fire Crackers' exulting voice returned in insolent exultation:

"Hard luck, Dickinson! Hard luck, you, old Hickey!"

Little Smeed, his hat askew, his collar rolled up, his bag at his feet, stood in the road, alone in the world, miserable and thoroughly frightened. One path led to the silent, hostile group on the steps, another went in safety to the master's entrance. He picked up his bag hastily.

"Hello, you—over there!"

Smeed understood it was a command. He turned submissively and approached with embarrassed steps. Face to face with these superior beings, tanned and muscular, stretched in Olympian attitudes, he realized all at once the hopelessness of his ever daring to associate with such demi-gods. Still he stood, shifting from foot to foot, eying the steps, waiting for the solemn ordeal of examination and classification to be over.

"Well, Hungry—what's your name?"

Smeed comprehended that the future was decided, and that to the grave he would go down as "Hungry" Smeed. With a sigh of relief he answered:

155

"Smeed—John Smeed."

"Sir!"

"Sir."

"How old?"

"Fifteen."

"Sir!!"

"Sir."

"What do you weigh?"

"One hundred and six—sir!"

A grim silence succeeded this depressing information. Then someone in the back, as a mere matter of form, asked:

"Never played football?"

"No, sir."

"Baseball?"

"No, sir."

"Anything on the track?"

"No, sir."

"Sing?"

"No, sir," said Smeed, humbly.

"Do anything at all?"

Little Smeed glanced at the eaves where the swallows were swaying and then down at the soft couch of green at his feet and answered faintly:

"No, sir—I'm afraid not."

Another silence came, then some one said, in a voice of deepest conviction:

"A dead loss!"

Smeed went sadly into the house.

At the door he lingered long enough to hear the chorus burst out:

"A fine football team we'll have!"

"It's a put-up job!"

"They don't want us to win the championship again—that's it!"

"I say, we ought to kick."

Then, after a little, the same deep voice:

"A dead loss!"

With each succeeding week Hungry Smeed comprehended more fully the enormity of his offense in doing nothing and weighing one hundred and six pounds. He saw the new boys arrive, pass through the

156

fire of christening, give respectable weights and go forth to the gridiron to be whipped into shape by Turkey and the Butcher, who played on the school eleven. Smeed humbly and thankfully went down each afternoon to the practice, carrying the sweaters and shinguards, like the grateful little beast of burden that he was. He watched his juniors, Spider and Red Dog, rolling in the mud or flung gloriously under an avalanche of bodies; but then, they weighed over one hundred and thirty, while he was still at one hundred and six—a dead loss! The fever of the house loyalty invaded him; he even came to look with resentment on the Faculty and to repeat secretly to himself that they never would have unloaded him on the Dickinson if they hadn't been willing to stoop to any methods to prevent the House again securing the championship.

The fact that the Dickinson, in an extraordinary manner, finally won by the closest of margins, consoled Smeed but a little while. There were no more sweaters to carry, or pails of barley water to fetch, or guard to be mounted on the old rail fence, to make certain that the spies from the Davis and Kennedy did not surprise the secret plays which Hickey and Slugger Jones had craftily evolved.

157

With the long winter months he felt more keenly his obscurity and the hopelessness of ever leaving a mark on the great desert of school life that would bring honor to the Dickinson. He resented even the lack of the mild hazing the other boys received—he was too insignificant to be so honored. He was only a "dead loss," good for nothing but to squeeze through his recitations, to sleep enormously, and to eat like a glutton with a hunger that could never be satisfied, little suspecting the future that lay in this famine of his stomach.

For it was written in the inscrutable fates that Hungry Smeed should leave a name that would go down imperishably to decades of school-boys, when Dibbles' touchdown against Princeton and Kafer's home run should be only tinkling sounds. So it happened, and the agent of this divine destiny was Hickey.

It so happened that examinations being still in the threatening distance, Hickey's fertile brain was unoccupied with methods of facilitating his scholarly progress by homely inventions that allowed formulas and dates to be concealed in the palm and disappear obligingly up the sleeve on the approach of the Natural Enemy. Moreover, Hickey and Hickey's friends were in straitened circumstances, with all credit gone at the jigger-shop, and the appetite for jiggers in an acute stage of deprivation.

In this keenly sensitive, famished state of his imagination, Hickey suddenly became aware of a fact fraught with possibilities. Hungry Smeed had an appetite distinguished and remarkable even in that company of aching voids.

No sooner had this pregnant idea become his property than Hickey confided his hopes to Doc Macnooder, his chum and partner in plans that were dark and mysterious. Macnooder saw in a flash the glorious and lucrative possibilities. A very short series of tests sufficed to convince the twain that in little Smeed they had a phenomenon who needed only to be properly developed to pass into history.

Accordingly, on a certain muddy morning in March, Hickey and Doc Macnooder, with Smeed in tow, stole into the jigger-shop at an hour in defiance of regulations and fraught with delightful risks of detection.

Al, the watch-dog of the jigger, was tilted back, near a farther window, the parted tow hair falling doglike over his eyes, absorbed in the reading of Spenser's Faerie Queene, an abnormal taste which made him absolutely incomprehensible to the boyish mind. At the sound of the

158

stolen entrance, Al put down the volume and started mechanically to rise. Then, recognizing his visitors, he returned to his chair, saying wearily:

"Nothing doing, Hickey."

"Guess again," said Hickey, cheerily. "We're not asking you to hang us up this time, Al."

"You haven't got any money," said Al, the recorder of allowances; "not unless you stole it."

"Al, we don't come to take your hard-earned money, but to do you good," put in Macnooder impudently. "We're bringing you a little sporting proposition."

"Have you come to pay up that account of yours?" said Al. "If not, run along, you Macnooder; don't waste my time, with your wildcat schemes."

"Al, this is a sporting proposition," took up Hickey.

"Has *he* any money?" said Al, who suddenly remembered that Smeed was not yet under suspicion.

"See here, Al," said Macnooder, "we'll back Smeed to eat the jiggers against you—for the crowd!"

"Where's your money?"

"Here," said Hickey; "this goes up if we lose." He produced a gold watch of Smeed's, and was about to tender it when he withdrew it with a sudden caution. "On the condition, if we win I get it back and you won't hold it up against my account."

"All right. Let's see it."

The watch was given to Al, who looked it over, grunted in approval, and then looked at little Smeed.

"Now, Al," said Macnooder softly, "give us a gambling chance; he's only a runt."

Al considered, and Al was wise. The proposition came often and he never lost. A jigger is unlike any other ice cream; it is dipped from the creamy tin by a cone-shaped scoop called a jigger, which gives it an unusual and peculiar flavor. Since those days the original jigger has been contaminated and made ridiculous by offensive alliances with upstart syrups, meringues and macaroons with absurd titles; but then the boy went to the simple jigger as the sturdy Roman went to the cold waters of the Tiber. A double jigger fills a large soda glass when ten cents has been laid on the counter, and two such glasses quench all desire in the normal appetite.

159

"If he can eat twelve double jiggers," Al said slowly, "I'll set them up and the jiggers for youse. Otherwise, I'll hold the watch."

At this there was a protest from the backers of the champion, with the result that the limit was reduced to ten.

"Is it a go?" Al said, turning to Smeed, who had waited modestly in the background.

"Sure," he answered, with calm certainty.

"You've got nerve, you have," said Al, with a scornful smile, scooping up the first jiggers and shoving the glass to him. "Ten doubles is the record in these parts, young fellow!"

Then little Smeed, methodically, and without apparent pain, ate the ten doubles.

Conover's was not in the catalogue that anxious parents study, but then catalogues are like epitaphs in a cemetery. Next to the jiggershop, Conover's was quite the most important institution in the school. In a little white Colonial Cottage, Conover, veteran of the late war, and Mrs. Conover, still in active service, supplied pancakes and maple syrup on a cash basis, two dollars credit to second-year boys in good repute. Conover's, too, had its traditions. Twenty-six pancakes, large and thick, in one continuous sitting, was the record, five years old, standing to the credit of Guzzler Wilkins, which succeeding classes had attacked in vain. Wily Conover, to stimulate such profitable tests, had solemnly pledged himself to the delivery of free pancakes to all comers during that day on which any boy, at one continuous sitting, unaided, should succeed in swallowing the awful number of thirty-two. Conover was not considered a prodigal.

This deed of heroic accomplishment and public benefaction was the true goal of Hickey's planning. The test of the jigger-shop was but a preliminary trying out. With medical caution, Doc Macnooder refused to permit Smeed to go beyond the ten doubles, holding very wisely that the jigger record could wait for a further day. The amazed Al was sworn to secrecy.

It was Wednesday, and the following Saturday was decided upon for the supreme test at Conover's. Smeed at once was subjected to a graduated system of starvation. Thursday he was hungry, but Friday he was so ravenous that a watch was instituted on all his movements.

The next morning the Dickinson House, let into the secret, accompanied Smeed to Conover's. If there was even a possibility of free pancakes, the House intended to be satisfied before the deluge broke.

160

Great was the astonishment at Conover's at the arrival of the procession.

"Mr. Conover," said Hickey, in the quality of manager, "we're going after that pancake record."

"Mr. Wilkins' record?" said Conover, seeking vainly the champion in the crowd.

"No—after that record of *yours*," answered Hickey. "Thirty-two pancakes—we're here to get free pancakes today—that's what we're here for."

"So, boys, so," said Conover, smiling pleasantly; "and you want to begin now?"

"Right off the bat."

"Well, where is he?"

Little Smeed, famished to the point of tears, was thrust forward. Conover, who was expecting something on the lines of a buffalo, smiled confidently.

"So, boys, so," he said, leading the way with alacrity. "I guess we're ready, too."

"Thirty-two pancakes, Conover—and we get 'em free!"

"That's right," answered Conover, secure in his knowledge of boyish capacity. "If that little boy there can eat thirty-two I'll make them all day free to the school. That's what I said, and what I say goes—and that's what I say now."

Hickey and Doc Macnooder whispered the last instructions in Smeed's ear.

"Cut out the syrup."

"Loosen your belt."

"Eat slowly."

In a low room, with the white rafters impending over his head, beside a basement window flanked with geraniums, little Smeed sat down to battle for the honor of the Dickinson and the record of the school. Directly under his eyes, carved on the wooden table, a name challenged him, standing out of the numerous initials—Guzzler Wilkins.

"I'll keep count," said Hickey. "Macnooder and Turkey, watch the pancakes."

"Regulation size, Conover," cried that cautious Red Dog; "no doubling now. All fair and above board."

"All right, Hickey, all right," said Conover, leering wickedly from the door; "if that little grasshopper can do it, you get the cakes."

161

"Now, Hungry," said Turkey, clapping Smeed on the shoulder. "Here is where you get your chance. Remember, Kid, old sport, it's for the Dickinson."

Smeed heard in ecstasy; it was just the way Turkey talked to the eleven on the eve of a match. He nodded his head with a grim little shake and smiled nervously at the thirty-odd Dickinsonians who formed around him a pit of expectant and hungry boyhood from the floor to the ceiling.

"All ready!" sang out Turkey, from the doorway.

"Six pancakes!"

"Six it is," replied Hickey, chalking up a monster 6 on the slate that swung from the rafters. The pancakes placed before the ravenous Smeed vanished like snow-flakes on a July lawn.

A cheer went up, mingled with cries of caution.

"Not so fast."

"Take your time."

"Don't let them be too hot."

"Not too hot, Hickey!"

Macnooder was instructed to watch carefully over the temperature as well as the dimensions.

"Ready again," came the cry.

"Ready—how many?"

"Six more."

"Six it is," said Hickey, adding a second figure to the score. "Six and six are twelve."

The second batch went the way of the first.

"Why, that boy is starving," said Conover, opening his eyes.

"Sure he is," said Hickey. "He's eating 'way back in last week—he hasn't had a thing for ten days."

"Six more," cried Macnooder.

"Six it is," answered Hickey. "Six and twelve is eighteen."

"Eat them one at a time, Hungry."

"No, let him alone."

"He knows best."

"Not too fast, Hungry, not too fast."

"Eighteen for Hungry, eighteen. Hurrah!"

"Thirty-two is a long ways to go," said Conover, gazing apprehensively at the little David who had come so impudently into his domain; "fourteen pancakes is an awful lot."

162

"Shut up, Conover."

"No trying to influence him there."

"Don't listen to him, Hungry."

"He's only trying to get you nervous."

"Fourteen more, Hungry—fourteen more."

"Ready again," sang out Macnooder.

"Ready here."

"Three pancakes."

"Three it is," responded Hickey. "Eighteen and three is twenty-one."

But a storm of protest arose.

"Here, that's not fair!"

"I say, Hickey, don't let them do that."

"I say, Hickey, it's twice as hard that way."

"Oh, go on."

"Sure it is."

"Of course it is."

"Don't you know that you can't drink a glass of beer if you take it with a teaspoon?"

"That's right, Red Dog's right! Six at a time."

"Six at a time!"

A hurried consultation was now held and the reasoning approved. Macnooder was charged with the responsibility of seeing to the number as well as the temperature and dimensions.

Meanwhile Smeed had eaten the pancakes.

"Coming again!"

"All ready here."

"Six pancakes!"

"Six," said Hickey; "twenty-one and six is twenty-seven."

"That'll beat Guzzler Wilkins."

"So it will."

"Five more makes thirty-two."

"Easy, Hungry, easy."

"Hungry's done it; he's done it."

"Twenty-seven and the record!"

"Hurrah!"

At this point Smeed looked about anxiously.

"It's pretty dry," he said, speaking for the first time.

Instantly there was a panic. Smeed was reaching his limit—a groan went up.

163

"Oh, Hungry."

"Only five more."

"Give him some water."

"Water, you loon; do you want to end him?"

"Why?"

"Water'll swell up the pancakes!"

"No water, no water."

Hickey approached his man with anxiety.

"What is it, Hungry? Anything wrong?" he said tenderly.

"No, only it's a little dry," said Smeed, unmoved. "I'm all right, but I'd like just a drop of syrup now."

The syrup was discussed, approved and voted.

"You're sure you're all right," said Hickey.

"Oh, yes."

Conover, in the last ditch, said carefully:

"I don't want no fits around here."

A cry of protest greeted him.

"Well, son, that boy can't stand much more. That's just like the Guzzler. He was taken short and we had to work over him for an hour."

"Conover, shut up!"

"Conover, you're beaten."

"Conover, that's an old game."

"Get out."

"Shut up."

"Fair play! Fair play!"

A new interruption came from the kitchen. Macnooder claimed that Mrs. Conover was doubling the size of her cakes. The dish was brought. There was no doubt about it. The cakes were swollen. Pandemonium broke loose. Conover capitulated, the cakes were rejected.

"Don't be feazed by that," said Hickey, warningly to Smeed.

"I'm not," said Smeed.

"All ready," came Macnooder's cry.

"Ready here."

"Six pancakes!"

"Regulation size?"

"Regulation."

"Six it is," said Hickey, at the slate. "Six and twenty-seven is thirty-three."

164

"Wait a moment," sang out the Butcher. "He has only to eat thirty-two."

"That's so—take one off."

"Give him five, Hickey—five only."

"If Hungry says he can eat six," said Hickey, firmly, glancing at his protégé, "he can. We're out for big things. Can you do it, Hungry?"

And Smeed, fired with the heroism of the moment, answered in disdainful simplicity:

"Sure!"

A cheer that brought two Davis House boys running in greeted the disappearance of the thirty-third. Then everything was forgotten in the amazement of the deed.

"Please, I'd like to go on," said Smeed.

"Oh, Hungry, can you do it?"

"Really?"

"You're goin' on?"

"Holy cats!"

"How'll you take them?" said Hickey, anxiously.

"I'll try another six," said Smeed, thoughtfully, "and then we'll see."

Conover, vanquished and convinced, no longer sought to intimidate him with horrid suggestions.

"Mr. Smeed," he said, giving him his hand in admiration, "you go ahead; you make a great record."

"Six more," cried Macnooder.

165

"Six it is," said Hickey, in an awed voice; "six and thirty-three makes thirty-nine!"

Mrs. Conover and Macnooder, no longer antagonists, came in from the kitchen to watch the great spectacle. Little Smeed alone, calm and unconscious, with the light of a great ambition on his forehead, ate steadily, without vacillation.

"Gee, what a stride!"

"By Jiminy, where does he put it?" said Conover, staring helplessly.

"Holy cats!"

"Thirty-nine—thirty-nine pancakes—gee!!!"

"Hungry," said Hickey, entreatingly, "do you think you could eat another—make it an even forty?"

"Three more," said Smeed, pounding the table with a new authority. This time no voice rose in remonstrance. The clouds had rolled away. They were in the presence of a master.

"Pancakes coming."

"Bring them in!"

"Three more."

"Three it is," said Hickey, faintly. "Thirty-nine and three makes forty-two—forty-two. Gee!"

In profound silence the three pancakes passed regularly from the plate down the throat of little Smeed. Forty-two pancakes!

"Three more," said Smeed.

Doc Macnooder rushed in hysterically.

"Hungry, go the limit—the limit! If anything happens I'll bleed you."

"Shut up, Doc!"

"Get out, you wild man."

Macnooder was sent ignominiously back into the kitchen, with the curses of the Dickinsons, and Smeed assured of their unfaltering protection.

"Three more," came the cry from the chastened Macnooder.

"Three it is," said Hickey. "Forty-two and three makes—forty-five."

"Holy cats!"

Still little Smeed, without appreciable abatement of hunger, continued to eat. A sense of impending calamity and alarm began to spread. Forty-five pancakes, and still eating! It might turn into a tragedy.

"Say, bub—say, now," said Hickey, gazing anxiously down into the pointed face, "you've done enough—don't get rash."

166

"I'll stop when it's time," said Smeed; "bring 'em on now, one at a time."

"Forty-six, forty-seven, forty-eight, forty-nine!"

Suddenly, at the moment when they expected him to go on forever, little Smeed stopped, gazed at his plate, then at the fiftieth pancake, and said:

"That's all."

Forty-nine pancakes! Then, and only then, did they return to a realization of what had happened. They cheered Smeed, they sang his praises, they cheered again, and then, pounding the table, they cried, in a mighty chorus:

"We want pancakes!"

"Bring us pancakes!"

"Pancakes, pancakes, we want pancakes!"

Twenty minutes later, Red Dog and the Egghead, fed to bursting, rolled out of Conover's, spreading the uproarious news.

"Free pancakes! Free pancakes!"

The nearest houses, the Davis and the Rouse, heard and came with a rush.

Red Dog and the Egghead staggered down into the village and over to the circle of houses, throwing out their arms like returning bacchanalians.

"Free pancakes!"

"Hungry Smeed's broken the record!"

"Pancakes at Conover's—free pancakes!"

The word jumped from house to house, the campus was emptied in a trice. The road became choked with the hungry stream that struggled, fought, laughed and shouted as it stormed to Conover's.

"Free pancakes! Free pancakes!"

"Hurrah for Smeed!"

"Hurrah for Hungry Smeed!!"

167

A PAIR OF SEXES

FRANKLIN P. ADAMS

I. A MAN TELEPHONES

"Ed? ... Lunch at one. Whyte's. Right."

II. A WOMAN TELEPHONES

"Hello. Operator. Operator? I want Caledonia five eight six seven, please. Oh, this *is* Caledonia five eight six seven? Oh, I beg your pardon. I'm terribly sorry. I thought it was the operator. I've had so much trouble with the telephone lately. May I speak to Miss Lucille Webster, please? Oh, *speaking?* Oh, I'm terribly sorry. Is this Miss Webster? Is this you, Lucille? I didn't recognize your voice at first. First I thought it was the operator, and then I thought it was somebody answering for you, Lucille. I didn't recognize your voice at first. Got a cold or something? Oh, you sound as though you had. There's so much of it around this wretched weather. I never saw anything like it in my whole life. Well, I'm glad you haven't got a cold, though at first you certainly sounded like it. . . . I was just talking to Ethel for a second, and she had such a cold she could hardly talk. That's the reason I asked you. There's an *awful* lot of it around this wretched weather. . . . Oh, nothing particular. . . . Oh, yes, there is too. How silly of me! I was so interested in what you were saying, I almost forgot. Lucille, what are you doing tomorrow? . . . No, about lunch time. Or a little earlier. Or a little later. It doesn't matter. Because I expect to be in your part of town about that time, around lunch time, oh, maybe one or one-thirty or so, I have an appointment at twelve-thirty, and it oughtn't to take me more than half an hour, or at the most three quarters, surely not over an hour, I'm almost certain, and probably I'll be through in half an hour, but, anyway, I ought to be all through by one-thirty, and I could meet you anywhere you say. . . . Oh, I know, but Maillard's is pretty crowded about that time, and isn't there some place nearer? My appointment is on Forty-seventh Street near Madison—no, it's near Fifth, I guess. But that doesn't matter. I'll take a cab. If I can get one. Did you ever see anything like how hard it is to get a cab nowadays? My dear, last night I was twenty-five minutes trying to get one, and it got me late for dinner, and I *know* they didn't believe me. But if I can't get one I'll walk. It's only a block. And I guess a little exercise wouldn't do me any harm . . . Maillard's . . . How about the Ritz? No, there's such a jam there. And it's hard to meet. Well, any place *you* say. . . . Oh, Lucille, that's a dreadful place. The food's so— oh, I don't know. You know. So—bad, if you know what I mean. Well, let's take a chance on Maillard's. Only it's so crowded. . . . Oh, no, I never heard that. . . . No, I haven't. I haven't read a thing in months, absolutely months. Where the time goes to I don't know. *I* simply do not know where the time goes to. Lucille, you're sure you've got tomorrow at lunch free? Because if you haven't, or there's something you'd rather do, just say so and we'll try again. Well, suppose we say at Maillard's at—oh, do you know that little tea shop on Forty-seventh? I think it's between Park and Madison on the—let's see—on the downtown, that's the south side of the street. I'll be there by one, or anyway one-thirty, and if I'm there first I'll get a table, and you do the same if you are. But I ought to be there by one. My appointment is for half-past twelve, and it may take me only a few minutes. I might be there before one. But surely by quarter past, and certainly by one-thirty. . . . All right, then. Suppose we say about one, at Maillard's. . . . Oh, no, what am I thinking of? We decided that would be too crowded, didn't we? Unless you'd rather go there. That little tea shop is very nice. . . . Well, yes, I'd just as soon go to Maillard's. It doesn't matter much. It's seeing you I care about. There's a *lot* I want to talk to you about. These little snatches at the telephone are so, well, so sort of unsatisfactory, if you know what I mean. . . . All right, suppose we say Maillard's, then. And then if we don't like the looks of things we can go somewhere else. . . . All right, then, at . . . oh, let's go to the tea room. It's quieter. . . . All right, then. I'm longing to see you, Lucille. . . . Tomorrow, then. At the tea shop, that's on Forty-seventh between

169

Park and Madison, on the downtown, that's the south side of the street. Tomorrow, then, about one. That's Wednesday. . . . What? Is it Tuesday? . . . Well, I'm *all* turned around. I thought it was Wednesday. I'm terribly sorry, Lucille. I can't possibly meet you tomorrow if it's Tuesday. I've got a luncheon appointment I've had for ages, simply for weeks, and I've postponed it so often I don't dare do it again. . . . You can't Wednesday? I'm terribly sorry. . . . Well, I'll try again. Ring me up. I'll be in all afternoon until five twenty-five, and then I have to go uptown. . . . Yes. . . . Well, I'm glad we had a nice little talk, anyway. . . . And I'll see you soon. . . . What? No, *soon*—S for Sam. . . . Yes, soon. . . . Good-bye, Lucille. . . . Good-bye. Good-bye."

ANTHOLOGISTICS

ARTHUR GUITERMAN

Since one anthologist put in his book
Sweet things by Morse, Bone, Potter, Bliss and Brook,
All subsequent anthologists, of course
Have quoted Bliss, Brook, Potter, Bone and Morse.
For, should some rash anthologist make free
To print selections, say, from you and me,
Omitting with a judgment all his own
The classic Brook, Morse, Potter, Bliss and Bone,
Contemptuous reviewers, passing by
Our verses, would unanimously cry,
"What manner of anthology is this
That leaves out Bone, Brook, Potter, Morse and Bliss!"

PIGS IS PIGS

ELLIS PARKER BUTLER

MIKE FLANNERY, the Westcote agent of the Interurban Express Company, leaned over the counter of the express office and shook his fist. Mr. Morehouse, angry and red, stood on the other side of the counter, trembling with rage. The argument had been long and heated, and at last Mr. Morehouse had talked himself speechless. The cause of the trouble stood on the counter between the two men. It was a soap box across the top of which were nailed a number of strips, forming a rough but serviceable cage. In it two spotted guinea-pigs were greedily eating lettuce leaves.

"Do as you loike, then!" shouted Flannery, "pay for thim an' take thim, or don't pay for thim and leave thim be. Rules is rules, Misther Morehouse, an' Mike Flannery's not goin' to be called down fer breakin' of thim."

"But, you everlastingly stupid idiot!" shouted Mr. Morehouse, madly shaking a flimsy printed book beneath the agent's nose, "can't you read it here—in your own plain printed rates? 'Pets, domestic, Franklin to Westcote, if properly boxed, twenty-five cents each.'" He threw the book on the counter in disgust. "What more do you want? Aren't they pets? Aren't they domestic? Aren't they properly boxed? What?"

He turned and walked back and forth rapidly; frowning ferociously.

Suddenly he turned to Flannery, and forcing his voice to an artificial calmness spoke slowly but with intense sarcasm.

"Pets," he said "P-e-t-s! Twenty-five cents each. There are two of them. One! Two! Two times twenty-five are fifty! Can you understand that? I offer you fifty cents."

Flannery reached for the book. He ran his hand through the pages and stopped at page sixty-four.

"An' I don't take fifty cints," he whispered in mockery. "Here's the rule for ut. 'Whin the agint be in anny doubt regardin' which of two rates applies to a shipment, he shall charge the larger. The consign-ey may file a claim for the overcharge.' In this case, Misther Morehouse, I be in doubt. Pets thim animals may be, an' domestic they be, but pigs I'm blame sure they do be, an' me rules says plain as the nose on yer face, 'Pigs Franklin to Westcote, thirty cints each.' An' Mister More-house, by me arithmetical knowledge two times thurty comes to sixty cints."

Mr. Morehouse shook his head savagely. "Nonsense!" he shouted, "confounded nonsense, I tell you! Why, you poor ignorant foreigner, that rule means common pigs, domestic pigs, not guinea-pigs!"

Flannery was stubborn.

"Pigs is pigs," he declared firmly. "Guinea-pigs, or dago pigs or Irish pigs is all the same to the Interurban Express Company an' to Mike Flannery. Th' nationality of the pig creates no differentiality in the rate, Misther Morehouse! 'Twould be the same was they Dutch pigs or Rooshun pigs. Mike Flannery," he added, "is here to tind to the expriss business and not to hould conversation wid dago pigs in sivinteen

172

languages fer to discover be they Chinese or Tipperary by birth an' nativity."

Mr. Morehouse hesitated. He bit his lip and then flung out his arms wildly.

"Very well!" he shouted, "you shall hear of this! Your president shall hear of this! It is an outrage! I have offered you fifty cents. You refuse it! Keep the pigs until you are ready to take the fifty cents, but, by George, sir, if one hair of those pigs' heads is harmed I will have the law on you!"

He turned and stalked out, slamming the door. Flannery carefully lifted the soap box from the counter and placed it in a corner. He was not worried. He felt the peace that comes to a faithful servant who has done his duty and done it well.

Mr. Morehouse went home raging. His boy, who had been awaiting the guinea-pigs, knew better than to ask him for them. He was a normal boy and therefore always had a guilty conscience when his father was angry. So the boy slipped quietly around the house. There is nothing so soothing to a guilty conscience as to be out of the path of the avenger.

Mr. Morehouse stormed into the house. "Where's the ink?" he shouted at his wife as soon as his foot was across the doorsill.

Mrs. Morehouse jumped, guiltily. She never used ink. She had not seen the ink, nor moved the ink, nor thought of the ink, but her husband's tone convicted her of the guilt of having borne and reared a boy, and she knew that whenever her husband wanted anything in a loud voice the boy had been at it.

173

"I'll find Sammy," she said meekly.

When the ink was found Mr. Morehouse wrote rapidly, and he read the completed letter and smiled a triumphant smile.

"That will settle that crazy Irishman!" he exclaimed. "When they get that letter he will hunt another job, all right!"

A week later Mr. Morehouse received a long official envelope with the card of the Interurban Express Company in the upper left corner. He tore it open eagerly and drew out a sheet of paper. At the top it bore the number A6754. The letter was short. "Subject—Rate on guinea-pigs," it said, "Dr. Sir—We are in receipt of your letter regarding rate on guinea-pigs between Franklin and Westcote, addressed to the president of this company. All claims for overcharge should be addressed to the Claims Department."

Mr. Morehouse wrote to the Claims Department. He wrote six pages of choice sarcasm, vituperation and argument, and sent them to the Claims Department.

A few weeks later he received a reply from the Claims Department. Attached to it was his last letter.

"Dr. Sir," said the reply. "Your letter of the 16th inst., addressed to this Department, subject rate on guinea-pigs from Franklin to Westcote, rec'd. We have taken up the matter with our agent at Westcote, and his reply is attached herewith. He informs us that you refused to receive the consignment or to pay the charges. You have therefore no claim against this company, and your letter regarding the proper rate on the consignment should be addressed to our Tariff Department."

Mr. Morehouse wrote to the Tariff Department. He stated his case clearly, and gave his arguments in full, quoting a page or two from the encyclopedia to prove that guinea-pigs were not common pigs.

With the care that characterizes corporations when they are systematically conducted, Mr. Morehouse's letter was numbered, O.K.'d, and started through the regular channels. Duplicate copies of the bill of lading, manifest, Flannery's receipt for the package and several other pertinent papers were pinned to the letter, and they were passed to the head of the Tariff Department.

The head of the Tariff Department put his feet on his desk and yawned. He looked through the papers carelessly.

"Miss Kane," he said to his stenographer, "take this letter. 'Agent, Westcote, N. J. Please advise why consignment referred to in attached papers was refused domestic pet rates.'"

174

Miss Kane made a series of curves and angles on her note book and waited with pencil poised. The head of the department looked at the papers again.

"Huh! guinea-pigs!" he said. "Probably starved to death by this time! Add this to that letter: 'Give condition of consignment at present.'"

He tossed the papers on to the stenographer's desk, took his feet from his own desk and went out to lunch.

When Mike Flannery received the letter he scratched his head.

"Give prisint condition," he repeated thoughtfully. "Now what do thim clerks be wantin' to know, I wonder! 'Prisint condition,' is ut? Thim pigs, praise St. Patrick, do be in good health, so far as I know, but I niver was no veterinairy surgeon to dago pigs. Mebby thim clerks wants me to call in the pig docther an' have their pulses took. Wan thing I do know, howiver, which is they've glorious appytites for pigs their soize. Ate? They'd ate the brass padlocks off of a barn door! If the paddy pig, by the same token, ate as hearty as these dago pigs do, there'd be a famine in Ireland."

To assure himself that his report would be up to date, Flannery went to the rear of the office and looked into the cage. The pigs had been transferred to a larger box—a dry goods box.

"Wan, — two, — t'ree, — four, — foive, — six, — sivin, — eight!" he counted. "Sivin spotted an' wan all black. All well an' hearty an' all eatin' loike ragin' hippypottymusses." He went back to his desk and wrote.

"Mr. Morgan, Head of Tariff Department," he wrote. "Why do I say dago pigs is pigs because they is pigs and will be til you say they ain't which is what the rule book says stop your jollying me you know it as well as I do. As to health they are all well and hoping you are the same. P.S. There are eight now the family increased all good eaters. P.S. I paid out so far two dollars for cabbage which they like shall I put in bill for same what?"

Morgan, head of the Tariff Department, when he received this letter, laughed. He read it again and became serious.

"By George!" he said, "Flannery is right, 'pigs is pigs.' I'll have to get authority on this thing. Meanwhile, Miss Kane, take this letter: Agent, Westcote, N. J. Regarding shipment guinea-pigs, File No. A6754. Rule 83, General Instructions to Agents, clearly states that agents shall collect from consignee all costs of provender, etc., etc., required for live stock while in transit or storage. You will proceed

175

to collect same from consignee."

Flannery received this letter next morning, and when he read it he grinned.

"Proceed to collect," he said softly. "How thim clerks do loike to be talkin'! *Me* proceed to collect two dollars and twinty-foive cints off Misther Morehouse! I wonder do thim clerks *know* Misther Morehouse? I'll get it! Oh, yes! 'Misther Morehouse, two an' a quarter, plaze.' 'Cert'nly, me dear frind Flannery. Delighted!' *Not!*"

Flannery drove the express wagon to Mr. Morehouse's door. Mr. Morehouse answered the bell.

"Ah, ha!" he cried as soon as he saw it was Flannery. "So you've come to your senses at last, have you? I thought you would! Bring the box in."

"I hev no box," said Flannery coldly. "I hev a bill agin Misther John C. Morehouse for two dollars and twinty-foive cints for kebbages aten by his dago pigs. Wud you wish to pay ut?"

"Pay— Cabbages—!" gasped Mr. Morehouse. "Do you mean to say that two little guinea-pigs—"

"Eight!" said Flannery. "Papa an' mamma an' the six childer. Eight!"

For answer Mr. Morehouse slammed the door in Flannery's face. Flannery looked at the door reproachfully.

"I take ut the con-*sign*-y don't want to pay for thim kebbages," he said. "If I know signs of refusal, the con-*sign*-y refuses to pay for wan dang kebbage leaf an' be hanged to me!"

Mr. Morgan, head of the Tariff Department, consulted the president of the Interurban Express Company regarding guinea-pigs, as to whether they were pigs or not pigs. The president was inclined to treat the matter lightly.

"What is the rate on pigs and on pets?" he asked.

"Pigs thirty cents, pets twenty-five," said Morgan.

"Then of course guinea-pigs are pigs," said the president.

"Yes," agreed Morgan, "I look at it that way, too. A thing that can come under two rates is naturally to be classed as the higher. But are guinea-pigs, pigs? Aren't they rabbits?"

"Come to think of it," said the president, "I believe they are more

like rabbits. Sort of half-way station between pig and rabbit. I think the question is this—are guinea-pigs of the domestic pig family? I'll ask Professor Gordon. He is authority on such things. Leave the papers with me."

The president put the papers on his desk and wrote a letter to Professor Gordon. Unfortunately the Professor was in South America collecting zoological specimens, and the letter was forwarded to him by his wife. As the Professor was in the highest Andes, where no white man had ever penetrated, the letter was many months in reaching him. The president forgot the guinea-pigs, Morgan forgot them, Mr. Morehouse forgot them, but Flannery did not. One-half of his time he gave to the duties of his agency; the other half was devoted to the guinea-pigs. Long before Professor Gordon received the president's letter Morgan received one from Flannery.

"About them dago pigs," it said, "what shall I do they are great in family life, no race suicide for them, there are thirty-two now shall I sell them do you take this express office for a menagerie, answer quick."

Morgan reached for a telegraph blank and wrote:

"Agent, Westcote. Don't sell pigs."

He then wrote Flannery a letter calling his attention to the fact that the pigs were not the property of the company but were merely being held during a settlement of a dispute regarding rates. He advised Flannery to take the best possible care of them.

Flannery, letter in hand, looked at the pigs and sighed. The drygoods box cage had become too small. He boarded up twenty feet of the rear of the express office to make a large and airy home for them, and went about his business. He worked with feverish intensity when out on his rounds, for the pigs required attention and took most of his time. Some months later, in desperation, he seized a sheet of paper and wrote "160" across it and mailed it to Morgan. Morgan returned it asking for explanation. Flannery replied:

"There be now one hundred sixty of them dago pigs, for heavens sake let me sell off some, do you want me to go crazy, what."

"Sell no pigs," Morgan wired.

Not long after this the president of the express company received a

letter from Professor Gordon. It was a long and scholarly letter, but the point was that the guinea-pig was the *Cavia aparoea* while the common pig was the genus *Sus* of the family *Suidae*. He remarked that they were prolific and multiplied rapidly.

"They are not pigs," said the president, decidedly, to Morgan. "The twenty-five cent rate applies."

Morgan made the proper notation on the papers that had accumulated in File A6754, and turned them over to the Audit Department. The Audit Department took some time to look the matter up, and after the usual delay wrote Flannery that as he had on hand one hundred and sixty guinea-pigs, the property of consignee, he should deliver them and collect charges at the rate of twenty-five cents each.

Flannery spent a day herding his charges through a narrow opening in their cage so that he might count them.

"Audit Dept." he wrote, when he had finished the count, "you are way off there may be was one hundred and sixty dago pigs once, but wake up don't be a back number. I've got even eight hundred, now shall I collect for eight hundred or what, how about sixty-four dollars I paid out for cabbages."

It required a great many letters back and forth before the Audit Department was able to understand why the error had been made of billing one hundred and sixty instead of eight hundred, and still more

time for it to get the meaning of the "cabbages."

Flannery was crowded into a few feet at the extreme front of the office. The pigs had all the rest of the room and two boys were employed constantly attending to them. The day after Flannery had counted the guinea-pigs there were eight more added to his drove, and by the time the Audit Department gave him authority to collect for eight hundred Flannery had given up all attempts to attend to the receipts or the delivery of goods. He was hastily building galleries around the express office, tier above tier. He had four thousand and sixty-four guinea-pigs to care for. More were arriving daily.

Immediately following its authorization the Audit Department sent another letter, but Flannery was too busy to open it. They wrote another and then they telegraphed:

"Error in guinea-pig bill. Collect for two guinea-pigs, fifty cents. Deliver all to consignee."

Flannery read the telegram and cheered up. He wrote out a bill as rapidly as his pencil could travel over the paper and ran all the way to the Morehouse home. At the gate he stopped suddenly. The house stared at him with vacant eyes. The windows were bare of curtains and he could see into the empty rooms. A sign on the porch said, "To Let." Mr. Morehouse had moved! Flannery ran all the way back to the express office. Sixty-nine guinea-pigs had been born during his absence. He ran out again and made feverish inquiries in the village. Mr. Morehouse had not only moved, but he had left Westcote. Flannery returned to the express office and found that two hundred and six guinea-pigs had entered the world since he left. He wrote a telegram to the Audit Department.

"Can't collect fifty cents for two dago pigs consignee has left town address unknown what shall I do? Flannery."

The telegram was handed to one of the clerks in the Audit Department, and as he read it he laughed.

"Flannery must be crazy. He ought to know that the thing to do is to return the consignment here," said the clerk. He telegraphed Flannery to send the pigs to the main office of the company at Franklin.

When Flannery received the telegram he set to work. The six boys he had engaged to help him also set to work. They worked with the haste of desperate men, making cages out of soap boxes, cracker boxes, and all kinds of boxes, and as fast as the cages were completed they filled them with guinea-pigs and expressed them to Franklin. Day after

179

day the cages of guinea-pigs flowed in a steady stream from Westcote to Franklin, and still Flannery and his six helpers ripped and nailed and packed—relentlessly and feverishly. At the end of the week they had shipped two hundred and eighty cases of guinea-pigs, and there were in the express office seven hundred and four more pigs than when they began packing them.

"Stop sending pigs. Warehouse full," came a telegram to Flannery. He stopped packing only long enough to wire back, "Can't stop," and kept on sending them. On the next train up from Franklin came one of the company's inspectors. He had instructions to stop the stream of guinea-pigs at all hazards. As his train drew up at Westcote station he saw a cattle-car standing on the express company's siding. When he reached the express office he saw the express wagon backed up to the door. Six boys were carrying bushel baskets full of guinea-pigs from the office and dumping them into the wagon. Inside the room Flannery, with his coat and vest off, was shoveling guinea-pigs into bushel baskets with a coal scoop. He was winding up the guinea-pig episode.

He looked up at the inspector with a snort of anger.

"Wan wagonload more an' I'll be quit of thim, an' niver will ye catch Flannery wid no more foreign pigs on his hands. No, sur! They near was the death o' me. Nixt toime I'll know that pigs of whatever nationality is domistic pets—an' go at the lowest rate."

He began shoveling again rapidly, speaking quickly between breaths.

"Rules may be rules, but you can't fool Mike Flannery twice wid the same trick—whin ut comes to live stock, dang the rules. So long as Flannery runs this expriss office—pigs is pets—an' cows is pets—an' horses is pets—an' lions an' tigers an' Rocky Mountain goats is pets—an' the rate on thim is twinty-foive cints."

He paused long enough to let one of the boys put an empty basket in the place of the one he had just filled. There were only a few guinea-pigs left. As he noted their limited number his natural habit of looking on the bright side returned.

"Well, annyhow," he said cheerfully, " 'tis not so bad as ut might be. What if thim dago pigs had been elephants!"

EIGHT BOTTLES OF LINIMENT

FRANCES EISENBERG

THE MONDAY after Miss Katy left, Aunt Pearl put out the "ROOM FOR RENT" sign, and before the day was over she had got a roomer, a lady who turned out to be a widow named Mrs. Byron Peacock. She was a large woman with earnest brown eyes. She talked in a low voice, hissing all her *s*'s and she gazed at the person she was speaking to in a fixed way as if she were trying to mesmerize them.

"I'll only be here a month while I'm working this territory," she explained to Aunt Pearl when she took the room. "I've been living in hotels so long, I thought a private home would be a nice change."

This was a nasty blow to Aunt Pearl, but after all, twenty dollars was better than an empty room.

"What does Mrs. Peacock do?" Ellen asked at the supper table.

"I don't know," Aunt Pearl replied. "I wanted to ask her, but I thought it was none of my business as long as she paid in advance."

"Don't worry," Uncle Newt said. "I don't care if she's a female tight-rope walker. I'm not gonna bother her. I've had enough of your roomers. If she leaves me alone, I'll leave her alone. All I want is a little peace and quiet."

"She's a nice, respectable woman," Aunt Pearl said, "and the way she talked, I feel right sorry for her. She seems to be all alone in the world. I told her to come down to the living room any time she wanted to and sit with us. She seemed so grateful it was sort of pitiful. I think the poor woman wants somebody to talk to."

181

"Just so she don't talk to me," Uncle Newt said, reaching for the butter.

Right after supper that night Mrs. Peacock took advantage of Aunt Pearl's invitation and came down to the living room. Uncle Newt had gone to a lodge meeting. Aunt Pearl was sitting by the fire knitting, and Ellen was writing lesson plans and listening to the radio at the same time.

Mrs. Peacock sat down on the sofa with an expression of pleasure. "My, you're comfortable here," she remarked, looking around with her large sad eyes. "There's nothing as homelike as a real home."

"No, there isn't," Aunt Pearl agreed. "A home is a wonderful place."

"It certainly is," Mrs. Peacock said. Then she looked serious. "But a home is a dangerous place too. Did you know that nearly all the fatal accidents that occur in the United States take place right in the home?"

"Is that so?" said Aunt Pearl brightly, counting stitches. "I didn't know that."

"Yes indeed, just think of all the ways that a person can get injured right under his own roof. Do you know how many people in the United States fell in the bathtub last year and suffered serious injuries? Roughly speaking, a thousand four hundred and fifty."

"Just think!" Aunt Pearl looked shocked. "I never dreamed of such a thing."

"And there are so many other menaces in the home. People injure themselves in so many different ways. Falling off stepladders and out windows, getting electrocuted by electric appliances, having heavy pieces of furniture fall on them, tripping on stairways, swallowing foreign substances, oh, I could enumerate them by the hour."

Aunt Pearl shook her head and made a clicking noise with her tongue. "It only goes to show that a person should be ready to go at any time," she remarked in a moral tone. "They should be ready to meet their Maker at any hour of the day or night."

"Yes, you're certainly right," Mrs. Peacock agreed. "And they should take out a good accident policy so that in case something happens to them they will get remuneration, or at least their beneficiaries will."

Suddenly it came to Ellen what it was Mrs. Peacock did. She tried to catch her aunt's eye and give her a warning, but it was no use. Aunt Pearl kept looking down at her knitting, and even when Ellen cleared her throat loudly she didn't look up.

182

Mrs. Peacock turned her gaze on Ellen. "And the sad thing is, youth is no protection," she said solemnly. "Young people under twenty-five are as often victims as older people."

"If you'll excuse me, I believe I'll go upstairs," Ellen interrupted hastily, gathering up her papers and switching off the radio. "There's something I need to do up there right away."

"Certainly," said Mrs. Peacock, "but I want to have a nice long talk with you, dear, sometime while I'm here. I have a plan I think you'll be interested in. We must get together some evening soon."

"Not if I see you first," Ellen thought rudely, but she murmured a polite rejoinder and left the room.

From the stairway she looked back and saw that Aunt Pearl was still rocking calmly away, unconscious of her danger, and that Mrs. Peacock was talking in a serious tone, leaning forward a little and staring earnestly at Aunt Pearl.

"Poor Aunt Pearl, she's a goner," Ellen thought, going into her room and closing the door. "She's so anxious to keep Mrs. Peacock here that she'll do anything to please her."

And sure enough, it wasn't an hour until Aunt Pearl came upstairs to bed, and on the way to her room she knocked on Ellen's door.

"I've found out what Mrs. Peacock does, Ellen," she said, coming in and sitting down. "She sells accident insurance."

"I know she does," Ellen said. "I tried to give you the high sign, but you wouldn't look. I guess you bought some?"

"Of course I did. I thought it was only right to do anything I could to help her out when she was nice enough to take the room. It's only two dollars a month. That's not so much; I'll still clear eighteen dollars on Mrs. Peacock."

"Yes, but you'll be paying accident insurance after Mrs. Peacock is gone. You'll be paying two dollars every month for the rest of your life. If you live twenty-five years that will be exactly six hundred dollars," she said, figuring rapidly.

Aunt Pearl gave a gasp and looked as if she were going to faint. "Oh my," she moaned. "I don't know why I didn't think of that. I never was any good at figures."

"Tell her you changed your mind," Ellen suggested.

"I've already signed the papers," Aunt Pearl said. "Oh, that makes me sick." Then she brightened. "But after all, who knows what will happen? If I break a leg I get six hundred dollars; and even if I break an arm I get two hundred."

"That's a cheerful thought," Ellen remarked.

"So maybe I'll come out all right in the end." Aunt Pearl was quiet a moment. "Ellen, I wish you wouldn't tell your Uncle Newt that Mrs. Peacock is selling anything. You know agents make him act sort of wild. And I certainly don't want anything to happen to Mrs. Peacock now that I've got all this money tied up in her."

"I won't tell him," Ellen promised.

The next night Uncle Newt was sitting in the living room when Mrs. Peacock came down. As soon as she came in the door Aunt Pearl started acting nervous. "Mrs. Peacock, this is my uncle, Mr. Dillion. Uncle Newt, don't you want to sit in your bedroom?" she asked hurriedly. "It's warmer in there."

"It's plenty warm in here for me," Uncle Newt said affably. "The thermometer reads sixty-eight. And that's just the right temperature."

"Yes, you're right, it is." Mrs. Peacock sat down, and fixed her gaze on Uncle Newt. "It's very comfortable in here. A nice warm home is certainly a pleasant place to be on a night like this. I've been out in the cold all day, and it certainly feels good to be inside."

Uncle Newt looked at her with interest. "You do outdoor work?" he asked.

"Uncle Newt, maybe you better go down and look at the furnace," Aunt Pearl suggested quickly. "Maybe it needs shaking up or something."

"No it don't," Uncle Newt said with finality. "Pearl, calm down. You act like a chicken on a hot stove lid. What's the matter with you, anyway?"

"The wind just whistled down the street today. It chilled me to the bone," Mrs. Peacock remarked. "Weather like this claims the lives of hundreds of people every winter."

"You're subject to rheumatism, eh?" Uncle Newt asked brightly. "You do a lot of walking?"

"Oh yes," Mrs. Peacock replied. "Did you know, Mr. Dillion, that next to the home, the most common source of accidents is on slippery pavements and sidewalks? It's so easy for an older person to get a sprain or even a broken limb weather like this."

Uncle Newt looked fondly at her. "That's a fact," he said. "Everybody that goes out much weather like this ought to have some kind of protection."

Mrs. Peacock's sad face looked almost cheerful. "They certainly ought. They owe it to themselves. Mr. Dillion, you're an extremely sensible man. It's a real pleasure to meet a person like you. Now while I have the opportunity I'd like to talk to you about—"

Aunt Pearl was sitting on the edge of her chair.

"Uncle Newt!" she cried loudly.

"What?" Uncle Newt said, looking pained.

"I forgot what I was going to say," Aunt Pearl said weakly. "It slipped my mind."

"Pearl, you act like you haven't got good sense sometimes," Uncle Newt said in disgust. "For God's sake, don't let out a shriek like that over nothing again. It goes through me like a knife." He turned to Mrs. Peacock, and his expression grew kindly. "You have trouble with your feet, I expect, being on them so much."

"Yes indeed, Mr. Dillion, as I was saying—"

"You suffer from muscular soreness?"

Mrs. Peacock began to look slightly annoyed. "At times," she said. "But I was about to—"

Uncle Newt jumped to his feet. "Excuse me," he exclaimed excitedly. "I'll be right back." He hurried out to the kitchen and there was a sound of rattling and the banging of the cupboard door where he kept his filled bottles.

Aunt Pearl opened her mouth to say something to Mrs. Peacock, but she evidently did not know what to say. She closed it again, and looked hopelessly over at Ellen who during the conversation had been a quiet but interested spectator.

Uncle Newt came charging back into the room carrying eight bottles of liniment. He was panting with exertion. He put the bottles down on the sofa. "There!" he said, looking down at them proudly. "There! That's the cure for all your trouble."

Mrs. Peacock glanced down at the bottles in a puzzled way. She started to speak, but Uncle Newt hurried on. "There's the thing you've been looking for." He picked up a bottle and held it in front of Mrs. Peacock's face. "What you see in there is a liquid," he said oratorically, "but what really is in there is two remedies in one. This liniment has preventative properties and curative properties. When you go out in the wind, rub some on your back and chest. It prevents chills and colds. When you come in with aching feet or sharp pains from over-exposure rub some on the afflicted parts. You get instant relief."

185

Mrs. Peacock drew back a little. "That's very—" she began.

"And that's not all," Uncle Newt went on enthusiastically. "In the winter this is a priceless protection, but in the summer it's even more priceless. Say you get bit by a snake or stung by a mosquito. Apply this liniment to the bite or sting and the swelling goes down the minute you apply it. And if you're subject to poison ivy, there's nothing like this for instant relief. Why, this bottle contains the most revolutionary remedy ever known to the human race. Nobody that values their well-being and comfort should be without it. It's indispensable." He rolled out the word with relish. "It's indispensable and compulsory."

Mrs. Peacock was staring at Uncle Newt with a hypnotized expression. "I don't—" she said feebly.

"These eight bottles are the very least you should have on hand," Uncle Newt informed her in a brisk tone. "And seeing that you're a roomer of my niece's I'm gonna let you have them at a discount. I'm gonna charge you only four dollars for the eight."

Mrs. Peacock finally found her voice. "I'm afraid I haven't any change," she said. "Five dollars is the least I have."

"Oh, I can change five dollars," Uncle Newt said carelessly. "I'll carry the bottles upstairs for you. And when you leave, I want you to take a good supply along with you to wherever you go. You can't buy this liniment everywhere."

Mrs. Peacock got up and went slowly toward the stairs, opening and closing her mouth as she went. Uncle Newt followed her smiling happily. All the way upstairs they could hear his cheerful voice enumerating the things Dillion's Wonder Rub was good for, but from Mrs. Peacock there was no sound at all.

Aunt Pearl sat back in her chair and gave a loud sigh. "Oh my, for a minute there I was holding my breath."

"I was holding mine the whole time," Ellen said. "You know in some ways Uncle Newt is a remarkable man," she added thoughtfully. "There's no telling what he might have amounted to under different circumstances."

Aunt Pearl began to look very pleased. "Ellen, we've made twenty-two dollars off of Mrs. Peacock, clear profit. Isn't that nice? And if Uncle Newt sells her some more liniment, we may do even better. So we haven't come out so bad after all."

But after that evening Uncle Newt never got within ten feet of Mrs. Peacock. When she came in at night she went straight to her room and locked the door. And when she came down in the morning she hurried past the dining room almost on a run. Once she passed Uncle Newt on the walk. He tipped his hat and began cheerfully, "About that—" but Mrs. Peacock gave him an alarmed look and hastened off in the opposite direction, leaving him standing there staring after her in bewilderment.

"She's a peculiar woman," he remarked to Aunt Pearl when he was telling her about the incident. "She acted real intelligent that first night, but since then she's behaved sort of queer, it seems to me. I wonder if there's not a screw loose somewhere in her brain?"

MONEY

RICHARD ARMOUR

Workers earn it,
Spendthrifts burn it,
Bankers lend it,
Women spend it,
Forgers fake it,
Taxes take it,
Dying leave it,
Heirs receive it,
Thrifty save it,
Misers crave it,
Robbers seize it,
Rich increase it,
Gamblers lose it . . .
I could use it.

DR. ATWOOD AND MR. ED

WALTER BROOKS

WELL, it was just after gas rationing set in that this Wilbur Pope began riding his horse from the house to the train and back every day. He did it so Mrs. Pope could have the car. Of course, four gallons a week wasn't a quarter of what Mrs. Pope felt she needed, but it was all there was, and Mr. Pope was able to point out that her reproaches were misdirected.

"You'll have to take it up with the Wilhelmstrasse," he said. Yet the gentle patriotic glow that pervaded him when he and Ed clumped off to the station mornings hardly made up for the feeling Mrs. Pope managed to give him that he was somehow responsible, not merely for the gas situation but for the entire war.

Well, things went along like that for a while, and then one Sunday Mr. Pope saddled Ed, and after they'd stopped in at Barney's for a couple of beers, they went up to their abandoned orchard and sat down under a tree. And Mr. Pope said, "Ed, I've got a piece of news for you."

"Yeah?" said Ed, looking sort of sour. "Well, I bet it's nothing I want to hear, or you wouldn't be starting off with a preamble."

Mr. Pope wasn't as surprised as you or I would have been when Ed spoke—in fact, he wasn't surprised at all, because Ed was really quite a talker. Of course, I know there are people who pooh-pooh the idea that a horse can talk, but they're the same isolationists who pooh-poohed the earth being round. And look at them now. Anyway, Ed never talked to anybody but Mr. Pope.

So Mr. Pope said, "Well, you know Carlotta is busy with this AWVS and the Red Cross and all these committees, and there just isn't enough

188

gas to cover all the ground she has to, and so she thought if I could get a ride to the train with Jed or some of the other men who go by here every morning, she could ride you to some of the meetings."

"Ride me!" said Ed, glaring. "After the things she's said about me? Unh-uh, Wilb. Nothing doing."

"Oh, come, Ed," said Mr. Pope. "Carlotta doesn't mean half she says—you know that."

"Yeah," said Ed. "Well, if she's only meant a tenth, any jury in the country'd give me damages for slander. Besides, suppose she does ride me and falls off. Then you'll blame me."

"She used to ride a lot," said Mr. Pope. "So, if she falls off, I certainly will blame you. I'll expect you to behave like a gentleman. No climbing trees or shying at butterflies or any of that funny stuff."

"Pooh," said Ed, "she'd be as safe with me as with a Shetland pony. It's her that don't like me, not me that don't like her. Anyway, your wife is sacrosanct, as it says in one of them old story papers I found out here in the barn." Ed was pretty well read for a horse.

Mr. Pope said that was nice, and went on to appeal to Ed's patriotism, and at last broke down his resistance to the idea. "O.K.," he said dismally. "C'est la guerre. But we don't need to dwell on it. Let's take a nap."

Well, Mrs. Pope dug out the boots and breeches she used to wear, and I must say she looked cute as all get-out in them, and after the first few days Ed began to feel that maybe there were compensations after all. For on the road people turned and looked at them. Of course, they had always turned and looked at him and Mr. Pope, too, but this was different. For now they said, "Ah!" and "Oh, boy!" whereas before they had just said, "Judas!" or something like that. And some of the more ill-bred ones had guffawed.

So Ed began to put on a little style. He held his head high and tried to put a little spirit into his usual clumping trot, and he even talked to Mr. Pope about having his mane roached.

"It's all right for you and me, Wilb," he said, "to go round kind of dégagé in our appearance. But I heard some remarks lately. As why as smart a woman as your wife would want to be seen riding something that ought to be on a milk wagon. Well, I ain't got any illusions about myself; I'm plain folks and proud of it. But it ain't right. I'm frank to say I never liked your wife much, but she treats me nice, and it ain't fair to her. And just combing out the burs in my mane ain't enough. Look

189

here, Wilb." He arched his neck. "I got a good neckline. Now you roach that mane and it'll emphasize that line. Give me a little chic, like."

Mr. Pope said he didn't think it would work. "You're plain folks, Ed," he said. "Your line is solid worth, not chic."

"Rats!" said Ed. "You know as well as I do that you put plain folks in a tail coat and you can't tell the difference."

"You can't tell them from the waiters, you mean," said Mr. Pope. "You'd better leave well enough alone. Anyway, it's the contrast that appeals to Carlotta. She knows she's smart, and if you aren't, why, that makes her look all the smarter."

"You mean the worse I look, the better she'd like it?" said Ed.

"Well, something like that," said Mr. Pope. "Only there isn't any need of making a special effort. Just be yourself."

"Gosh, you don't encourage any illusions, do you?" said Ed gloomily.

Well, it was about this time that Mrs. Pope started taking a first-aid course. The classes were held at Mrs. Mervin Van Tessart's, which was a large estate about five miles from the Popes', and Ed didn't like it there because as soon as Mrs. Pope had dismounted under the elaborate portecochere, he was seized by a groom and led off to the stables. On one occasion he did succeed in getting out of the box stall where he was incarcerated and sneaking up behind the shrubbery to within earshot of the group of notetaking women on the lawn.

"And I give you my word, Wilb," he said to Mr. Pope, "I was never so shocked in my life. If I'd had the sayso, I'd have taken your wife right out of there and brought her home. There was a woman standing there and lecturing to 'em—decent looking girl too. 'And now,' she says, 'we have convulsions.' Well, that kind of startled me, till I see she was just going to talk about 'em, not have 'em. But then she went on to talk about—my gosh, Wilb—bleeding and gangrene and protruding

190

viscera—and all those women hashing it over! By the Lord Harry, in my day women didn't talk about such things!"

"Your delicacy does you credit," said Mr. Pope.

"Yeah, you can laugh," said Ed. "I call it morbid. But say, who's this Van Tessart dame where these classes are at? Grim old girl, ain't she?"

Mr. Pope explained that the Van Tessarts were unreconstructed society of the old school. Between them they headed most of the local volunteer organizations. Mrs. Van Tessart had taken a fancy to Mrs. Pope and had got her appointed as her lieutenant in the AWVS, as well as to several important committees. "Don't, for heaven's sake, try any funny business with Mrs. Van Tessart," said Mr. Pope, "or your popularity with Carlotta will be just a fond, vanished dream."

"Trust your old Uncle Ed to know which side his hay is buttered on," said the horse. "I could see they all kind of smooch up to her. I never see a woman could sit up so straight in a chair."

"It's partly her corsets, which I understand are specially made for her at the Baldwin Locomotive Works," said Mr. Pope. "But mostly it's her determination to be correct. She's never made a social or tactical error in her life. And her husband runs her a close second. They say he admits to one error: he voted for Harding."

"Well, I know one mistake she made," said Ed. "In a box stall you hear things folks in the front parlor don't know about." He rolled his eyes toward Mr. Pope. "But I dunno's I ought to tell you. I ain't much of a believer in repeating gossip."

"I know," said Mr. Pope; "you prefer to invent your own."

"You want to hear it or not?" Ed demanded.

Mr. Pope assured him that he was not interested.

"Oh, well, you'll worm it out of me sooner or later," said the horse. "Yes, sir, she made the mistake of being born on the wrong side of the tracks. She ain't any more society than what I am."

"Nonsense!" said Mr. Pope. "The Van Tessarts——"

"I'm not talking about Van Tessart," interrupted Ed; "I'm talking about her. I might have known anyone who was as high and mighty as her was poor stock. Listen, Wilb. I was standing in my stall, sort of dreamin' about this and that, and I heard Mrs. Van Tessart's voice ordering the stableman to go up to the house and fix some faucet, and then she came into the stall next to me. And a minute later I heard some other footsteps, and a man's voice says, 'Hello, May.'

" 'I told you never to come here in the daytime,' says Mrs. Van, very

191

sharp, and the man says, 'I need a lot of money, May. Never mind what for . . . No, wait a minute,' he says. 'You got to hear my proposition. How much would you pay if I turned over all those letters to you—the whole bunch?'

"She kind of hesitates, and I got my eye to a crack. This guy was middle-aged and pretty seedy looking. Finally she says, kind of off-hand, 'I've given you money, off and on, for twenty years, Sam. But I did it because I was sorry for you. I don't think letters written thirty years ago would be of much interest to Mr. Van Tessart, or to anyone else. If you want forty or fifty dollars——'

"The old guy snorted and says, 'You ain't foolin' anybody, May. Love letters written thirty years ago to a livery hand—no, they ain't anything in themselves to stir up trouble. It's what they tell about who your folks was before you went splurgin' around Europe on the money Wes left you. I guess you didn't tell Van Tessart you'd been the wife of a garage mechanic, and your money come from an invention he invented. How'd he like to know your ma was a scrubwoman, and about your Uncle Joe goin' to the pen? It's all referred to plain in the letters.'

" 'And how would you manage to connect me with them today?' she says.

" 'I guess you forgot the snapshots,' Sam says. 'You took your maiden name when you went to Europe, and that's the name that's signed to them—May Gregg. I guess one of these tabloid newspapers wouldn't have much trouble seein' the connection.'

"Well, she kinda weakened when he mentioned newspapers, but she said she'd have to get back to her guests, and she'd see him again in a week. He kind of griped about that, but had to give in. Funny, never mentioned his price. But ain't that a story, Wilb?"

"It is indeed," said Mr. Pope.

"She'll have to keep this old boy dark, whatever it costs," said Ed. "Sam don't fit into the Van Tessart mealyou any better'n a toad in a fruitcake. You and me, Wilb, we're vulgar, but we ain't common. We can pass any time we have to. But this old wump, he's commoner'n red suspenders." He thought a minute. "But, boy, she's tough! I dunno's I blame her. You can't ever afford to pay these birds their asking price. Because they'll ask for more, anyway."

"I wouldn't know," said Mr. Pope. "I haven't your experience in blackmail."

"Hey, listen," said Ed; "don't look down your long nose at black-

192

mail. Any time you want to start a nice little business, just say the word. No capital required, as it says in the ads. I got enough raw material to split this county wide open. And, boy, what I mean, it's raw! You'd be surprised what some of these nice folks'll say in front of a horse. You think they'd blush."

Well, it was one afternoon about a week later that Mr. Pope came home and found trouble.

Mrs. Pope came rushing out to meet him, and she said, "Oh, Wilbur, I'm so glad you've come! That terrible horse! He's ruined everything!" And she began to cry.

"You mean Ed?" said Mr. Pope, and she said, "I certainly do mean Ed. He attacked Mrs. Van Tessart. He rushed into the garden where we were having our first-aid class—Wilbur, you never saw anything look so fiendish—and he threw Mrs. Van Tessart right over a hedge. It was horrible! One of her men came running and got hold of him and managed to quiet him, and I had Evelyn bring me home."

"Where's Ed?" said Mr. Pope, and Mrs. Pope said, "I had to leave him there, of course. They locked him up, and I told them to send for a vet or something and have him disposed of. Wilbur, he's simply gone mad!"

Mr. Pope didn't wait to hear any more.

"I'll settle this," he said, and he ran out and got into his car and drove over to the Van Tessarts'.

193

Well, he didn't stop at the house, but went right around to the stable. Ed was locked in a box stall with a man on guard at the door.

"I want my horse," said Mr. Pope.

The man shook his head. "I'm sorry, Mr. Pope," he said. "I can't let you have him. The vet says he's dangerous, and we're waiting for the truck to take him away."

"Is that so?" said Mr. Pope. "Well, the horse is my property, and nobody's going to take him away but me. Open up."

"Well, I don't know," said the man. "I'll have to phone the madam. But I don't know can she talk, and Mr. Van Tessart ain't got here yet."

"You mean she's been hurt?" said Mr. Pope, and the man said, "Well, not exactly, but she's kind of shattered, like."

"There's no sense telephoning," answered Mr. Pope. "Come on, get out of the way."

But at that moment there was a tremendous crash and the door of the box stall was driven from its hinges. The man vanished with a yell, and Ed stepped out.

"Hi, Wilb," he said. " I knew you wouldn't leave me to languish in a prison cell. Let's get out of here."

"What on earth have you been up to?" demanded Mr. Pope as they cantered unmolested down the drive and through the iron gates.

"I been framed," said Ed. "Judas, Wilb, I only done what you or anybody else'd have done. I come over here with your wife, and this lackey led me off to a stall just like always. By and by I got kind of bored and full of onwee, so I slipped my halter and sneaked over to see how the first-aiders was getting on.

"My gosh, when I peeked over the hedge there was a regular free-for-all going on! Half the women had the others down and was pommelin' 'em, and this Van Tessart dame was sittin' astride your wife's back and jabbin' her in the short ribs.

"Well, if your wife had been on top, I wouldn't have interfered, but being she was under my protection, I just sailed over the hedge and grabbed this old devil by the —— Say, Wilb, you were right about those corsets. You couldn't get a grip on her any more'n you could on a hot-water boiler. I was going to kick her first, but I thought: *That's no way to treat a lady, however savage.* So I grabs her by the slack of her slacks and heaves her over the hedge."

"Oh, good Lord!" moaned Mr. Pope.

"Yeah?" said Ed. "Well, what would you have done?"

194

"Hardly that," said Mr. Pope. "Gosh, Ed, they were just practicing artificial respiration. It's part of the course."

It was some time, however, before he could convince Ed. "If I ever saw a barroom fight," said the horse, "that was it. Why, a couple of 'em had even dropped out of the fight and was getting bandaged up on the side lines." But the fact that Mrs. Pope had abandoned him, had even acquiesced in the death sentence imposed by Mrs. Van Tessart, convinced him. "Gosh, Wilbur," he said, "I'm awful sorry. But how could I know? I never seen a bunch of ladies acting like that before. I guess I got too old-fashioned ideas to understand these modern women."

"Well," said Mr. Pope, "you acted in good faith, and I'll stand by you. We'll drop these keys at the garage and have someone go after my car, and then go home and see what happens."

Late that evening Mr. Pope went out to the stable. He snapped on the light and sat down on a box and sighed wearily, and then he said, "Well, I've partly squared you with Carlotta."

Ed said he guessed she took some squaring.

"I told her the truth," said Mr. Pope. "I painted a pretty touching picture of you, Ed. Rushing to the defense of your mistress. 'Faithful old Ed,' I said; he's devoted to you, Carlotta, and——' "

"That ain't the truth," said Ed.

"Well, you were trying to protect her, anyway," said Mr. Pope. "She sees that. But she feels she has got to stand well with the Van Tessarts. Aside from Mrs. Van Tessart's liking her and putting her on committees and things, they're great friends of the Kimshaws. And as you know, Kimshaw controls my best account. So when old Van Tessart called me up a little while ago—well, I guess it was kind of an indignity his wife suffered. Anyway, he says I have to get rid of you."

"Oh, yeah?" said Ed.

"No use being truculent," said Mr. Pope. "He says he hasn't consulted his lawyers yet, or the police. But if I persist in my refusal to get rid of an animal which is plainly a public menace, the police will take you away and the lawyers will sue. Now, whether they could do it or not, I don't know. My guess is, they could."

"Public menace, eh?" said Ed, looking pleased. "Look, Wilb, we got the squeezers on that dame. All you got to do is drop a word about——"

"No!" said Mr. Pope sharply. "Let's hear no more about that, Ed. We can't go in for blackmail."

"O.K.," said Ed bitterly. "You're one of these noble jerks that'll sac-

195

rifice their best friend rather than do something ungentlemanly. Well, I guess there's nothing further to say. Dish me up to the lions and let's get it over with."

"Oh, don't be a fool!" said Mr. Pope. "I said I'd stand by you. But Carlotta insists that you must be sold. So I've got a plan——"

"Reject it unconditionally," said Ed. "I know you won't stand between me and those Van Tessarts. A horse ain't got any social position. Look, Wilb; I don't mind discussing my own funeral when the date ain't set. It's kinda nice and weepy figurin' out your own last words and thinking how bad folks'll feel. But if I got to face the firing squad tomorrow morning——"

"For heaven's sake, shut up!" said Mr. Pope. "Nobody's going to shoot you. My idea is, you get under cover for a few weeks, and I'll tell everybody I've sold you. Then, after a decent period of mourning, I'll show up with a new horse. If he looks a good deal like you, nobody'll think it strange, because, naturally, being so fond of you, I'd have picked another as near like you as possible. That'll satisfy the Van Tessarts, and if Carlotta gets wise, she won't dare say anything."

"Yeah," said Ed, "and what's the alternative?"

"I'm very much afraid," said Mr. Pope, "that it's the S.P.C.A. wagon."

Ed moaned. "The S.P.C.A. wagon! Me that's been what I have been and done what I done; me that should have died like my noble forebears on a stricken field, defeated mayhap, but unconquered; me that—— Get me my smelling salts, Wilb."

So Mr. Pope unlocked the harness closet and brought out a bottle of Scotch, and when this restorative had been applied, he said, "I've called up Barney, and he's agreed to take you in. I'll ride you over there tonight."

196

"Couldn't you make it Joe Canelli's?" said Ed. "Joe's still got a couple cases of that imported beer left."

"And where would you be put up?" said Mr. Pope. "There's nothing at Joe's but the barroom and that dance hall."

"I slept in a barroom before this," pleaded Ed, but Mr. Pope said, "Barney's got a good barn. He even keeps a cow."

"She'll be company for me, I suppose," said Ed sarcastically. "Oh, well, this is what I get for rescuing ladies in distress. The knight-errant ends up as companion for a cow."

For the next two weeks, every evening that Mr. Pope could get away he went over to Barney's and saddled Ed and took him for a ride. At first Ed seemed resigned to his exile. Barney's beer was good, and the horse picked up many items of local gossip with which to astound Mr. Pope. But after a while he got homesick.

"There's no place like home, Wilb," he said. "I guess I'm just a sentimental old fool, but when those boys in the barroom get to singing all them moldy old carry-me-back songs, it's all I can do to choke back the sobs."

"Well, you choke 'em back for a couple more weeks," said Mr. Pope, "and then I'll take you home as—— Let me see—'Atwood,' I think, would be a good name. We'll have to make you look different somehow—maybe your idea of roaching your mane would be enough. People probably never noticed you much."

"I suppose that's meant for an insult," said Ed, and Mr. Pope said, "Not at all. The true gentleman is always inconspicuous."

Ed snorted, but after a minute he said, "Well, I got no choice. Atwood it is. The gentlemanly Atwood, hey? That ought to fool 'em. Oh, I can be gentlemanly if I put my mind to it. Look at you, Wilb. You get away with it every day. We all of us got double natures. I read a story about it once."

"Doctor Jekyll and Mr. Hyde," said Mr. Pope.

"Sure," said the horse. "Doctor Atwood and Mr. Ed." He thought for a minute. "I expect Atwood could learn to like beer, though," he said. "You could say you were trainin' him, and I could splutter a little when I drink it."

"You do anyway," said Mr. Pope.

A few days later, when Mr. Pope brought the gentlemanly Atwood home and showed him to his wife, Mrs. Pope seemed to suspect nothing. Least of all, apparently, did she suspect his gentility.

197

"You do have the damnedest taste in horses, Wilbur," she said. "If you think I'm going to ride that monster around the country——"

"He's a darned good horse," said Mr. Pope. "Not so good as Ed, of course."

"He certainly isn't," said Mrs. Pope. "Though there's a look of Ed too. Paleozoic. And what happened to his mane? Did the moths get in it?"

Elsewhere, Atwood was accepted without comment. But though Mr. Pope pointed out that this was a distinct triumph for Ed's histrionic ability, the horse was not happy about it. "This being a gentleman," he said, "it's easy as falling off a log. And just about as much point to it. Because who wants to fall off a log, anyway? It used to be, when we rode around the country, folks would wave to me and come up and whack me on the rump, and guys I never saw before would fight for the privilege of buying me a drink. I was to home everywhere. But now all is changed, Wilb. I'm just a stranger in this earthly vale. I've become so darn inconspicuous and gentlemanly that nobody pays any attention to me."

But Ed was wrong. A night or two later Mr. Pope came out to the stable and slumped down on the box. "We're over the dam, Ed," he said. "Van Tessart has been here. He wanted to see the bill of sale for Atwood."

"Yeah?" said Ed. "I hope you told him where he got off at."

"Listen, my poor numbskull," said Mr. Pope. "We are in no position to bandy insults with Van Tessart. Somebody who has seen you in your double role reported to him on the odd similarity between Atwood and Ed, and he got suspicious."

"I'd hate to have a mean nature like that," said Ed. "You told him you'd sold me and bought another horse. Ain't your word good enough for him?"

"I tried to stall him," said Mr. Pope, "but he says I'll have to give him proof of the sale or he'll go ahead with his original action."

"Aw, heck!" said Ed. "If your word ain't any good, what's the use of this gentleman stuff? Well, our little coop de theayter didn't come off. We'll have to think of something more suited to our talents."

"Maybe you can think of something," said Mr. Pope. "Frankly, I can't. It's either selling you, or the S.P.C.A. wag——"

"Don't *talk* that way!" interrupted Ed. "I hear the rumble of tumbrel wheels." He shuddered. "Come on, Wilb," he said. "Pull yourself to-

gether. Let's take a little ride. We can think better on the road. And stick my smelling salts in your pocket. I don't believe in waiting for inspiration when I got it right handy in a bottle."

But when, some five miles from home, the empty bottle was tossed into the ditch, no plan had revealed itself to them. Indeed they had begun to feel that no plan was necessary. Something, they assured each other, would turn up.

"Something always does," said Ed, "even if it's only your toes. Just sniff this air; it's like wine."

"Don't mix your drinks," said Mr. Pope. "My gosh, look where we are! That's the Van Tessart place ahead. How'd we get here?"

"Criminal always returns to the scene of the crime," said Ed. He began to giggle. "I like to die laughing every time I think of her soarin' over that eight-foot hedge like a hawk after a rabbit. Only she didn't get no rabbit; only a couple dents in her fenders."

"Eight-foot hedge nothing," said Mr. Pope. "It's fairly bore—I mean barely four."

"You would pick on some little unimportant detail," said Ed disgustedly. "Well, have it your own way. But I stick to it, it's eight if it's an inch."

"I don't follow you," said Mr. Pope. "You say, have it my own way, which is four, and then you say it's eight. We can't—I mean, it's——"

"Why is it?" said Ed.

"Why is what?" said Mr. Pope. "Look, Ed; if I had paper and pencil——"

"Oh, let's go down and measure it," said Ed. "It's cool tonight; they'll all be indoors."

So they rode down and through the service gate, and then, keeping on the grass, made a detour through a plantation of evergreens to come up to the terrace hedge on the side away from the house. It was dark and there was little chance of discovery if they kept out of the bands of light that streamed from the windows. But it was through one of these bands, as they came opposite the end of the hedge, that they saw a figure move furtively and then disappear.

Mr. Pope leaned forward and whispered in Ed's ear, "A burglar. We ought to warn them."

Ed shrugged, but carefully, in order not to dislodge Mr. Pope, who seldom sat firmly in the saddle after the second round. "Let him burgle," he murmured. "Psst!" he whispered. "Look!" For one of the French windows had opened and Mrs. Van Tessart stepped out.

She walked quickly across the terrace to the hedge. Out of the light, they could only make her out as a darker moving shadow. But presently she was joined by another shadow—evidently the presumed burglar, and for a minute or two there was a whispering in the dark.

Then, with a cautious glance at the windows, the burglar stepped out into the light.

Ed turned his head carefully. "My gosh," he whispered, "it's that Sam—the old guy that she wrote the letters to!"

The man had a sheaf of bills in his hand and was counting them in the light from the window. He nodded and stuffed them in his pocket, then turned and looked thoughtfully toward where, in the darkness close by, a shaded flashlight glimmered on hands that shuffled a packet of letters.

"It's the pay-off, Wilb," Ed whispered. "She's bought 'em and she'll burn 'em. It's our last chance to make a deal. You grab the letters and I'll give Sam a toss. Then we can—— Oh, Judas!"

For Sam, with a sudden pounce, had grabbed the letters, the flashlight went out, and then heavy feet came pounding toward them.

Just what it was that impelled him to interfere, Mr. Pope was never afterward able to explain. Ed said it was automatic gentlemanliness, and added that it was a prime example of the utter stupidity of the whole gentleman tradition. But whatever it was, it brought Mr. Pope into the path of the fleeing Sam.

"Stop!" commanded Mr. Pope sternly, and the next thing he knew

200

he was sitting on the grass holding his nose, while Sam, seizing his chance and Ed's bridle, scrambled aboard the startled horse and was off through the evergreens in a shower of divots.

Mr. Pope continued to hold his nose. He held it because it was completely numb, and he could not otherwise be sure that it still formed part of his face. It also felt at least ten times its normal size, but he knew that this could not be so or he would not have been able to see Mrs. Van Tessart, who now came toward him.

"Mr. Pope!" she exclaimed. "What are you doing here? Was that your horse?"

"Bust have butted be betweed the eyes," said Mr. Pope. Then he staggered to his feet and withdrew his hand from his nose. In this crisis it would have to look after itself. Which the return of his normal voice, when he spoke, assured him it could do. "Yes," he said, "the fellow took my horse. But don't worry, he won't get far—not on Ed."

"I am not worrying, Mr. Pope," she said coldly, though he thought her voice trembled. "I came out a moment ago for a breath of air and heard the sound of a struggle, and saw some man jump on a horse and ride off. And then I find you here. I am curious to know what is going on."

"I was curious myself," said Mr. Pope. "That's why I'm here. I was riding by, and saw a man sneak through the gate and up toward the house. I followed and tried to capture him, but he knocked me down and took my horse and got away. Shouldn't you call the police?"

"Hardly necessary now," said Mrs. Van Tessart. "He's taken nothing. And the police couldn't find him now. Unless you wish to call them to recover your horse. Which, by the way, I think you just referred to as Ed."

"At," said Mr. Pope. "Short for Atwood. But what's the difference?" he added bitterly. "In coming here, I was merely trying to protect your property. And that, in spite of the fact that you and your husband are doing your best to deprive me of some of my property—namely, my horse. Whose only fault is an excess of fidelity."

"I haven't time to discuss that with you now," said Mrs. Van Tessart. "Perhaps your explanation of your presence here is true, but it doesn't entirely satisfy me. I am sure it will not satisfy Mr. Van Tessart. You threatened him this evening."

Evidently, thought Mr. Pope, she felt sure that he hadn't seen anything. And she was trying to distract and get rid of him by bringing up the horse issue, which she could hardly at the moment be very much concerned about.

Well, he only had to tell her what he'd seen. Maybe it was blackmail, but if blackmail was the only thing that would save Ed——

"I told your husband that I'd punch his head if he he didn't lay off Ed," he said. "But I hardly think that will be necessary, however pleasant it would be. For——"

The thud of rapidly approaching hoofbeats interrupted him. Mrs. Van Tessart blenched. She blenched from her iron pompadour to her shoes. And over the hedge sailed Ed. She caught up her skirts and started to run. But Mr. Pope put a hand on her arm.

"Please," he said. "He's quite harmless. And he seems to have something for you," he added, pointing.

She turned, then stared fascinated at the packet of letters which Ed held in his mouth.

"Give them to Mrs. Van Tessart, Ed," said Mr. Pope.

The horse looked at Mr. Pope's nose and gave a loud and vulgar giggle. Mrs. Van Tessart started away in alarm, but Mr. Pope said, "That's nothing. Just his way of showing affection. He always does that when he sees me." At which Ed giggled again.

And at that moment the French window flew open and Mr. Van Tessart came out. He was a small man with rather more dignity than he had been constructed to carry.

"What's going on here?" he demanded. He didn't at first see Mr. Pope and Ed, who were outside the band of illumination. "Oh, it's you, May." He looked down at the grass. "I wish you wouldn't make prac-

tice mashie shots on this lawn, May. There's a place provided——"

"I'm afraid my horse did that," said Mr. Pope, stepping forward. "You see——"

Mr. Van Tessart retreated hastily to the doorway. "By heaven, Pope," he said, "I'm going to settle this once for all. Evidently you're not content with that murderous attack on my wife; you dare to bring that vicious brute here——"

"Be quiet, Mervin," said Mrs. Van Tessart. "Mr. Pope has done us a service. He—or rather his horse—has driven off a gang of thieves who were trying to break into the house. After what I have seen, I am convinced that the attack on me was, however mistaken, an act of remarkable intelligence. Under the circumstances, we have no choice but to overlook it and drop the whole thing."

"You're making a mistake, May," said Mr. Van Tessart.

"*I* do not make mistakes," she replied firmly.

The reference to that disastrous vote for Harding crumpled Mr. Van Tessart. He turned without a word and went in.

"Now, Mr. Pope," she said. And he nodded to Ed, and the horse dropped the letters into her outstretched hand. She looked at Mr. Pope sharply. "I think——" she began.

"The matter is closed," he said, swinging into the saddle. "Good night, Mrs. Van Tessart."

"Well," he said as they went back through the evergreens, "that's the last of Atwood. And I must say, he went out in a blaze of gentility. That was the gentlemanly gesture—handing over those letters."

"Uh-huh," said Ed. "Well, I could have knocked Sam over when he hit you, but I needed time to think things over, so I took him on a tour of the flower beds." He grinned. "I've always wanted to have a little roll among the petunias. And I did; boy, I did! So did Sam. Only his roll ended in a barberry hedge. His language kind of shocked the Atwood in me."

"There's some stuff hanging on your bit," said Mr. Pope. "Looks like gents' suiting."

"Pants," said Ed. "Had to rip 'em a bit to get the—— Oh, that reminds me. Let's go this way." And he turned right through the trees into another part of the grounds. "Must be about here." He ducked his head under a bush and drew out the sheaf of bills, which he passed back to Mr. Pope. "Little something for our piggy bank."

"Good Lord, Ed!" said Mr. Pope. "We can't keep this!"

Ed groaned. "Don't explain," he said; "I can't bear it. All right, send it back to her. Probably you'll add interest for the time I had it in my possession. Just one more gentlemanly word and I'll go over to the boneyard and give myself up."

"By the way," said Mr. Pope, "that hedge was four feet."

"Yeah?" said Ed. "Well, what's the matter with you, Wilb? When you're right you usually crow your head off. Sick or something?"

"Yes," said Mr. Pope. "I still have to explain to Carlotta. Can you see me issuing a reasonable explanation from behind this nose?"

"If it swells any more," said Ed, looking around, "she won't be able to see you. Maybe," he said brightly, "she won't even know it's you."

But Mrs. Pope was more concerned with the nose than with the explanation.

"Oh, Wilbur!" she said. "Oh, you poor darling! We must get a dressing on it right away. Look, dear; can you wiggle it? I mean with your fingers. That'll tell if it's broken."

Mr. Pope said firmly that to wiggle it would certainly send him into pronounced shock, so Mrs. Pope kissed the nose lightly and then brought her first-aid kit and put on a bandage which left nothing of Mr. Pope visible but his right eye and half his chin. Under the circumstances he thought it best not to complain, and it was from within these stifling folds that he mumbled his explanation.

"My poor Wilbur," said Mrs. Pope, "you fooled nobody. We all knew it was Ed. It's been one of the chief items of speculation—whether you'd get away with it. I wish I knew who told!" she said viciously. "But it's all right now," she said. "Shall I get you a cup of tea, darling?"

"Tea!" Mr. Pope nearly blew the bandage off.

"It's the only stimulant you can have," she said. "The Red Cross says alcohol is not a stimulant."

Mr. Pope said that he must go and fix Ed up first, and retreated to the stable.

"Wow!" said the horse, staring. Then he came closer. "Symbolic," he mused aloud. "The worm at last weaves him a cocoon, to emerge—— My Lord, Wilb, I wonder what will hatch out of there! It makes me feel kind of weak."

"Me too," said Mr. Pope. "How about a nice cup of tea?" And as Ed stared he went over to the harness closet. "The Red Cross says alcohol isn't stimulating, Ed. You suppose we have been on the wrong track all these years?"

"We better do a little research on it ourselves," said the horse. "Make mine a double, Wilb."

"It's no use plying me with drinks, Morton,
I still say I love another."

SPRING OVER BROOKLYN

ZACHARY GOLD

"HELLO, Dolly," I shouted into the telephone.

"Who is this?" Dolly said. "Where are you?"

"I'm in a phone booth." I looked out and saw the corner of a counter and medicine bottles piled in a pyramid and a poster with shades of red smeared on it and a sign that read: BE BEAUTIFUL. "I'm in a drugstore," I said.

"Who is this?"

"Willie," I said. "You remember. Willie."

"Willie?"

"I live two blocks away from you. The house with the shutters."

"Willie?"

When did you see her last, Willie? I said to myself. The church bazaar? A school dance? A family bingo game? I couldn't remember.

"Nice Willie," I said.

"Oh," said Dolly. "Crazy Willie."

"That's a fine thing to say to me. That's a fine thing to hear over a telephone."

"What do you want, Willie?"

"Come out with me, Dolly. I looked through my little black book today, because it's spring; and, Willie, I said, who'll you see tonight, who'll you make happy? Come out with me, Dolly, and let me hold your hand, because it's spring and I haven't seen you in three years."

"I'll go out with you," said Dolly.

"You won't regret it," I said and hung up.

From the drugstore to my house it's two blocks, and from my house to Dolly's it's two blocks; and I hadn't seen Dolly in three years. That's the world for you; that's Brooklyn.

Two blocks and three years. In three years I could walk from my house to San Francisco and halfway back; but I couldn't walk two blocks.

After supper I went upstairs to get dressed. Wear a bow tie, Willie, I said to myself. Don't ask me why. Don't ask me if Dolly likes bow ties; I don't know. Wear your sport slacks, Willie. Wear your pork-pie hat with the yellow brush.

I washed and shaved and looked in the top drawer of my bureau. I had two dollars and eighty cents in the little glass. Spend it all, Willie, I said to myself; do it right. I folded the bills into my wallet and dropped the change into my pocket.

"So long, ma," I called, and closed the door easy.

"Remember you work tomorrow," ma said.

I should worry about Caesar and Company. I should worry about the shipping department. Who is Dolly, what is she? That's like a song, I thought. I walked down the street and I clipped the hedges as I passed and I banged the wires around the front lawns.

It was so clear you could see Coney Island; I swear you could see Coney Island. You could see the sky, too, all the way up; not a cloud, just blue, all blue from Avenue N to Coney Island. And from Coney Island to Sandy Hook, and from Sandy Hook to Europe, I bet. But I should worry about the color of the sky in Europe. I should worry about anything except that it was spring and the sky was blue and the lawns were fuzzy with green and the trees weren't brown any more and Dolly was only two blocks away.

When I got to the house I checked with my little black book. This is the place, Willie, I said.

"Dolly," I said, when the door opened, "Dolly, you're beautiful."

"I'm not Dolly," the girl said. "I'm her sister."

"I'm sorry," I said. "I haven't seen Dolly in three years and I forgot what she looks like."

That was a mistake, all right, but I should cry over spilt milk. I took off my hat and sat down on the porch swing. I whistled awhile and looked at my wrist watch. It was 7:38. My watch is never wrong. It is an heirloom. My brother gave it to me last year. I don't know where he got it.

This time it was Dolly. She was blond and she had a smile and she wasn't too fat and she wasn't too skinny. That was Dolly, all right.

Don't ask me how I knew. I just knew.

"Let's go, Dolly," I said.

Dolly said good-by to her ma and pa, and I said hello and good-by; and I said good-by and I'm sorry to her sister, Janet, and I got Dolly into the street in five minutes.

"Dolly," I said, "you have a wonderful family. I always loved them."

"You never saw them before," Dolly said.

"Didn't I?"

"No."

"I think they're swell. I think you're swell. I've seen you before."

"At a party once," Dolly said. "You never took me out."

That's the world for you; that's Brooklyn. Three years and two blocks, and I never took her out before. Willie, I said to myself, you're slipping.

We did it right that night. Loge seats in the movies, forty cents per; sodas afterward, twenty cents per.

"Dolly," I said, "would you like a chocolate bar; would you like some candy drops, some chewing gum?"

"No, thanks."

"I have a dollar sixty to burn. What do you want to do?"

"Save it, Willie," she said. "Let's go home."

The sky was like a blot of blue-black ink.

"Home?" I said. "I don't want to go home. Let's take a walk in the park."

We got in the Ocean Avenue entrance and we walked around past the zoo and the boathouse, past the rose garden and the lily pool, under the covered bridge.

"I'm tired," I said. "Let's sit down."

Out on a point in the lake I found a bench and we sat down. "Dolly," I said, "this is the life. This reminds me of college. We used to sit on the steps of the frat house and sing songs. Those were the times. Willie, they'd say to me, tell us how you made that touchdown. Willie, did you hit that home run on a curve or a straight ball? That was a great game of basketball you played tonight, Willie. Those were the times."

"You never went to college," Dolly said.

"Be technical," I said. "It sounds nice, doesn't it? It could have been. What do you want me to say?"

"I don't know," Dolly said.

"The only reason I said it was because I wanted to get around to holding your hand. It works too. Ask me; I know."

"You can't hold my hand."

"That's a fine thing to tell me now. Why didn't you say that on the phone? Aw, come on, Dolly. It's spring and it's Willie asking."

"I'll let you hold my hand when you see a seal waiting for a trolley car," Dolly said, and laughed.

"You're not giving me a run-around?"

"No."

"Come on home, Dolly," I said.

So we walked back the way we came, past the rose garden and the lily pool and the zoo, out on to Ocean Avenue, and the first thing we saw was a trolley stalled on the tracks.

"What's the matter, bud?" I said to a fellow.

"Go look," he said. "How should I know?"

That's the world for you; that's Brooklyn.

I pushed through the crowd, and there was an animal sitting on the tracks.

"What is it?" I said to the fellow next to me.

"It's a seal," he said. "Escaped from the zoo."

"What's he doing here?" I said.

"He's waiting for a trolley car, bright boy."

"I believe you," I said.

So all the way home I held Dolly's hand.

"You're not sore at me?" I said.

"No."

I wanted to sit on the porch swing awhile, but Dolly said: "Go on home, Willie. You're not so tired that you need a rest, and it's only two blocks away."

When I got home I didn't feel like sleeping. Read a book, Willie, I said to myself. So I went down to the bookcase and I looked through every shelf, and I'd read them all. I looked through all the magazines, and I'd read them too. Willie, I said to myself, you read too much. So all I did was make a lettuce-and-tomato sandwich and eat it, looking out of the window, waiting for a car to pass, so I'd know I wasn't the last one in New York to go to sleep. When a car passed I got into bed.

The next morning the sun was shining. Lord, it was a beautiful day. It was a baseball day; it was a day to go swimming. It was a day for anything except work.

"Ma," I said at breakfast. "I could call up the place and tell them I was sick. I could tell them I broke my arm or something."

"You go to work, Willie," ma said.

"Why can't I tell them, ma? They'll never know."

"It's a lie," ma said.

"You don't understand about lying, ma. Sometimes you have to lie. Sometimes things aren't just right and a lie helps straighten it out. Sometimes things sound nicer when you lie. Suppose you're out with a girl. Do you have to tell the truth all the time?"

"If you're serious about the girl," ma said.

"I want you to know the truth, ma. I was out with a girl last night."

"Get out," ma said. "Go to work."

I slapped ma on the back and pulled her apron loose, and while she was still laughing I went out. On the way to the subway I stopped at the telegraph office and wrote a telegram.

MEET ME SAME PLACE STOP SAME TIME STOP URGENT
                                                    WILHELM

It cost me thirty cents. I addressed it to Dearest Dolly.

When I got to the shipping room of Caesar and Company, I felt good. "Buck," I said to the head clerk, "I'm going to ship out the whole place by myself today."

"That's fine," Buck said.

"Buck, you don't know how to say things. It's wonderful. It'll be the most stupendous thing that ever happened in Caesar and Company. Today I'm Atlas. I'm Hercules. I'm Tarzan. I'm Willie the Giant Killer."

"What's the matter with you?"

"How should I know?" I said. "How should I know?"

I worked like a demon. I tied; I packaged. I sent things out so fast the top of the shipping table burned from the friction. Don't ask me why; I don't know. Willie, I said to myself, you're terrific, you're a one-man department.

I went to the park and sat down on the bench at the point. You're sad, Willie, I said to myself; you're deep in sorrow.

By the time Dolly came, I really felt sad. I felt terrible. Nobody ever felt the way I did.

"What's the matter, Willie?" Dolly said. "Your telegram scared me."

"It's come, Dolly," I said. "It's come. Be brave."

210

"For heaven's sake, tell me what's the matter?"

"The company," I said. "A secret mission. I may never come back. But don't take it too hard, Dolly. I'm not worth it."

"A secret mission?" Dolly said. "You may never come back? Willie, you're not just making it up?"

"Dolly!"

"I knew it," Dolly said. "I knew it. Wilhelm. Of all the silly things."

I felt better. I didn't have to feel sad any more. "Well, it was for your sake I did it," I said.

"My sake?"

"It's spring," I said. "Let me hold your hand and hug you, because it's spring and it's Willie asking."

"You can hold my hand," Dolly said.

"Suppose I were really going away? Suppose you might never see me again?"

"You're not going away."

"What's a hug?" I said. "You talk as if it was the most important thing in the world."

"When the stars fall down," Dolly said, laughing, "I'll hug you."

"That's a fine thing to tell me," I said.

I looked up into the sky. "Look," I said. "Make a wish. It's a falling star. Make two; there's another."

They came down fizz and bang; gone.

"Dolly," I said.

"Yes."

"They fell down."

"What?"

"You said stars. You didn't say all the stars. You just said stars. Two stars are stars."

So I hugged her.

I was glad I wore my crepe-soled shoes and my hand-painted tie. I was glad I wore my tab-collar shirt. Willie, I said to myself, you look swell. Willie, I said to myself, you feel swell too.

"You're not sore?" I said to Dolly.

"No."

Walking home from Dolly's that night I met old Mr. Pranzer. "Hello, sir," I said. "It's a beautiful night."

"I have hay fever," said Mr. Pranzer.

That night I dreamt about my little black book. I dreamt I tore out

211

all the pages. I tore out Lily's and Flo's; Jane and Jean and Helen, Phyllis, Corinne, Dorothy, Joan and Norma and Anne. The only page left was Dolly's.

As soon as I got up I looked for the book. It was there, and so were all the pages. That was close, Willie, I said to myself; be careful of the little black book.

That morning I didn't feel like working. That's how it goes. I was going to take a taxi downtown, but I only had a quarter with me. I asked the taxi driver about it and he told me I could go take a jump. I told him I'd pay him off a nickel a week.

I heard the train coming and ran for the turnstile. I just made the station as the doors were closing. A fat lady held it open for me.

"Thanks," I said to her.

"I couldn't help it," said the lady; "somebody was trying to push me off the train."

That's the world for you; that's Brooklyn.

Lunchtime I went out and had a roll and coffee. I used a nickel to call Dolly.

"This is Jay Freling Matton," I said, "counselor-at-law. We have just received word that you are the beneficiary of a large estate left by a Mr. Dubelo, of Kansas, China. If you will meet us in front of the lions at the Public Library, we will be happy to further discuss the matter with you."

"Willie?" said Dolly. "Is that you, Willie?"

212

"You'll come?" I said.

"I didn't say that."

"Remember, it is to your benefit."

"The Public Library?"

"No," I said, remembering the nickel I had left. "I'll pick you up at home."

I heard Dolly say, "Willie——" just as I hung up.

"Why do you lie to me?" Dolly said. "Why do you make up all those stories?"

"It isn't lying," I said. "Why can't you have an uncle in Kansas or in China?"

"I haven't. That's all. I haven't."

"Dolly, you're wonderful. You're beautiful. Your eyes are like stars. Your mouth is a red, red ruby. Your hair is like spun gold. Your hands are like pale pieces of jade."

"Jade is green."

"There's white jade too."

"Well, my hands aren't like jade," Dolly said.

"I say they are."

"You read it in a book, Willie."

"No, I didn't. It was in a movie. The girl was in Malay and the fellow who told it to her was an international thief. It was a wonderful, wonderful scene."

"I don't like it," Dolly said.

"All right. You make up something better."

"I don't want to make up anything. I want you to tell the truth."

"I was going to tell you that your mouth was like a ripe melon. I was going to say that if I could kiss you once, just once, ah, then death would be sweet. There's a speech."

"Why didn't you just ask for a kiss?"

"You will?" I said. "Oh, Dolly!"

"I didn't say that."

"There. There you have it. I suppose if I said, 'How about it, babe?' it would have been all right?"

"No."

"That's fine," I said. "You just won't kiss me. That's fine. Aw, Dolly, it's spring and it's me, Willie, asking. Come on."

"No."

213

"What if I see a seal waiting for a trolley car?"

"No."

"If the stars fall down?"

"No."

"What then?"

Dolly laughed and leaned over. "Because you're such a crazy loon, Willie."

"That's a fine thing to say to me," I said.

But I kissed her.

Wonderful. Like running a strike right down the alley; like clicking off a rack in pool; like a cannon-ball ace in tennis. You're in the groove, Willie, I said to myself. You did it, Willie, you did it.

I reached down and tore off a snowball from the bush in the lawn. "Here, keep it," I said. "This is a night to remember."

"Willie——"

"What?"

"Do you love me, Willie?"

"I don't know, Dolly. It's spring; and sure I love you. Kiss me again, because it's spring and it's Willie asking."

"You better go home, Willie."

"I'm Don Juan," I said. "You're standing on a balcony and I'm sere-nading you. I'm singing you a love song. I'm Casanova and I'm sitting beside you whispering poetry in your ear."

"You better go home, Willie."

"Is something the matter?" I said. "Did I say something?"

"Go home, Willie." And she got up and she was crying. And before I could say anything she was in the house and the door was locked and I was standing on the porch all alone.

Willie, I said to myself, be sad; you've got a right to be sad now.

Walking home, I met Mr. Pranzer. "The trouble with you, Willie," he said, "is that you've never had hay fever. If you'd ever had hay fever you'd know how it's possible to be sad in the spring."

"Go jump in the lake, sir," I said courteously.

You do your best. You make everything nice. You think of things to say. You try to be different. You try to be romantic and glamorous. What happens?

She runs into the house crying.

You're a fool, Willie, I said to myself. You're a crazy fool. I should

214

worry about one girl. I have a million girls. I have a choice, anyone I want. They're all mine. Brooklyn is full of girls. Look in the little black book, Willie, I said to myself.

It was no good. I looked in the little black book and I got out a number. "Hello," I said. "Is Joan home?"

"This is Joan talking."

"This is Willie. How are you?"

"Fine. And you, Willie?"

"Fine."

And then it was no good. Joan has knock-knees, I said to myself. Joan talks with a lisp.

"What is it you wanted, Willie?" Joan said.

"I'm working for the telephone company," I said. "I'm just testing the connection. Good-by, Joan," I said, and hung up.

The same with Phyllis. Ditto on Anne. Corinne has hair like wet grass. Jane always sings. Lily has a job and a boss. Flo wanted classical music.

There was something wrong with all of them.

I took out the little black book and I tore out all the pages except Dolly's. I tore them all out and scattered them in the wind. What's the good of a little black book if you don't like any of them?

Ma said I didn't sleep enough. Buck told me I looked like the devil. Every time I ran for a train I missed it. When I went out to eat lunch I wasn't hungry.

It was Dolly all right.

Dolly was the one.

A week later I wrote her a letter:

Dolly: He had your name on his lips; I who am his closest friend have undertaken the sacred duty of telling you what he said.

However, do not grieve, since I know it was his wish that we who knew him should continue to carry on in the carefree happy way he knew, despite the fact that he no longer will be with us.

But I feel that all of us must feel that something fine, something grand has disappeared now that Willie has left.

So it is with both grief and the happiness he wanted us to continue to feel that I write you this news. Be brave, my dear, be brave.

His friend,

CARTER WAINWRIGHT, JR.

I went all the way up to the Bronx to mail it.

I waited three hours and ten minutes, on my brother's watch, in front of the lions, and when Dolly came, I was good and angry.

"That's it," I said to her; "keep me waiting. I don't matter at all."

"You didn't say what time to meet you in the letter," Dolly said.

"What letter? I never sent you any letter."

"Please, Willie," Dolly said. "What is it you wanted?"

"Marry me, Dolly," I said. "I'll give you a penthouse and a limousine. I'll shower you with diamonds and furs. You'll live in a house of flowers. I will be your slave. Step on me. Do as you will with me. But marry me."

"No," Dolly said.

"You let me hold your hand," I said.

"That was because of the seal."

"You let me hug you."

"The stars fell down."

"I kissed you."

"I liked your crazy talk, Willie."

"You cried over me."

"That was because I thought you didn't love me."

"I do," I said. "I do. Why won't you marry me, Dolly?"

"Willie," Dolly said. "Oh, Willie. I'll let you hold my hand and hug me because you're lucky; and I'll let you kiss me because I like you. But I won't marry you."

"I'll give you everything you want. Luxuries. Anything. Just ask for it."

"No, you won't. You know you can't do that, Willie."

So that was it. And maybe she wasn't wrong. Maybe I was wrong. Maybe, Willie, I said to myself, you're not good enough for her. I felt all washed up. I felt like the stone lions must feel in a rain.

"Dolly," I said, "you're right. I can't give you anything. I work in a shipping room and I make twenty-two-fifty a week. I haven't got any money in the bank, and I'm always lying. Don't ever believe me,

Dolly. All I have is myself. That's all I can give you."
"No limousine?" Dolly said.
"No."
"No furs?"
"No."
"No diamonds?"
"No."
"Just you?"
"Just me, Dolly."
"And you'd like it that way: Just you and me?"
"Oh, Dolly!" I said.
"Without lies or stories?"
"Dolly," I said, "you're breaking my heart."
"How much do you make a week, again?" Dolly said.
"Twenty-two-fifty."
"I make eighteen," Dolly said. "What do you think?"
"Dolly," I said. "Dolly!"
"Crazy Willie," Dolly said. "Who wants all those things?"
Imagine that. Furs, diamonds, limousines, penthouses—pouf, in the garbage pail; all in exchange for me—Willie. There's a girl for you. I didn't know what to do. "Hey, lions," I yelled.
"Willie," she said. "Willie, kiss me, because it's spring and it's me, Dolly, asking."
That's the world for you; that's Brooklyn.

SPRING TONIC

MARGARET FISHBACK

When crocuses poke through the ground
To promise springtime's just around
The corner, that's a sure-fire sign
A tonic's due . . . I don't mean wine,
Or even sulphur and molasses,
Or kisses, or rose-colored glasses.
What Mamma needs at times like that
Is just a brand-new cockeyed hat.

217

THE HIPPOPOTAMUS

OGDEN NASH

Behold the hippopotamus!
We laugh at how he looks to us,
And yet in moments dank and grim,
I wonder how we look to him.
Peace, peace, thou hippopotamus!
We really look all right to us,
And you no doubt delight the eye
Of other hippopotami.

"Open wide, please—say AH!"

THE COMPLETE DANGLER

JOHN MASON BROWN

THE unveiling had taken place in the presence of Miss Brickley, though she did not remove her cap, and had been eagerly attended by me. With a modesty uncommon in sculptors, Dr. Smith had stayed away. He was already working on another figure.

Dr. Wright served him as his deputy. To my disappointment I noticed he carried no prepared speech. It was he, however, who had walked up calmly to the monument. It was he who released the enveloping tape.

This turned out to be a job more difficult than ticklish. Because of the heat and incipient reforestation, the tape was militantly adhesive. A bulldog's bite could not have been more unrelenting, a mule more unbudgeable.

I never expect to see anything depart as regretfully as did this tape. Plainly it hated to leave me. Had I not been hurt, I would have been flattered, by its devotion. It had to be torn away. Once so torn it would rush back to cling to me again. The result was the kind of farewell

219

known as painful. Indeed, it was an enforced separation which must be described not as one yank but as a long series of yanks.

Dr. Wright had shocked me by talking throughout the ceremonies. His conversation was meant to take the place of those yellow pills and that needle. But, though diverting enough to amuse Miss Brickley and him, it left me unamused. I found it a poor substitute.

Little by little, after much huffing and puffing on Dr. Wright's part, the tape had submitted to removal—and Dr. Smith's handiwork inched into view. At first I was sickened by what I peeked at with dread. Horror, however, soon gave way to pride as I surveyed, running across my body, the only Norwegian fjord I had ever seen which was lighted by an Arizona sunset and crossed with stitches.

The sight made me as happy as a student with a diploma. I now fully understood for the first time how a city father feels when a park in his town is populated with a new statue, and shared the emotions of a curator whose museum has been blessed with an important acquisition.

"A beauty," I had cried in tones equalling in professionalism any that Dr. Smith could have mustered.

Miss Brickley smiled. Dr. Wright smiled. So did I. Evidently the unveiling had been a great success. I could hardly wait for the reviews.

"It will be a beauty in a minute," said Dr. Wright. "We're not through yet."

Whereupon he began to undo Dr. Smith's sewing with as much relish as Penelope had undone her own. As he snipped at the stitches here and there, my heart sank. I had found them rather attractive. I knew they broke the line. Yet for this reason I believed they softened it. To my mind they had been what the ribbons and the holly are to a Christmas box, or what an artist's signature is to a painting. I missed their personal touch, and the sense of the fiesta their streamers brought to the basement.

Dr. Wright would have none of them.

"A building looks better without the scaffolding," was his only comment as he plucked at me with his scissors.

When he had let out my hem, he added a sentence which rang a bell, however lightly.

"Tomorrow's another big day."

"Tomorrow?"

Dr. Wright shook his head in assent.

"Un-hunh, you'll dangle."

Dangle? Yes, that was the word, the perplexing word, my wife had used long ago, before we had been separated. Before I had been separated, too, for that matter. I did not like its sound. As the novelists say, I searched Miss Brickley's face. But found nothing. Since her expression did not change, my courage rose.

"Dangle?" I gulped.

"Yes," Dr. Wright answered. "Tomorrow you can sit up, with your feet hanging over the edge of the bed for twenty minutes in the morning and for twenty minutes in the afternoon. Then, the next day, you can get up for an hour, and walk a little, and read in the big chair."

The dangling day had come and gone, presenting more problems and excitements than anyone could believe who has not dangled or looked

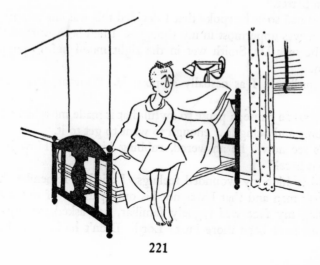

221

forward to so doing. Before it was over I realized why grammarians frown on participles that weakly do what I had weakly done.

Sitting on the edge of a bed and dropping your feet over the side sounds easy enough. Certainly, it sounds easier than rolling off a log, a diversion which has never tempted me. But it can be hard, as to my sorrow I now know well. The morning I tried it I recalled the time when I could even do it myself without anyone's aid, or without feeling that hatpins were sheathed in all my pores and that my head belonged to a drunk on a Merry-Go-Round bar.

If the morning's experience overtook me as an Alpine adventure braved by a man cursed with vertigo, the afternoon's repetition was somewhat more encouraging. By then my feet no longer belonged to a paper doll. They had ceased to secede from me. They seemed almost anxious to be readmitted to my union.

The next morning, which was Thursday, Dr. Smith had arrived when, dressed for the occasion in pajamas, I was about to set out on a maiden voyage to the chair.

"How do we feel today?" he asked, incorporating my weakness in his strength in one of those medical "we's" which can so outdistance their editorial cousins in comfort.

"Fine," said I. "And guess what? Yesterday I dangled."

"Good," said Dr. Smith as if he were about to pin a Congressional Medal upon me. "And walking today?"

"About to try."

"Even better."

He beamed so as he spoke that I decided this was the moment to ask him what was uppermost in my thoughts. I had been warned that you had to be sure Dr. Smith was in the right mood before popping the question.

"Doctor," said I as casually as possible. "Doctor, when can I go home?"

There was a pause; a pause so awful that it made me ashamed of having a home and being low enough to want to get to it.

"Let's see now," he answered, rubbing his chin. "How long have you been here?"

I tried to hide my wounded feelings. I tried to remember he was a very busy man and that I was not his only patient. If my wife, after confessing my face was vaguely familiar, had asked me my name, I could not have been more hurt. Lord! Didn't he know what I had

222

been through? How could he forget those days and nights, every hour of which had seemed longer to me than the Passion Play?

I was proud of saying as calmly as I did, "Two weeks this coming Saturday."

There was another pause. 429 was as silent as a courtroom at a murder trial's end when the judge is about to read the sentence.

"Why, Saturday, of course!" exclaimed Dr. Smith. "Saturday morning."

While muttering my thanks, I was forced to wonder if Dr. Smith remembered why he had operated on me. I was so grateful by now that I would not have blamed him had he forgotten.

"Would you like to see my scar?" I asked archly, feeling this might remind him and eager to express my gratitude.

He looked at it. He even felt it. Modest though he was, I gathered he approved. At least he attempted to make no changes. As a writing man, accustomed to filling galley proofs with author's alterations, I marveled at this.

He merely grunted like a stage Indian. "Un-un-un," as he circumnavigated his handiwork. "Yes, Saturday morning will be fine." And in a cloud of such civilities as "It's been a pleasure," "No, the pleasure has been all mine," he was gone.

"Let's get back to walking," said Miss Brickley.

The prospect of getting home had so flooded me with joy that I was confident my bedroom slippers were Seven League Boots. As I

223

sat on the edge of my bed, dangling now undizzily, I told myself that, if necessary, I could foot it to Canossa.

But walking is a funny business. It is amazing in what a short time it can become a lost art. It's like playing the piano, making Stradivariuses, or tying your shoes. You have to keep at it to be good. Swimming, bicycling, and riding come back to you much more quickly. Give up walking for a while, and it will give you up. Lie in bed for even a week and a half, and the quadruped in you will do its best to down the biped.

When my feet touched the floor my body tried to follow them there. Only Miss Brickley kept it from oozing into my slippers. Had Sir Isaac Newton been in the room, and Miss Brickley out, I could have taught him more than the ripest apple. Miss Brickley, however, was there. By turning herself into crutches and a cane, she kept me safely out of the grasp of the law of gravity.

One foot moved forward. It pushed away from me like a ship getting free of a pier. I watched its departure with impersonal interest, forgetting I was a passenger. After considerable concentration, I remembered the other foot should follow. But it did not. Although I tried to give it its proceed orders, my lines of communications were hopelessly broken.

I could not blame Miss Brickley for the baby-talk with which she once again abused me.

224

"One and two! Two and one! This footie, now that footie! *That's* a big boy."

Encouraged by such exhortations, my little piggies at last went to the big chair, though not to market. I sank into it, with my head still bent forward over my knees and my body throbbing as if from a misplaced hangover.

Miss Brickley crossed over to the bed table to get me a book. I don't think that I have ever seen anything more remarkable than the way in which she negotiated this cross. Her head was held high. Her feet followed one another without her looking at them or entreating them. Her body moved briskly. She did not moan. Her face was not distorted with pain. She neither carried a cane nor draped herself like a valance over a crutch. Moreover, she was able to talk while walking; a feat which struck me as stupendous. I surveyed her with the admiration navigators feel for Captain Bligh.

Miss Brickley saw the green envy on my face.

"Never mind," she said. "It'll come back to you."

It did—reluctantly.

By the next morning I was shuffling around, bent over like an old-fashioned razor, and a rusty one at that. I was still relying on my hands as much as my feet, balancing with them, grabbing on to the furniture, flapping penguinwise against the wall. But I was walking, and ferociously proud of it.

I could even go to the bathroom by myself. A simple thing, you may say, and unexceptional. Yet an event—a St. Crispin's day—in the lives of the imbedded, and a blessing not properly appreciated by those whose good health has never left them at the mercy of a middleman.

That afternoon I was swaying up and down the corridor under my own steam. Someone had added several miles to it since I had last been pushed down it on my bed when heading for the sun roof. The solarium looked so far away that I could have sworn it was slipping behind the horizon. It was my goal, however. By it I set my course.

My eyes were still fixed on the floor as if I were searching for pennies. Each step disturbed the shell crater which Dr. Smith had left in my midriff. And I was still finding that my feet belonged to irreconcilable political parties. Even so I considered myself a second Nurmi, uncrowned as yet, though deserving of applause.

When I finally reached the solarium, to my sorrow it was empty. Not a person was on hand to greet me at Le Bourget. I smoked a cig-

225

arette in bored silence, and took off with difficulty for the return voyage. On the way back I could not resist crawling into the control room to speak to the Floor Nurse who sat there reading a paper.

"Look!" I cried.

"What's that?"

"Look," I repeated, pitifully anxious for praise.

"At what?" she asked.

"At me."

An expression of amazement—or was it fear?—washed over her face, but, from her point of view, she handled the situation well.

"Why?"

This deflated me.

"I'm walking," I stammered. "I came all the way down the hall by myself."

"Really?" she smiled. "That's fine." There was no genuine excitement in her voice. I was glad to have saved my ace.

"What is more, I'm going home tomorrow."

Although I had not expected the Floor Nurse to cry at this, her self-control exceeded my expectations.

"You're in 429, aren't you?" she asked, and consulted a diagram. "Yes, I knew you were leaving then. You see, Dr. Smith has already engaged the room for someone who's coming in tomorrow night."

226

"Do they ever get mixed on their signals?"

HELL'S BELLS

MARGARET FISHBACK

The ambulance flies at a furious gait
That registers utter defiance of Fate,
As clanging through traffic quite agile and supple,
It picks up one person and knocks down a couple.

THE WIDOW'S CRUISE

FRANK R. STOCKTON

THE Widow Ducket lived in a small village about ten miles from the New Jersey seacoast. In this village she was born, here she had married and buried her husband, and here she expected somebody to bury her; but she was in no hurry for this, for she had scarcely reached middle age. She was a tall woman with no apparent fat in her composition, and full of activity both muscular and mental.

She rose at six o'clock in the morning, cooked breakfast, set the table, washed the dishes when the meal was over, milked, churned, swept, washed, ironed, worked in her little garden, attended to the flowers in the front yard and in the afternoon knitted and quilted and sewed, and after tea she either went to see her neighbors or had them come to see her. When it was really dark she lighted the lamp in her parlor and read for an hour.

Dorcas Networthy, who was a small, plump woman, with a solemn face, had lived with the widow for many years and had become her devoted disciple. Whatever the widow did, that also did Dorcas—not so well, for her heart told her she could never expect to do that, but with a yearning anxiety to do everything as well as she could.

She rose at five minutes past six, and in a subsidiary way she helped to get the breakfast, to eat it, to wash up the dishes, to work in the garden, to quilt, to sew, to visit and receive, and no one could have tried harder than she did to keep awake when the widow read aloud in the evening.

All these things happened every day in the summer time, but in the winter the widow and Dorcas cleared the snow from their little front path instead of attending to the flowers, and in the evening they lighted a fire as well as a lamp in the parlor.

Sometimes, however, something different happened, but this was not often, only a few times in the year. One of the different things occurred when Mrs. Ducket and Dorcas were sitting on their little front porch one summer afternoon, one on the little bench on one side of the door, and the other on the little bench on the other side of the door, each waiting until she should hear the clock strike five, to prepare tea. But it was not yet a quarter to five when a one-horse wagon containing four men came slowly down the street. Dorcas first saw the wagon, and she instantly stopped knitting.

"Mercy on me!" she exclaimed. "Whoever those people are, they are strangers here, and they don't know where to stop, for they first go to one side of the street and then to the other."

The widow looked around sharply. "Humph!" said she. "Those men are sailormen. You might see that in a twinklin' of an eye. Sailormen always drive that way, because that is the way they sail ships. They first tack in one direction and then in another."

"Mr. Ducket didn't like the sea?" remarked Dorcas, for about the three hundredth time.

"No, he didn't," answered the widow, for about the two hundredth and fiftieth time, for there had been occasions when she thought Dorcas put this question inopportunely. "He hated it, and he was drowned in it through trustin' a sailorman, which I never did nor shall. Do you really believe those men are comin' here?"

"Upon my word I do!" said Dorcas, and her opinion was correct.

The wagon drew up in front of Mrs. Ducket's little white house, and the two women sat rigidly, their hands in their laps, staring at the man who drove.

This was an elderly personage with whitish hair, and under his chin a thin whitish beard, which waved in the gentle breeze and gave Dorcas the idea that his head was filled with hair which was leaking out from below.

"Is this the Widow Ducket's?" inquired this elderly man, in a strong, penetrating voice.

"That's my name," said the widow, and laying her knitting on the bench beside her, she went to the gate. Dorcas also laid her knitting on the bench beside her and went to the gate.

"I was told," said the elderly man, "at a house we touched at about a quarter of a mile back, that the Widow Ducket's was the only house in this village where there was any chance of me and my mates getting a meal. We are four sailors, and we are making from the bay over to Cuppertown, and that's eight miles ahead yet, and we are all pretty sharp set for something to eat."

"This is the place," said the widow, "and I do give meals if there is
229

enough in the house and everything comes handy."

"Does everything come handy today?" said he.

"It does," said she, "and you can hitch your horse and come in; but I haven't got anything for him."

"Oh, that's all right," said the man, "we brought along stores for him, so we'll just make fast and then come in."

The two women hurried into the house in a state of bustling preparation, for the furnishing of this meal meant one dollar in cash.

The four mariners, all elderly men, descended from the wagon, each one scrambling with alacrity over a different wheel.

A box of broken ship biscuit was brought out and put on the ground in front of the horse, who immediately set himself to eating with great satisfaction.

Tea was a little late that day, because there were six persons to provide for instead of two, but it was a good meal, and after the four seamen had washed their hands and faces at the pump in the back yard and had wiped them on two towels furnished by Dorcas, they all came in and sat down. Mrs. Ducket seated herself at the head of the table with the dignity proper to the mistress of the house, and Dorcas seated herself at the other end with the dignity proper to the disciple of the mistress. No service was necessary, for everything that was to be eaten or drunk was on the table.

When each of the elderly mariners had had as much bread and butter, quickly baked soda biscuit, dried beef, cold ham, cold tongue, and preserved fruit of every variety known, as his storage capacity would permit, the mariner in command, Captain Bird, pushed back his chair, whereupon the other mariners pushed back their chairs.

"Madam," said Captain Bird, "we have all made a good meal, which didn't need to be no better nor more of it, and we're satisfied; but that horse out there has not had time to rest himself enough to go the eight miles that lie ahead of us, so, if it's all the same to you and this good lady, we'd like to sit on that front porch awhile and smoke our pipes. I was a-looking at that porch when I came in, and I bethought to myself what a rare good place it was to smoke a pipe in."

"There's pipes been smoked there," said the widow, rising, "and it can be done again. Inside the house I don't allow tobacco, but on the porch neither of us minds."

So the four captains betook themselves to the porch, two of them seating themselves on the little bench on one side of the door, and two of

230

them on the little bench on the other side of the door, and lighted their pipes.

"Shall we clear off the table and wash up the dishes," said Dorcas, "or wait until they are gone?"

"We will wait until they are gone," said the widow, "for now that they are here we might as well have a bit of a chat with them. When a sailorman lights his pipe he is generally willin' to talk, but when he is eatin' you can't get a word out of him."

Without thinking it necessary to ask permission, for the house belonged to her, the Widow Ducket brought a chair and put it in the hall close to the open front door, and Dorcas brought another chair and seated herself by the side of the widow.

"Do all you sailormen belong down there at the bay?" asked Mrs. Ducket; thus the conversation began, and in a few minutes it had reached a point at which Captain Bird thought it proper to say that a great many strange things happen to seamen sailing on the sea which lands-people never dream of.

"Such as anything in particular?" asked the widow, at which remark Dorcas clasped her hands in expectancy.

At this question each of the mariners took his pipe from his mouth and gazed upon the floor in thought.

"There's a good many things strange happened to me and my mates at sea. Would you and that other lady like to hear any of them?" asked Captain Bird.

"We would like to hear them if they are true," said the widow.

"There's nothing happened to me and my mates that isn't true," said Captain Bird, "and there is something that once happened to me. I was on a whaling v'yage when a big sperm whale, just as mad as a fiery bull, came at us, head on, and struck the ship at the stern with such tremendous force that his head crashed right through her timbers and he went nearly half his length into her hull. The hold was mostly filled with empty barrels, for we was just beginning our v'yage, and when he had made kindling wood of these there was room enough for him. We all expected that it wouldn't take five minutes for the vessel to fill and go to the bottom, and we made ready to take to the boats; but it turned out we didn't need to take to no boats, for as fast as the water rushed into the hold of the ship, that whale drank it and squirted it up through the two blowholes in the top of his head, and as there was an open hatchway just over his head, the water all went into the sea again, and that whale kept

231

working day and night pumping the water out until we beached the vessel on the island of Trinidad—the whale helping us wonderful on our way over by the powerful working of his tail, which, being outside in the water, acted like a propeller. I don't believe anything stranger than that ever happened to a whaling ship."

"No," said the widow, "I don't believe anything ever did."

Captain Bird now looked at Captain Sanderson, and the latter took his pipe out of his mouth and said that in all his sailing around the world he had never known anything queerer than what happened to a big steamship he chanced to be on, which ran into an island in a fog. Everybody on board thought the ship was wrecked, but it had twin screws, and was going at such a tremendous speed that it turned the island entirely upside down and sailed over it, and he had heard tell that even now people sailing over the spot could look down into the water and see the roots of the trees and the cellars of the houses.

Captain Sanderson now put his pipe back into his mouth, and Captain Burress took out his pipe.

"I was once in an obelisk-ship," said he, "that used to trade regular between Egypt and New York, carrying obelisks. We had a big obelisk on board. The way they ship obelisks is to make a hole in the stern of the ship, and run the obelisk in, p'inted end foremost; and this obelisk filled up nearly the whole of that ship from stern to bow. We was about ten days out, and sailing afore a northeast gale with the engines at full speed, when suddenly we spied breakers ahead, and our captain saw we was about to run on a bank. Now if we hadn't had an obelisk on board we might have sailed over that bank, but the captain knew that with an obelisk on board we drew too much water for this, and that we'd be

232

wrecked in about fifty-five seconds if something wasn't done quick. So he had to do something quick, and this is what he did: He ordered all steam on, and drove slambang on that bank. Just as he expected, we stopped so suddint that that big obelisk bounced for'ard, it p'inted end foremost, and went clean through the bow and shot out into the sea. The minute it did that the vessel was so lightened that it rose in the water and we then steamed over the bank. There was one man knocked overboard by the shock when we struck, but as soon as we missed him we went back after him and we got him all right. You see, when the obelisk went overboard, its butt end, which was heaviest, went down first, and when it touched the bottom it just stood there, and as it was such a big obelisk there was about five and a half feet of it stuck out of the water. The man who was knocked overboard, he just swam for that obelisk and he climbed up the hiryglyphics. It was a mighty fine obelisk, and the Egyptians had cut their hiryglyphics good and deep, so that the man could get hand and foot hold; and when we got to him and took him off, he was sitting high and dry on the p'inted end of that obelisk. It was a great pity about the obelisk, for it was a good obelisk, but as I never heard the company tried to raise it I expect it is standing there yet."

Captain Burress now put his pipe back into his mouth and looked at Captain Jenkinson, who removed his pipe and said:

"The queerest thing that ever happened to me was about a shark. We was off the Banks, and the time of year was July, and the ice was coming down, and we got in among a lot of it. Not far away, off our weather bow, there was a little iceberg which had such a queerness about it that the captain and three men went in a boat to look at it. The ice was mighty clear ice, and you could see almost through it, and right inside of it, not more than three feet above the waterline, and about two feet, or maybe

233

twenty inches, inside the ice, was a whooping big shark, about fourteen feet long—a regular man-eater—frozen in there hard and fast. 'Bless my soul,' said the captain, 'this is a wonderful curiosity, and I'm going to git him out.' Just then one of the men said he saw that shark wink, but the captain wouldn't believe him, for he said that shark was frozen stiff and hard and couldn't wink. You see, the captain had his own idees about things, and he knew that whales was warm-blooded and would freeze if they was shut up in ice, but he forgot that sharks was not whales and that they're cold-blooded just like toads. And there is toads that has been shut up in rocks for thousands of years, and they stayed alive, no matter how cold the place was, because they was cold-blooded, and when the rocks was split, out hopped the frog. But, as I said before, the captain forgot sharks was cold-blooded, and he determined to get that one out.

"Now you both know, being housekeepers, that if you take a needle and drive it into a hunk of ice you can split it. The captain had a sail-needle with him, and so he drove it into the iceberg right alongside of the shark and split it. Now the minute he did it he knew that the man was right when he said he saw the shark wink, for it flopped out of that iceberg quicker nor a flash of lightning."

"What a happy fish he must have been!" ejaculated Dorcas, forgetful of precedent, so great was her emotion.

"Yes," said Captain Jenkinson, "it was a happy fish enough, but it wasn't a happy captain. You see, that shark hadn't had anything to eat, perhaps for a thousand years, until the captain came along with his sail-needle."

"Surely you sailormen do see strange things," now said the widow, "and the strangest thing about them is that they are true."

"Yes, indeed," said Dorcas, "that is the most wonderful thing."

"You wouldn't suppose," said the Widow Ducket, glancing from one bench of mariners to the other, "that I have a sea story to tell, but I have, and if you like I will tell it to you."

Captain Bird looked up a little surprised.

"We would like to hear it—indeed, we would, madam," said he.

"Ay, ay!" said Captain Burress, and the two other mariners nodded.

"It was a good while ago," she said, "when I was living on the shore near the head of the bay, that my husband was away and I was left alone in the house. One mornin' my sister-in-law, who lived on the other side of the bay, sent me word by a boy on a horse that she hadn't

234

any oil in the house to fill the lamp that she always put in the window to light her husband home, who was a fisherman, and if I would send her some by the boy she would pay me back as soon as they bought oil. The boy said he would stop on his way home and take the oil to her, but he never did stop, or perhaps he never went back, and about five o'clock I began to get dreadfully worried, for I knew if that lamp wasn't in my sister-in-law's window by dark she might be a widow before midnight. So I said to myself, 'I've got to get that oil to her, no matter what happens or how it's done.' Of course I couldn't tell what might happen, but there was only one way it could be done, and that was for me to get into the boat that was tied to the post down by the water, and take it to her, for it was too far for me to walk around by the head of the bay. Now, the trouble was, I didn't know no more about a boat and the managin' of it than any one of you sailormen knows about clear-starchin'. But there wasn't no use of thinkin' what I knew and what I didn't know, for I had to take it to her, and there was no way of doin' it except in that boat. So I filled a gallon can, for I thought I might as well take enough while I was about it, and I went down to the water and I unhitched that boat and I put the oilcan into her, and then I got in, and off I started, and when I was about a quarter of a mile from the shore—"

"Madam," interrupted Captain Bird, "did you row or—or was there a sail to the boat?"

The widow looked at the questioner for a moment. "No," said she, "I didn't row. I forgot to bring the oars from the house; but it didn't matter, for I didn't know how to use them, and if there had been a sail I couldn't have put it up, for I didn't know how to use it, either. I used the rudder to make the boat go. The rudder was the only thing I knew anything about. I'd held a rudder when I was a little girl, and I knew how to work it. So I just took hold of the handle of the rudder and turned it round and round, and that made the boat go ahead, you know, and—"

"Madam!" exclaimed Captain Bird and the other elderly mariners took their pipes from their mouths.

"Yes, that is the way I did it," continued the widow, briskly. "Big steamships are made to go by a propeller turning round and round at their back ends, and I made the rudder work in the same way, and I got along very well, too, until suddenly, when I was about a quarter of a mile from the shore, a most terrible and awful storm arose. There must have been a typhoon or a cyclone out at sea, for the waves came up the

235

bay bigger than houses, and when they got to the head of the bay they turned around and tried to get out to sea again. So in this way they continually met, and made the most awful and roarin' pilin' up of waves that ever was known.

"My little boat was pitched about as if it had been a feather in a breeze, and when the front part of it was cleavin' itself down into the water the hind part was stickin' up until the rudder whizzed around like a patent churn with no milk in it. The thunder began to roar and the lightnin' flashed, and three sea gulls, so nearly frightened to death that they began to turn up the whites of their eyes, flew down and sat on one of the seats of the boat, forgettin' in that awful moment that man was their nat'ral enemy. I had a couple of biscuits in my pocket, because I had thought I might want a bite in crossin', and I crumpled up one of these and fed the poor creatures. Then I began to wonder what I was goin' to do, for things were gettin' awfuller and awfuller every instant, and the little boat was a-heavin' and a-pitchin' and a-rollin' and h'istin' itself up, first on one end then on the other, to such an extent that if I hadn't kept tight hold of the rudder-handle I'd slipped off the seat I was sittin' on.

"All of a sudden I remembered that oil in the can; but as I was puttin' my fingers on the cork my conscience smote me. 'Am I goin' to use this oil,' I said to myself, 'and let my sister-in-law's husband be wrecked for want of it?' And then I thought that he wouldn't want it all that night, and perhaps they would buy oil the next day, and so I poured out about a tumblerful of it on the water, and I can just tell you sailormen that you never saw anything act as prompt as that did. In three seconds, or perhaps five, the water all around me, for the distance of a small front yard, was just as flat as a table and as smooth as glass, and so invitin' in appearance that the three gulls jumped out of the boat and began to swim about on it, primin' their feathers and lookin' at themselves in the transparent depths, though I must say that one of them made an awful face as he dipped his bill into the water and tasted kerosene.

"Now I had time to sit quiet in the midst of the placid space I had made for myself, and rest from workin' of the rudder. Truly it was a wonderful and marvelous thing to look at. The waves was roarin' and leapin' up all around me higher than the roof of this house, and sometimes their tops would reach over so that they nearly met and shut out all view of the stormy sky, which seemed as if it was bein' torn to pieces by blazin' lightnin', while the thunder pealed so tremendous that it

236

almost drowned the roar of the waves. Not only above and all around me was everything terrific and fearful, but even under me it was the same, for there was a big crack in the bottom of the boat as wide as my hand, and through this I could see down into the water beneath, and there was—"

"Madam!" ejaculated Captain Bird, the hand which had been holding his pipe a few inches from his mouth now dropping to his knee; and at this motion the hands which held the pipes of the three other mariners dropped to their knees.

"Of course it sounds strange," continued the widow, "but I know that people can see down into clear water, and the water under me was clear, and the crack was wide enough for me to see through, and down under me was sharks and swordfishes and other horrible water creatures, which I had never seen before, all driven into the bay, I haven't a doubt, by the violence of the storm out at sea. The thought of my bein' upset and fallin' in among those monsters made my very blood run cold, and involuntary-like I began to turn the handle of the rudder, and in a moment I shot into a wall of ragin' sea water that was towerin' around me. For a second I was fairly blinded and stunned, but I had the cork out of that oilcan in no time, and very soon—you'd scarcely believe it if I told you how soon—I had another placid millpond surroundin' of me. I sat there a-pantin' and fannin' with my straw hat, for you'd better believe I was flustered, and then I begun to think how long it would take me to make a line of millponds clean across the head of the bay, and how much oil it would need, and whether I had enough. So I sat and calculated that if a tumblerful of oil would make a smooth place about seven yards across, which I would say was the width of the one I was in —which I calculated by a measure of my eye as to how many breadths of carpet it would take to cover it—and if the bay was two miles across betwixt our house and my sister-in-law's, and, although I couldn't get the thing down to exact figures, I saw pretty soon that I wouldn't have oil enough to make a level cuttin' through all those mountainous billows, and besides, even if I had enough to take me across, what would be the good of goin' if there wasn't any oil left to fill my sister-in-law's lamp?

"While I was thinkin' and calculatin' a perfectly dreadful thing happened, which made me think if I didn't get out of this pretty soon I'd find myself in a mighty risky predicament. The oilcan, which I had forgotten to put the cork in, toppled over, and before I could grab it every drop of the oil ran into the hind part of the boat, where it was soaked up by a lot of dry dust that was there. No wonder my heart sank when I saw this. Glancin' wildly around me, as people will do when they are scared, I saw the smooth place I was in gettin' smaller and smaller, for the kerosene was evaporatin', as it will do even off woolen clothes if you give it time enough. The first pond I had come out of seemed to be covered up, and the great, towerin', throbbin' precipice of sea water was a-closin' around me.

"Castin' down my eyes in despair, I happened to look through the crack in the bottom of the boat, and oh, what a blessed relief it was! Far down there everything was smooth and still, and I could see the sand on the bottom, as level and hard, no doubt, as it was on the beach. Suddenly the thought struck me that that bottom would give me the only chance I had of gettin' out of the frightful fix I was in. If I could fill that oilcan with air, and then puttin' it under my arm and takin' a long breath if I could drop down on that smooth bottom, I might run along toward shore, as far as I could, and then, when I felt my breath was givin' out, I could take a pull at the oilcan and take another run, and then take

238

another pull and another run, and perhaps the can would hold air enough for me until I got near enough to shore to wade to dry land. To be sure, the sharks and other monsters were down there, but then they must have been awfully frightened, and perhaps they might not remember that man was their nat'ral enemy. Anyway, I thought it would be better to try the smooth-water passage down there than stay and be swallowed up by the ragin' waves on top.

"So I blew the can full of air and corked it, and then I tore up some of the boards from the bottom of the boat so as to make a hole big enough for me to get through—and you sailormen needn't wriggle so when I say that, for you all know a divin'-bell hasn't any bottom at all and the water never comes in—and so when I got the hole big enough I took the oilcan under my arm, and was just about to slip down through it when I saw an awful turtle a-walkin' through the sand at the bottom. Now, I might trust sharks and swordfishes and sea serpents to be frightened and forget about their nat'ral enemies, but I never could trust a gray turtle as big as a cart, with a black neck a yard long, with yellow bags to its jaws, to forget anything or to remember anything. I'd as lieve get into a bathtub with a live crab as to go down there. It wasn't of no use even so much as thinkin' of it, so I gave up that plan and didn't once look through that hole again."

"And what did you do, madam?" asked Captain Bird, who was regarding her with a face of stone.

"I used electricity," she said. "Now don't stare as if you had a shock of it. That's what I used. When I was younger than I was then, and sometimes visited friends in the city, we often amused ourselves by rubbing our feet on the carpet until we got ourselves so full of electricity that we could put up our fingers and light the gas. So I said to myself that if I could get full of electricity for the purpose of lightin' the gas I could get full of it for other purposes, and so, without losin' a moment, I set to work. I stood up on one of the seats, which was dry, and rubbed the bottoms of my shoes backward and forward on it with such violence and swiftness that they pretty soon got warm and I began fillin' with electricity, and when I was fully charged with it from my toes to the top of my head, I just sprang into the water and swam ashore. Of course I couldn't sink, bein' full of electricity."

Captain Bird heaved a long sigh and rose to his feet, whereupon the other mariners rose to their feet. "Madam," said Captain Bird, "what's to pay for the supper and—the rest of the entertainment?"

239

"The supper is twenty-five cents apiece," said the Widow Ducket, "and everything else is free, gratis."

Whereupon each mariner put his hand into his trousers pocket, pulled out a silver quarter, and handed it to the widow. Then, with four solemn "Good evenin's," they went out to the front gate.

"Cast off, Captain Jenkinson," said Captain Bird, "and you, Captain Burress, clew him up for'ard. You can stay in the bow, Captain Sanderson and take the sheetlines. I'll go aft."

All being ready, each of the elderly mariners clambered over a wheel, and having seated themselves, they prepared to lay their course for Cuppertown.

But just as they were about to start, Captain Jenkinson asked that they lay to a bit, and clambering down over his wheel, he re-entered the front gate and went up to the door of the house, where the widow and Dorcas were still standing.

"Madam," said he, "I just came back to ask what became of your brother-in-law through his wife's not bein' able to put no light in the window?"

"The storm drove him ashore on our side of the bay," said she, "and the next mornin' he came up to our house, and I told him all that had happened to me. And when he took our boat and went home and told that story to his wife, she just packed up and went out West, and got divorced from him. And it served him right, too."

"Thank you, ma'am," said Captain Jenkinson, and going out of the gate, he clambered up over the wheel, and the wagon cleared for Cuppertown.

When the elderly mariners were gone, the Widow Ducket, still standing at the door, turned to Dorcas.

"Think of it!" she said. "To tell all that to me, in my own house! And after I had opened my one jar of brandied peaches, that I'd been keepin' for special company!"

"In your own house!" ejaculated Dorcas. "And not one of them brandied peaches left!"

The widow jingled the four quarters in her hand before she slipped them into her pocket.

"Anyway, Dorcas," she remarked, "I think we can now say we are square with all the world, and so let's go in and wash the dishes."

"Yes," said Dorcas, "we're square."

THE LAST DAY

ROBERT BENCHLEY

WHEN, during the long winter evenings, you sit around the snap-shot album and recall the merry, merry times you had on your vacation, there is one day which your memory mercifully overlooks. It is the day you packed up and left the resort to go home.

This Ultimate Day really begins the night before, when you sit up until one o'clock trying to get things into the trunks and bags. This is when you discover the well-known fact that summer air swells articles to twice or three times their original size; so that the sneakers which in June fitted in between the phonograph and the book (which you have never opened), in September are found to require a whole tray for themselves and even then one of them will probably have to be carried in the hand.

Along about midnight, the discouraging process begins to get on your nerves and you snap at your wife and she snaps at you every time it is

241

found that something won't fit in the suitcase. As you have both gradually dispensed with the more attractive articles of clothing under stress of the heat and the excitement, these little word passages take on the sordid nature of a squabble in an East Side tenement, and all that is needed is for one of the children to wake up and start whimpering. This it does.

It is finally decided that there is no sense in trying to finish the job that night. General nervousness, combined with a specific fear of over-sleeping, results in a troubled tossing of perhaps three hours in bed, and ushers in the dawn of the last day on just about as irritable and bleary-eyed a little family as you will find outside an institution.

The trouble starts right away with the process of getting dressed in traveling clothes which haven't been worn since the trip up. Junior's shoulders are still tender, and he decides that it will be impossible for him to wear his starched blouse. One of Philip's good shoes, finding that there has been no call for it during the summer, has become hurt and has disappeared; so Philip has to wear a pair of Daddy's old bathing shoes which had been thrown away. (After everything has been locked and taken out of the room, the good shoe is found in the closet and left for dead.)

You, yourself, aren't any too successful in reverting to city clothes. Several weeks of soft collars and rubber-soled shoes have softened you to a point where the old "Deroy-14½" feels like a napkin-ring around your neck, and your natty brogans are so heavy that you lose your balance and topple over forward if you step out suddenly. The whole effect of your civilian costume when surveyed in a mirror is that of a Maine guide all dressed up for an outing "up to Bangor."

Incidentally, it shapes up as one of the hottest days of the season—or any other season.

"Oh, look how funny Daddy looks in his straw hat!"

"I never realized before, Fred, how much too high the crown is for the length of your face. Are you sure it's your hat?"

"It's my hat, all right," is the proper reply, "but maybe the face belongs to somebody else."

This silences them for a while, but on and off during the day a lot of good-natured fun is had in calling the attention of outsiders to the spectacle presented by Daddy in his "store" clothes.

Once everyone is dressed, there must be an excursion to take one last look at the ocean, or lake, or whatever particular prank of Nature it

may have been which served as an inducement to you to leave the city. This must be done before breakfast. So down to the beach you go, getting your shoes full of sand, and wait while Sister, in a sentimental attempt to feel the water for the last time, has tripped and fallen in, soaking herself to the garters. There being no dry clothes left out, she has to go to the kitchen and stand in front of the stove until at least one side of her is dry.

Breakfast bears no resemblance to any other meal eaten in the place. There is a poorly-suppressed feeling that you must hurry, coupled with the stiff collar and tight clothes, which makes it practically impossible to get any food down past the upper chest.

Then follows one of the worst features of the worst of all vacation days—the goodbyes. It isn't that you hate to part company with these people. They too, as they stand there in their summer clothes, seem to have undergone some process whereby you see them as they really are and not as they seemed when you were all together up to your necks in water or worrying a tennis ball back and forth over a net. And you may be sure that you, in your town clothes, seem doubly unattractive to them.

Here is Mrs. Tremble, who lives in Montclair, N. J., in the winter. That really is a terrible hat of hers, now that you get a good look at it. "Well, goodbye, Mrs. Tremble. Be sure to look us up if you ever get out our way. We are right in the telephone book, and we'll have a regular get-together meeting. . . . Goodbye, Marian. Think of us to-night in the hot city, and be sure to let us know when you are going through. . . . Well, so long, Mr. Prothero; look out for those girls up at the post office. Don't let any of them marry you. . . . Well, we're off,

Mrs. Rostetter. Yes, we're leaving today. On the 10-45. We have to be back for Junior's school. It begins on the 11th. *Goodbye!*"

It is then found that there is about an hour to wait before the machine comes to take you to the station; so all these goodbyes have been wasted and have to be gone through with again.

In the meantime, Mother decides that she must run over to the Bide-a-Wee cottage and say goodbye to the Sisbys. The children feel that they are about due for another last look at the ocean. And Daddy remembers that he hasn't been able to shut the big suitcase yet. So the family disperses in various directions and each unit gets lost. Mother, rushing out from the Sisbys' in a panic thinking that she hears the automobile, is unable to find the others. Little Mildred, having taken it upon herself to look out for the other children while they are gazing on the ocean, has felt it incumbent on her to spank Philip for trying to build one last tunnel in the sand, resulting in a bitter physical encounter in which Philip easily batters his sister into a state of hysteria. Daddy, having wilted his collar and put his knee through his straw hat in an attempt to jam the suitcase together, finds that the thing can't be done and takes out the box of sea-shells that Junior had planned to take home for his cabinet, and hides them under the bed.

The suitcase at last having been squeezed shut and placed with the rest of the bags in the hall, the maid comes running up with five damp bathing suits which she has found hanging on the line and wants to know if they belong there. Daddy looks cautiously down the hall and whispers: "No!"

At last the automobile arrives and stands honking by the roadside. "Come, Junior, quick, put your coat on! . . . Have you got the bag with the thermos? . . . Hurry, Philip! . . . Where's Sister? . . . Come, Sister! . . . Well, it's too late now. You'll have to wait till we get on the train. . . . Goodbye, Mrs. Tremble. . . . Be sure to look us up. . . . Goodbye, everybody! . . . Here, Junior! Put that down! You can't take that with you. No, no! That belongs to that other little boy. . . . *Junior!* . . . Goodbye, Marian! . . . Goodbye, Mrs. McNerdle. . . . Philip, say goodbye to Mrs. McNerdle, she's been so good to you, don't you remember? . . . Goodbye, Mrs. McNerdle, that's right. . . . Goodbye!"

And with that the automobile starts, the friends on the porch wave and call out indistinguishable pleasantries, Junior begins to cry, and it is found that Ed has no hat.

244

The trip home in the heat and cinders is enlivened by longing reminiscences: "Well, it's eleven o'clock. I suppose they're all getting into their bathing suits now. How'd you like to jump into that old ocean right this minute, eh?" (As a matter of fact, the speaker has probably not been induced to go into "that old ocean" more than three times during the whole summer.)

The fact that they reach home too late to get a regular dinner and have to go to bed hungry, and the more poignant impressions in the process of opening a house which has been closed all summer, have been treated of before in an article called "The Entrance Into the Tomb." And so we will leave our buoyant little family, their vacation ended, all ready to jump into the swing of their work, refreshed, invigorated, and clear-eyed.

245

THE THREE MUSKETEERS

RUDYARD KIPLING

MULVANEY, Ortheris and Learoyd are Privates in B Company of a Line Regiment, and personal friends of mine. Collectively I think, but am not certain, they are the worst men in the regiment so far as genial blackguardism goes.

They told me this story, the other day, in the Umballa Refreshment Room while we were waiting for an uptrain. I supplied the beer. The tale was cheap at a gallon and a half.

Of course you know Lord Benira Trig. He is a Duke, or an Earl, or something unofficial; also a Peer; also a Globe-trotter. On all three counts, as Ortheris says, " 'e didn't deserve no consideration." He was out here for three months collecting materials for a book on "Our Eastern Impedimenta," and quartering himself upon everybody, like a Cossack in evening-dress.

His particular vice—because he was a Radical, I suppose—was having garrisons turned out for his inspection. He would then dine with the Officer Commanding, and insult him, across the Mess table, about the appearance of the troops. That was Benira's way.

He turned out troops once too often. He came to Helanthami Cantonment on a Tuesday. He wished to go shopping in the bazaars on Wednesday, and he "desired" the troops to be turned out on a Thursday. *On—a—Thursday!* The Officer Commanding could not well refuse; for Berina was a Lord. There was an indignation meeting of subalterns in the Mess Room, to call the Colonel pet names.

"But the rale dimonstrashin," said Mulvaney, "was in B Comp'ny barricks; we three headin' it."

Mulvaney climbed on to the refreshment bar, settled himself comfortably by the beer, and went on:—"Whin the row was at ut's foinest an' B Comp'ny was fur goin' out to murther this man Thrigg on the p'rade-groun', Learoyd here takes up his helmut an' sez—fwhat was ut ye said?"

"Ah said," said Learoyd, "gie us t' brass. Tak oop a subscripshun, lads, for to put off t' p'rade, an' if t' p'rade's not put off, ah'll gie t' brass back agean. Thot's wot ah said. All B Coomp'ny knawed me. Ah took oop a big subscripshun—fower rupees eight annas 'twas—an' ah went oot to turn t' job over. Mulvaney an' Orth'ris coom with me."

"We three raises the Divil in couples gin'rally," explained Mulvaney. Here Ortheris interrupted. " 'Ave you read the papers?" said he.

"Sometimes," I said.

"We 'ad read the papers, an' we put hup a faked decoity, a—a sedukshun."

"*Ab*dukshin, ye cockney," said Mulvaney.

"*Ab*dukshun or *s*edukshun—no great odds. Any'ow, we arrange to taik an' put Mister Benhira out o' the way till Thursday was hover, or 'e too busy to rux 'isself about p'raids. *Hi* was the man wot said:— 'We'll make a few rupees off o' the business.' "

"We hild a Council av War," continued Mulvaney, "walkin' roun' by the Artill'ry Lines. I was Prisidint, Learoyd was Minister av Finance, an' little Orth'ris here was——"

"A bloomin' Bismarck! *Hi* made the 'ole show pay." "This interferin' bit av a Benira man," said Mulvaney, "did the thrick for us himself; for, on me sowl, we hadn't a notion av what was to come afther the next minut. He was shoppin' in the bazar on fut. 'Twas dhrawin' dusk thin, an' we stud watchin' the little man hoppin' in an' out av the shops, thryin' to injuce the naygurs to *mallum* his *bat*. Prisintly, he sthrols up, his arrums full av thruck, an' he sez in a consiquinshal way, shticking out his little belly:—'Me good men,' sez he, 'have ye seen the Kernel's b'roosh?' 'B'roosh?' says Learoyd. 'There's no b'roosh here— nobbut a *hekka*.' 'Fwhat's that?' sez Thrigg. Learoyd shows him wan down the sthreet, an' he sez:—'How thruly Orientil! I will ride on a *hekka*.' I saw thin that our Rigimintal Saint was for givin' Thrigg over to us neck an' brisket. I purshued a *hekka*, an' I sez to the dhriver-divil, I sez—'Ye black limb, there's a *Sahib* comin' for this *hekka*. He wants to go *jildi* to the Padsahi Jhil'—'twas about tu moiles away—to shoot snipe—*chirria*. 'You dhrive *Jehannum ke marfik, mallum?* 'Tis no man- ner av *faider bukkin'* to the *Sahib*, bekaze he doesn't *samjao* your *bat*. Av he *bolos* anything, just you *choop* and *chel*. *Dekker?* Go *arsty* for the first *arder*-mile from cantonmints. Then *chel, Shaitan ke marfik,* an' the *chooper* you *choops* an' the *jilder* you *chels* the better *kooshy* will that *Sahib* be; an' here's a rupee for ye.'

"The *hekka*-man knew there was somethin' out av the common in the air. He grinned and sez:—'*Bote achee!* I goin' damn fast.' I prayed that the Kernel's b'roosh wudn't arrive till me darlin' Benira by the grace av God was undher weigh. The little man puts his thruck into the *hekka* an' scuttles in like a fat guinea-pig; niver offerin' us the price of a dhrink for our services in helpin' him home. 'He's off to the Padsahi *jhil*,' sez I to the others."

Ortheris took up the tale:—

"Jist then, little Buldoo kim up, 'oo was the son of one of the Artillery *Saises*—'e would 'av made a 'evinly newspaper-boy in London, bein' sharp and fly to all manner o' games. 'E 'ad bin watchin' us puttin' Mister Benhira into 's temporary baroush, an' 'e sez:—'What '*ave* you been a doin' of, *Sahibs?*' sez 'e. Learoyd 'e caught 'im by the ear an' 'e sez—"

"Ah says," went on Learoyd: " 'Young mon, that mon's gooin' to hav't goons out o' Thursday—*kul*—an' thot's more work for you, young mon. Now, sitha, tak a *tat* an' a *lookri*, an' ride tha domdest to t' Padsahi Jhil. Cotch thot there *hekka*, and tell t' driver iv your lingo thot you've coom to tak' his place. T' *Sahib* doesn't speak t' *bat*, an' he's a little mon. Drive t' *hekka* into t' Padsahi Jhil into t' watter. Leave t' *Sahib* theer an' roon hoam; an' here's a rupee for tha.' "

Then Mulvaney and Ortheris spoke together in alternate fragments: Mulvaney leading [You must pick out the two speakers as best you can.]—"He was a knowin' little devil was Bhuldoo,—'e sez *bote achee* an' cuts—wid a wink in his oi—but *Hi* sez there's money to be made— an' I want to see the end av the campaign—so *Hi* says we'll double hout to the Padsahi Jhil—and save the little man from bein' dacoited by the murtherin' Bhuldoo—an' turn hup like reskoors in a Ryle Victoria Theayter Melodrama—so we doubled for the *Jhil*, an' prisintly there was the divil of a hurroosh behind us an' three bhoys on grasscuts' *tats* come by, pounding along for the dear life—s'elp me Bob, hif Buldoo 'adn't raised a regular *harmy* of decoits—to do the job in shtile. An' we ran, an' they ran, shplittin' with laughin', till we gets near the *jhil*—and 'ears sounds of distress floatin' molloncally on the heavenin' hair." [Ortheris was growing poetical under the influence of the beer. The duet recommenced; Mulvaney leading again.]

"Thin we heard Bhuldoo, the dacoit, shoutin' to the *hekka* man, an' wan of the young divils brought his *lakri* down on top av the *hekka*-cover, an' Benira Thrigg inside howled 'Murther an' Death.' Buldoo

248

takes the reins and dhrives like mad for the *jhil*, havin' dishpersed the *hekka*-dhriver—'oo cum up to us an' e' sez, sezie:—'That *Sahib's* nigh *gawbry* with funk! Wot devil's work 'ave you led me into?' 'Hall right,' sez we, 'you *puckrow* that there pony an' come along. This *Sahib's* been decoited, an' we're going to resky 'im!' Says the driver: 'Decoits! Wot decoits? That's Buldoo the *budmash*'—'Bhuldoo be shot!' sez we. ''Tis a woild dissolute Pathan frum the hills. There's about eight av 'im coercin' the *Sahib*. You remimber that an' you'll get another rupee!' Then we heard the *whop-whop-whop* av the *hekka* turnin' over, an' a splash av water an' the voice av Benira Thrigg callin' upon God to forgive his sins—an' Buldoo an' 'is friends squotterin' in the water like boys in the Serpentine."

Here the Three Musketeers retired simultaneously into the beer.

"Well? What came next?" said I.

"Fwhat nex'?" answered Mulvaney, wiping his mouth. "Wud you let three bould sodger-bhoys lave the ornamint av the House av Lords to be dhrowned an' dacoited in a *jhil?* We formed line av quarther-column an' we desinded upon the inimy. For the better part av tin minutes you could not hear yerself spake. The *tattoo* was screamin' in chune wid Benira Thrigg an' Bhuldoo's army, an' the shticks was whistlin' roun' the *hekka*, an' Orth'ris was beatin' the *hekka*-cover wid his fistes, an' Learoyd yellin':—'Look out for their knives!' an' me cuttin' into the dark, right an' lef', dishpersin' arrmy corps av Pathans. Holy Mother av Moses! 'twas more disp'rit than Ahmid Kheyl wid Maiwund thrown in. Afther a while Bhuldoo an' his bhoys flees. Have ye iver seen a rale live Lord thryin' to hide his nobility undher a fut an' a half av brown *jhil* wather? 'Tis the livin' image av a *bhisti's mus-sick* wid the shivers. It tuk toime to pershuade me frind Benira he was not disimbowilled: an' more toime to get out the *hekka*. The dhriver come up afther the battle, swearin' he tuk a hand in repulsin' the inimy. Benira was sick wid the fear. We escorted him back, very slow, to cantonmints, for that an' the chill to soak into him. *It suk!* Glory be to the Rigimintil Saint, but it suk to the marrow av Lord Benira Thrigg!"

Here Otheris, slowly, with immense pride:—" 'E sez:—'You har my noble preservers,' sez 'e. 'You har a *honor* to the British Harmy,' sez 'e. With that 'e describes the hawful band of decoits wot set on 'im. There was about forty of 'em an' 'e was hoverpowered by numbers, so 'e was; but 'e never lost 'is presence of mind, so 'e didn't. 'E guv the *hekka*-

249

driver five rupees for 'is noble hassistance, an' 'e said 'e would see to us after 'e 'ad spoken to the Kernul. For we was a *honor* to the Regiment, we was."

"An' we three," said Mulvaney, with a seraphic smile, "have dhrawn the par-ti-cu-lar attinshin av Bobs Bahadur more than wanst. But he's a rale good little man is Bobs. Go on, Orth'ris, me son."

"Then we leaves 'im at the Kernul's 'ouse, werry sick, an' we cuts over to B Comp'ny barrick an' we sez we 'ave saved Benira from a bloody doom, an' the chances was agin there bein' p'raid on Thursday. About ten minutes later come three envelicks, one for each of us. S'elp me Bob, if the old bloke 'adn't guv us a fiver apiece—sixty-four dibs in the bazar! On Thursday 'e was in 'orspital recoverin' from 'is sanguinary encounter with a gang of Pathans, an' B Comp'ny was drinkin' 'emselves inter clink by squads. So there never was no Thursday p'raid. But the Kernul, when 'e 'eard of our galliant conduct, 'e sez:—'Hi know there's been some devilry somewheres,' sez 'e, 'but hi can't bring it 'ome to you three.'"

"An' my privit imprisshin is," said Mulvaney, getting off the bar and turning his glass upside down, "that, av they had known they wudn't have brought ut home. 'Tis flyin' in the face, firstly av Nature, second, av the Rig'lations, an' third, the will av Terence Mulvaney, to hold p'rades av Thursdays."

"Good, ma son!" said Learoyd; "but, young mon, what's t' note-book for?"

"Let be," said Mulvaney; "this time next month we're in the *Sherapis*. 'Tis immortial fame the gentleman's goin' to give us. But kape it dhark till we're out av the range av me little frind Bobs Bahadur."

And I have obeyed Mulvaney's order.

SONG OF THE OPEN ROAD

OGDEN NASH

> I think that I shall never see
> A billboard lovely as a tree.
> Indeed, unless the billboards fall
> I'll never see a tree at all.

AUNT AGATHA SPEAKS HER MIND

P. G. WODEHOUSE

I SUPPOSE in the case of a chappie of really fine fibre and all that sort of thing, a certain amount of gloom and anguish would have followed the dishing of young Bingo's matrimonial plans. I mean, if mine had been a noble nature, I would have been all broken up. But, what with one thing and another, I can't say I let it weigh on me very heavily. The fact that less than a week after he had had the bad news I came on young Bingo dancing like an untamed gazelle at Ciro's helped me to bear up.

A resilient bird, Bingo. He may be down, but he is never out. While

251

these little love-affairs of his are actually on, nobody could be more earnest and blighted; but once the fuse has blown out and the girl has handed him his hat and begged him as a favour never to let her see him again, up he bobs as merry and bright as ever. If I've seen it happen once, I've seen it happen a dozen times.

So I didn't worry about Bingo. Or about anything else, as a matter of fact. What with one thing and another, I can't remember ever having been chirpier than at about this period in my career. Everything seemed to be going right. On three separate occasions horses on which I'd invested a sizable amount won by lengths instead of sitting down to rest in the middle of the race, as horses usually do when I've got money on them.

Added to this, the weather continued topping to a degree; my new socks were admitted on all sides to be just the kind that mother makes; and, to round it all off, my Aunt Agatha had gone to France and wouldn't be on hand to snooter me for at least another six weeks. And, if you knew my Aunt Agatha, you'd agree that that alone was happiness enough for anyone.

It suddenly struck me so forcibly, one morning while I was having my bath, that I hadn't a worry on earth that I began to sing like a bally nightingale as I sploshed the sponge about. It seemed to me that everything was absolutely for the best in the best of all possible worlds.

But have you ever noticed a rummy thing about life? I mean the way something always comes along to give it to you in the neck at the very moment when you're feeling most braced about things in general. No sooner had I dried the old limbs and shoved on the suiting and toddled into the sitting-room than the blow fell. There was a letter from Aunt Agatha on the mantelpiece.

"Oh gosh!" I said when I'd read it.

"Sir?" said Jeeves. He was fooling about in the background on some job or other.

"It's from my Aunt Agatha, Jeeves. Mrs. Gregson, you know."

"Yes, sir?"

"Ah, you wouldn't speak in that light, careless tone if you knew what was in it," I said with a hollow, mirthless laugh. "The curse has come upon us, Jeeves. She wants me to go and join her at—what's the name of the dashed place?—at Roville-sur-mer. Oh, hang it all!"

"I had better be packing, sir?"

"I suppose so."

To people who don't know my Aunt Agatha I find it extraordinarily difficult to explain why it is that she has always put the wind up me to such a frightful extent. I mean, I'm not dependent on her financially or anything like that. It's simply personality, I've come to the conclusion. You see, all through my childhood and when I was a kid at school she was always able to turn me inside out with a single glance, and I haven't come out from under the 'fluence yet. We run to height a bit in our family, and there's about five-foot-nine of Aunt Agatha, topped with a beaky nose, an eagle eye, and a lot of grey hair, and the general effect is pretty formidable. Anyway, it never even occurred to me for a moment to give her the miss-in-baulk on this occasion. If she said I must go to Roville, it was all over except buying the tickets.

"What's the idea, Jeeves? I wonder why she wants me."

"I could not say, sir."

Well, it was no good talking about it. The only gleam of consolation, the only bit of blue among the clouds, was the fact that at Roville I should at last be able to wear the rather fruity cummerbund I had bought six months ago and had never had the nerve to put on. One of those silk contrivances, you know, which you tie round your waist instead of a waistcoat, something on the order of a sash only more substantial. I had never been able to muster up the courage to put it on so far, for I knew that there would be trouble with Jeeves when I did, it being a pretty brightish scarlet. Still, at a place like Roville, presumably dripping with the gaiety and *joie de vivre* of France, it seemed to me that something might be done.

Roville, which I reached early in the morning after a beastly choppy crossing and a jerky night in the train, is a fairly nifty spot where a chappie without encumbrances in the shape of aunts might spend a somewhat genial week or so. It is like all these French places, mainly sands and hotels and casinos. The hotel which had had the bad luck to draw Aunt Agatha's custom was the Splendide, and by the time I got there wasn't a member of the staff who didn't seem to be feeling it deeply. I sympathised with them. I've had experience of Aunt Agatha at hotels before. Of course, the real rough work was all over when I arrived, but I could tell by the way every one grovelled before her that she had started by having her first room changed because it hadn't a southern exposure and her next because it had a creaking wardrobe and that she had said her say on the subject of the cooking, the

253

waiting, the chambermaiding and everything else, with perfect freedom and candour. She had got the whole gang nicely under control by now. The manager, a whiskered cove who looked like a bandit, simply tied himself into knots whenever she looked at him.

All this triumph had produced a sort of grim geniality in her, and she was almost motherly when we met.

"I am so glad you were able to come, Bertie," she said. "The air will do you so much good. Far better for you than spending your time in stuffy London night clubs."

"Oh, ah," I said.

"You will meet some pleasant people, too. I want to introduce you to a Miss Hemmingway and her brother, who have become great friends of mine. I am sure you will like Miss Hemmingway. A nice, quiet girl, so different from so many of the bold girls one meets in London nowadays. Her brother is curate at Chipley-in-the-Glen in Dorsetshire. He tells me they are connected with the Kent Hemmingways. A very good family. She is a charming girl."

I had a grim foreboding of an awful doom. All this boosting was so unlike Aunt Agatha, who normally is one of the most celebrated right-and-left-hand knockers in London society. I felt a clammy suspicion. And by jove, I was right.

"Aline Hemmingway," said Aunt Agatha, "is just the girl I should like to see you marry, Bertie. You ought to be thinking of getting married. Marriage might make something of you. And I could not wish you a better wife than dear Aline. She would be such a good influence in your life."

"Here, I say!" I chipped in at this juncture, chilled to the marrow.

"Bertie!" said Aunt Agatha, dropping the motherly manner for a bit and giving me the cold eye.

"Yes, but I say . . ."

"It is young men like you, Bertie, who make the person with the future of the race at heart despair. Cursed with too much money, you fritter away in idle selfishness a life which might have been made useful, helpful and profitable. You do nothing but waste your time on frivolous pleasures. You are simply an anti-social animal, a drone. Bertie, it is imperative that you marry."

"But, dash it all . . ."

"Yes! You should be breeding children to . . ."

"No, really, I say, please!" I said, blushing richly. Aunt Agatha belongs to two or three of these women's clubs, and she keeps forgetting she isn't in the smoking-room.

"Bertie," she resumed, and would no doubt have hauled up her slacks at some length, had we not been interrupted. "Ah, here they are!" she said. "Aline, dear!"

And I perceived a girl and a chappie bearing down on me smiling in a pleased sort of manner.

"I want you to meet my nephew, Bertie Wooster," said Aunt Agatha. "He has just arrived. Such a surprise! I had no notion that he intended coming to Roville."

I gave the couple the wary-up-and-down, feeling rather like a cat in the middle of a lot of hounds. Sort of trapped feeling, you know what I mean. An inner voice was whispering that Bertram was up against it.

The brother was a small round cove with a face rather like a sheep. He wore pince-nez, his expression was benevolent, and he had on one of those collars which button at the back.

"Welcome to Roville, Mr. Wooster," he said.

"Oh, Sidney!" said the girl. "Doesn't Mr. Wooster remind you of Canon Blenkinsop, who came to Chipley to preach last Easter?"

"My dear! The resemblance is most striking!"

They peered at me for a while as if I were something in a glass case, and I goggled back and had a good look at the girl. There's no doubt about it, she was different from what Aunt Agatha had called the bold girls one meets in London nowadays. No bobbed hair and gaspers about *Her!* I don't know when I've met anybody who looked so— respectable is the only word. She had on a kind of plain dress, and her hair was plain, and her face was sort of mild and saint-like. I don't pretend to be a Sherlock Holmes or anything of that order, but the moment I looked at her I said to myself, "The girl plays the organ in a village church!"

Well, we gazed at one another for a bit, and there was a certain amount of chit-chat, and then I tore myself away. But before I went I had been booked up to take brother and the girl for a nice drive that afternoon. And the thought of it depressed me to such an extent that I felt there was only one thing to be done. I went straight back to my room, dug out the cummerbund, and draped it round the old tum. I turned round and Jeeves shied like a startled mustang.

"I beg your pardon, sir," he said in a sort of hushed voice. "You are surely not proposing to appear in public in that thing?"

"The cummerbund?" I said in a careless, debonair way, passing it off. "Oh, rather!"

"I should not advise it sir, really I shouldn't."

"Why not?"

"The effect, sir, is loud in the extreme."

I tackled the blighter squarely. I mean to say, nobody knows better than I do that Jeeves is a master mind and all that, but, dash it, a fellow must call his soul his own. You can't be a serf to your valet. Besides, I was feeling pretty low and the cummerbund was the only thing which could cheer me up.

"You know, the trouble with you, Jeeves," I said, "is that you're too— what's the word I want?—too bally insular. You can't realise that you aren't in Piccadilly all the time. In a place like this a bit of colour and touch of the poetic is expected of you. Why, I've just seen a fellow downstairs in a morning suit of yellow velvet."

"Nevertheless, sir——"

"Jeeves," I said firmly, "my mind is made up. I am feeling a little low spirited and need cheering. Besides, what's wrong with it? This cummerbund seems to me to be called for. I consider that it has rather a Spanish effect. A touch of the hidalgo. Sort of Vicente y Blasco What's-his-name stuff. The jolly old hidalgo off to the bull fight."

"Very good, sir," said Jeeves coldly.

Dashed upsetting, this sort of thing. If there's one thing that gives me the pip, it's unpleasantness in the home; and I could see that relations were going to be pretty fairly strained for a while. And, coming on top of Aunt Agatha's bombshell about the Hemmingway girl, I don't mind confessing it made me feel more or less as though nobody loved me.

The drive that afternoon was about as mouldy as I had expected. The curate chappie prattled on of this and that; the girl admired the view; and I got a headache early in the proceedings which started at the soles of my feet and got worse all the way up. I tottered back to my room to dress for dinner, feeling like a toad under the harrow. If it hadn't been for that cummerbund business earlier in the day I could have sobbed on Jeeve's neck and poured out all my troubles to him. Even as it was, I couldn't keep the thing entirely to myself.

"I say, Jeeves," I said.

"Sir?"

"Mix me a stiffish brandy and soda."

"Yes, sir."

"Stiffish, Jeeves. Not too much soda, but splash the brandy about a bit."

"Very good, sir."

After imbibing, I felt a shade better.

"Jeeves," I said.

"Sir?"

"I rather fancy I'm in the soup, Jeeves."

"Indeed, sir?"

I eyed the man narrowly. Dashed aloof his manner was. Still brooding over the cummerbund.

"Yes. Right up to the hocks," I said, suppressing the pride of the Woosters and trying to induce him to be a bit matier. "Have you seen a girl popping about here with a parson brother?"

"Miss Hemmingway, sir? Yes, sir."

"Aunt Agatha wants me to marry her."

"Indeed, sir?"

"Well, what about it?"

"Sir?"

"I mean, have you anything to suggest?"

"No, sir."

The blighter's manner was so cold and unchummy that I bit the bullet and had a dash at being airy.

"Oh, well, tra-la-la!" I said.

"Precisely, sir," said Jeeves.
And that was, so to speak, that.

I remember—it must have been when I was at school because I don't go in for that sort of thing very largely nowadays—reading a poem or something about something or other in which there was a line which went, if I've got it rightly, "Shades of the prison house begin to close upon the growing boy." Well, what I'm driving at is that during the next two weeks that's exactly how it was with me. I mean to say, I could hear the wedding bells chiming faintly in the distance and getting louder and louder every day, and how the deuce to slide out of it was more than I could think. Jeeves, no doubt, could have dug up a dozen brainy schemes in a couple of minutes, but he was still aloof and chilly and I couldn't bring myself to ask him point-blank. I mean, he could see easily enough that the young master was in a bad way and, if that wasn't enough to make him overlook the fact that I was still gleaming brightly about the waist-band, well, what it amounted to was that the old feudal spirit was dead in the blighter's bosom and there was nothing to be done about it.

It really was rummy the way the Hemmingway family had taken to me. I wouldn't have said off-hand that there was anything particularly fascinating about me—in fact, most people look on me as rather an ass; but there was no getting away from the fact that I went like a breeze with this girl and her brother. They didn't seem happy if they were away from me. I couldn't move a step, dash it, without one of them popping out from somewhere and freezing on. In fact, I'd got into the habit now of retiring to my room when I wanted to take it easy for a bit. I had managed to get a rather decent suite on the third floor, looking down onto the promenade.

I had gone to earth in my suite one evening and for the first time that day was feeling that life wasn't so bad after all. Right through the day from lunch time I'd had the Hemmingway girl on my hands, Aunt Agatha having shooed us off together immediately after the mid-day meal. The result was, as I looked down on the lighted promenade and saw all the people popping happily about on their way to dinner and the Casino and what not, a kind of wistful feeling came over me. I couldn't help thinking how dashed happy I could have contrived to be in this place if only Aunt Agatha and the other blisters had been elsewhere.

258

I heaved a sigh, and at that moment there was a knock at the door.

"Someone at the door, Jeeves," I said.

"Yes, sir."

He opened the door, and in popped Aline Hemmingway and her brother. The last person I had expected. I really had thought that I could be alone for a minute in my own room.

"Oh, hallo!" I said.

"Oh, Mr. Wooster!" said the girl in a gasping sort of way. "I don't know how to begin."

Then I noticed that she appeared considerably rattled, and as for the brother, he looked like a sheep with a secret sorrow.

This made me sit up a bit and take notice. I had supposed that this was just a social call, but apparently something had happened to give them a jolt. Though I couldn't see why they should come to me about it.

"Is anything up?" I said.

"Poor Sidney—it was my fault—I ought never to have let him go there alone," said the girl. Dashed agitated.

At this point the brother, who after shedding a floppy overcoat and parking his hat on a chair had been standing by wrapped in the silence, gave a little cough, like a sheep caught in the mist on a mountain top.

"The fact is, Mr. Wooster," he said, "a sad, a most deplorable thing has occurred. This afternoon, while you were so kindly escorting my sist-ah, I found the time hang a little heavy upon my hands and I was tempted to—ah—gamble at the Casino."

I looked at the man in a kindlier spirit than I had been able to up to date. This evidence that he had sporting blood in his veins made him seem more human, I'm bound to say. If only I'd known earlier that he went in for that sort of thing, I felt that we might have had a better time together.

"Oh!" I said. "Did you click?"

He sighed heavily.

"If you mean was I successful, I must answer in the negative. I rashly persisted in the view that the colour red, having appeared no fewer than seven times in succession, must inevitably at no distant date give place to black. I was in error. I lost my little all, Mr. Wooster."

"Tough luck," I said.

"I left the Casino," proceeded the chappie, "and returned to the hotel. There I encountered one of my parishioners, a Colonel Musgrave, who chanced to be holiday-making over here. I—er—induced him to cash me a cheque for one hundred pounds on my little account in my London bank."

"Well, that was all to the good, what?" I said, hoping to induce the poor fish to look on the bright side. "I mean, bit of luck finding someone to slip it into first crack out of the box."

"On the contrary, Mr. Wooster, it did but make matters worse. I burn with shame as I make the confession, but I immediately went back to the Casino and lost the entire sum—this time under the mistaken supposition that the colour black was, as I believe the expression is, due for a run."

"I say!" I said. "You *are* having a night out!"

"And," concluded the chappie, "the most lamentable feature of the whole affair is that I have no funds in the bank to meet the cheque when presented."

I'm free to confess that, though I realised by this time that all this was leading up to a touch and that my ear was shortly going to be bitten in no uncertain manner, my heart warmed to the poor prune. Indeed, I gazed at him with no little interest and admiration. Never before had I encountered a curate so genuinely all to the mustard. Little as he might look like one of the lads of the village, he certainly appeared to be the real tabasco, and I wished he had shown me this side of his character before.

260

"Colonel Musgrave," he went on, gulping somewhat, "is not a man who would be likely to overlook the matter. He is a hard man. He will expose me to my vic-ah. My vic-ah is a hard man. In short, Mr. Wooster, if Colonel Musgrave presents that cheque I shall be ruined. And he leaves for England to-night."

The girl, who had been standing by biting her handkerchief and gurgling at intervals while the brother got the above off his chest, now started in once more.

"Mr. Wooster," she cried, "won't you, won't you help us? Oh, do say you will! We must have the money to get back the cheque from Colonel Musgrave before nine o'clock—he leaves on the nine-twenty. I was at my wits' end what to do when I remembered how kind you had always been. Mr. Wooster, will you lend Sidney the money and take these as security?" And before I knew what she was doing she had dived into her bag, produced a case, and opened it. "My pearls," she said. "I don't know what they are worth—they were a present from my poor father——"

"Now, alas, no more——" chipped in the brother.

"But I know they must be worth ever so much more than the amount we want."

Dashed embarrassing. Made me feel like a pawnbroker. More than a touch of popping the watch about the whole business.

"No, I say, really," I protested. "There's no need of any security, you know, or any rot of that kind. Only too glad to let you have the money. I've got it on me, as a matter of fact. Rather luckily drew some this morning."

And I fished it out and pushed it across. The brother shook his head.

"Mr. Wooster," he said, "we appreciate your generosity, your beautiful, heartening confidence in us, but we cannot permit this."

"What Sidney means," said the girl, "is that you really don't know anything about us when you come to think of it. You mustn't risk lending all this money without any security at all to two people who, after all, are almost strangers. If I hadn't thought that you would be quite business-like about this I would never have dared to come to you."

"The idea of—er—pledging the pearls at the local Mont de Pieté was, you will readily understand, repugnant to us," said the brother.

"If you will just give me a receipt, as a matter of form——"

"Oh, right-o!"

I wrote out the receipt and handed it over, feeling more or less of an ass.

"Here you are," I said.

The girl took the piece of paper, shoved it in her bag, grabbed the money and slipped it to brother Sidney, and then, before I knew what was happening, she had darted at me, kissed me, and legged it from the room.

I'm bound to say the thing rattled me. So dashed sudden and unexpected. I mean, a girl like that. Always been quiet and demure and what not—by no means the sort of female you'd have expected to go about the place kissing fellows. Through a sort of mist I could see that Jeeves had appeared from the background and was helping the brother on with his coat; and I remember wondering idly how the dickens a man could bring himself to wear a coat like that, it being more like a sack than anything else. Then the brother came up to me and grasped my hand.

"I cannot thank you sufficiently, Mr. Wooster!"

"Oh, not at all."

"You have saved my good name. Good name in man or woman, dear my lord," he said, massaging the fin with some fervour, "is the immediate jewel of their souls. Who steals my purse steals trash. 'Twas mine, 'tis his, and has been slave to thousands. But he that filches from me my good name robs me of that which enriches not him and makes me poor indeed. I thank you from the bottom of my heart. Good night, Mr. Wooster."

"Good night, old thing," I said.

I blinked at Jeeves as the door shut. "Rather a sad affair, Jeeves," I said.

"Yes, sir."

"Lucky I happened to have all that money handy."

"Well—er—yes, sir."

"You speak as though you didn't think much of it."

"It is not my place to criticise your actions, sir, but I will venture to say that I think you behaved a little rashly."

"What, lending that money?"

"Yes, sir. These fashionable French watering places are notoriously infested by dishonest characters."

This was a bit too thick.

"Now look here, Jeeves," I said, "I can stand a lot but when it comes to your casting asp-whatever-the-word-is at a bird in Holy Orders——"

"Perhaps I am over-suspicious, sir. But I have seen a great deal of
262

these resorts. When I was in the employment of Lord Frederick Ranelagh, shortly before I entered your service, his lordship was very neatly swindled by a criminal known I believe, by the sobriquet of Soapy Sid, who scraped an acquaintance with us in Monte Carlo with the assistance of a female accomplice. I have never forgotten the circumstances."

"I don't want to butt in on your reminiscences, Jeeves," I said coldly, "but you're talking through your hat. How can there have been anything fishy about this business? They've left me the pearls, haven't they? Very well, then, think before you speak. You had better be tooling down to the desk now and having these things shoved in the hotel safe." I picked up the case and opened it. "Oh, Great Scott!"

The bally thing was empty!

"Oh, my Lord!" I said, staring. "Don't tell me there's been dirty work at the crossroads after all!"

"Precisely, sir. It was in exactly the same manner that Lord Frederick was swindled on the occasion to which I have alluded. While his female accomplice was gratefully embracing his lordship, Soapy Sid substituted a duplicate case for the one containing the pearls and went off with the jewels, the money and the receipt. On the strength of the receipt he subsequently demanded from his lordship the return of the pearls, and his lordship, not being able to produce them, was obliged to pay a heavy sum in compensation. It is a simple but effective ruse."

I felt as if the bottom had dropped out of things with a jerk.

"Soapy Sid? Sid! *Sidney!* Brother Sidney! Why, by Jove, Jeeves, do you think that parson was Soapy Sid?"

"Yes, sir."

"But it seems so extraordinary. Why, his collar buttoned at the back —I mean, he would have deceived a bishop. Do you really think he was Soapy Sid?"

"Yes, sir, I recognised him directly he came into the room."

I stared at the blighter.

"You recognised him?"

"Yes, sir."

"Then, dash it all," I said, deeply moved, "I think you might have told me."

"I thought it would save disturbance and unpleasantness if I merely abstracted the case from the man's pocket as I assisted him with his coat, sir. Here it is."

He laid another case on the table beside the dud one, and, by Jove, you couldn't tell them apart. I opened it and there were the good old pearls, as merry and bright as dammit, smiling up at me. I gazed feebly at the man. I was feeling a bit overwrought.

"Jeeves," I said. "You're an absolute genius!"

"Yes, sir."

Relief was surging over me in great chunks by now. Thanks to Jeeves I was not going to be called on to cough up several thousand quid.

"It looks to me as though you had saved the old home. I mean, even a chappie endowed with the immortal rind of dear old Sid is hardly likely to have the nerve to come back and retrieve these little chaps."

"I should imagine not, sir."

"Well, then—— Oh, I say, you don't think they are just paste or anything like that?"

"No, sir. These are genuine pearls and extremely valuable."

"Well, then, dash it, I'm on velvet. Absolutely reclining on the good old plush! I may be down a hundred quid but I'm up a jolly good string of pearls. Am I right or wrong?"

"Hardly that, sir. I think that you will have to restore the pearls."

"What! To Sid? Not while I have my physique!"

"No sir. To their rightful owner."

"But who is their rightful owner?"

"Mrs. Gregson, sir."

"What! How do you know?"

"It was all over the hotel an hour ago that Mrs. Gregson's pearls had been abstracted. I was speaking to Mrs. Gregson's maid shortly before you came in and she informed me that the manager of the hotel is now in Mrs. Gregson's suite."

"And having a devil of a time, what?"

"So I should be disposed to imagine, sir."

The situation was beginning to unfold before me.

"I'll go and give them back to her, eh? It'll put me one up, what?"

"Precisely, sir. And if I may make the suggestion, I think it might be judicious to stress the fact that they were stolen by——"

"Great Scott! By the dashed girl she was hounding me on to marry, by Jove!"

"Exactly, sir."

"Jeeves," I said, "this is going to be the biggest score off my jolly old relative that has ever occurred in the world's history."

"It is not unlikely, sir."

"Keep her quiet for a bit, what? Make her stop snootering me for a while?"

"It should have that effect, sir."

"Golly!" I said, bounding for the door.

Long before I reached Aunt Agatha's lair I could tell that the hunt was up. Divers chappies in hotel uniform and not a few chambermaids of sorts were hanging about in the corridor, and through the panels I could hear a mixed assortment of voices, with Aunt Agatha's topping the lot. I knocked but no one took any notice, so I trickled in. Among those present I noticed a chambermaid in hysterics, Aunt Agatha with her hair bristling, and the whiskered cove who looked like a bandit, the hotel manager fellow.

"Oh, hallo!" I said. "Hallo-allo-allo!"

Aunt Agatha shooshed me away. No welcoming smile for Bertram.

"Don't bother me now, Bertie," she snapped, looking at me as if I were more or less the last straw.

"Something up?"

"Yes, yes, yes! I've lost my pearls."

"Pearls? Pearls? Pearls?" I said. "No, really? Dashed annoying. Where did you see them last?"

"What does it matter where I saw them last? They have been stolen."

Here Wilfred the Whisker King, who seemed to have been taking a rest between rounds, stepped into the ring again and began to talk rapidly in French. Cut to the quick he seemed. The chambermaid whooped in the corner.

"Sure you've looked everywhere?" I said.

"Of course I've looked everywhere."

"Well, you know, I've often lost a collar stud and——"

265

"Do try not to be so maddening, Bertie! I have enough to bear without your imbecilities. Oh, be quiet! Be quiet!" she shouted in the sort of voice used by sergeant-majors and those who call the cattle home across the Sands of Dee. And such was the magnetism of her forceful personality that Wilfred subsided as if he had run into a wall. The chambermaid continued to go strong.

"I say," I said, "I think there's something the matter with this girl. Isn't she crying or something? You may not have spotted it, but I'm rather quick at noticing things."

"She stole my pearls! I am convinced of it."

This started the whisker specialist off again, and in about a couple of minutes Aunt Agatha had reached the frozen grande-dame stage and was putting the last of the bandits through it in the voice she usually reserves for snubbing waiters in restaurants.

"I tell you, my good man, for the hundredth time——"

"I say," I said, "don't want to interrupt you and all that sort of thing, but these aren't the little chaps by any chance, are they?"

I pulled the pearls out of my pocket and held them up.

"These look like pearls, what?"

I don't know when I've had a more juicy moment. It was one of those occasions about which I shall prattle to my grandchildren—if I ever have any, which at the moment of going to press seems more or less of a hundred-to-one shot. Aunt Agatha simply deflated before my eyes. It reminded me of when I once saw some chappies letting the gas out of a balloon."

"Where—where—where——" she gurgled.

"I got them from your friend, Miss Hemmingway."

Even now she didn't get it.

"From Miss Hemmingway. Miss *Hemmingway!* But—but how did they come into her possession?"

"How?" I said. "Because she jolly well stole them. Pinched them! Swiped them! Because that's how she makes her living, dash it—palling up to unsuspicious people in hotels and sneaking their jewelry. I don't know what her alias is, but her bally brother, the chap whose collar buttons at the back, is known in criminal circles as Soapy Sid."

She blinked.

"Miss Hemmingway a thief! I—I——" She stopped and looked feebly at me. "But how did you manage to recover the pearls, Bertie dear?"

"Never mind," I said crisply. "I have my methods." I dug out my entire stock of manly courage, breathed a short prayer and let her have it right in the thorax.

"I must say, Aunt Agatha, dash it all," I said severely, "I think you have been infernally careless. There's a printed notice in every bedroom in this place saying that there's a safe in the manager's office where jewelry and valuables ought to be placed, and you absolutely disregarded it. And what's the result? The first thief who came along simply walked into your room and pinched your pearls. And instead of admitting that it was your fault, you started biting this poor man here in the gizzard. You have been very, very unjust to this poor man."

"Yes, yes," moaned the poor man.

"And this unfortunate girl, what about her? Where does she get off? You've accused her of stealing the things on absolutely no evidence. I think she would be jolly well advised to bring an action for —for whatever it is and soak you for substantial damages."

"*Mais oui, mais oui, c'est trop fort!*" shouted the Bandit Chief, backing me up like a good 'un. And the chambermaid look up inquiringly, as if the sun was breaking through the clouds.

"I shall recompense her," said Aunt Agatha feebly.

"If you take my tip you jolly well will, and that eftsoons or right speedily. She's got a cast-iron case, and if I were her I wouldn't take a penny under twenty quid. But what gives me the pip most is the way you've unjustly abused this poor man here and tried to give his hotel a bad name——"

"Yes, by damn! It's too bad!" cried the whiskered marvel. "You careless old woman! You give my hotel bad names, would you or wasn't it? Tomorrow you leave my hotel, by great Scotland!"

And more to the same effect, all good, ripe stuff. And presently having said his say he withdrew, taking the chambermaid with him, the latter a crisp tenner clutched in a vise-like grip. I suppose she and the bandit split it outside. A French hotel manager wouldn't be likely to let real money wander away from him without counting himself in on the division.

I turned to Aunt Agatha, whose demeanor was now rather like that of one who, picking daisies on the railway, has just caught the down express in the small of the back.

"I don't want to rub it in, Aunt Agatha," I said coldly, "but I should just like to point out before I go that the girl who stole your pearls is

267

the girl you've been hounding me on to marry ever since I got here. Good heavens! Do you realize that if you had brought the thing off I should probably have had children who would have sneaked my watch while I was dandling them on my knee? I'm not a complaining sort of chap as a rule, but I must say that another time I do think you might be more careful how you go about egging me on to marry females."

I gave her one look, turned on my heel and left the room.

"Ten o'clock, a clear night, and all's well, Jeeves," I said, breezing back into the good old suite.

"I am gratified to hear it, sir."

"If twenty quid would be of any use, to you, Jeeves——"

There was a pause. And then—well, it was a wrench, but I did it. I unstripped the cummerbund and handed it over.

"Do you wish me to press this, sir?"

I gave the thing one last, longing look. It had been very dear to me.

"No," I said, "take it away; give it to the deserving poor—I shall never wear it again."

"Thank you very much, sir," said Jeeves.

THE RICH MAN

FRANKLIN P. ADAMS

The rich man has his motor-car,
   His country and his town estate.
He smokes a fifty-cent cigar
   And jeers at Fate.

He frivols through the livelong day,
   He knows not Poverty, her pinch.
His lot seems light, his heart seems gay;
   He has a cinch.

Yet though my lamp burns low and dim,
   Though I must slave for livelihood—
Think you that I would change with him?
   You bet I would!

TRIAL AND ERROR

*Lament Composed While Returning from Town with
Oliver on the 5:39*

PHYLLIS MC GINLEY

A lady is smarter than a gentleman, maybe.
She can sew a fine seam, she can have a baby.
She can use her intuition instead of her brain.
But she can't fold a paper on a crowded train.

269

THE LADIES

RICHARD ARMOUR

Liking their looks
  But not their notions,
I view the sex
  With mixed emotions.

MR. POTTLE AND THE ONE MAN DOG

RICHARD CONNELL

"AMBROSE! Ambrose dear!" The new Mrs. Pottle put down the book she was reading—Volume Dec to Erd of the encyclopedia.

"Yes, Blossom dear." Mr. Pottle's tone was fraught with the tender solicitude of the recently wed. He looked up from his book—Volume Ode to Pay of the encyclopedia.

"Ambrose, we must get a dog!"

"A dog, darling?"

His tone was still tender but a thought lacking in warmth. His smile, he hoped conveyed the impression that while he utterly approved of Blossom, herself, personally, her current idea struck no responsive chord in his bosom.

"Yes, a dog."

She sighed as she gazed at a large framed steel-engraving of Landseer's St. Bernards that occupied a space on the wall until recently tenanted by a crayon enlargement of her first husband in his lodge regalia.

"Such noble creatures," she sighed. "So intelligent. And so loyal."

"In the books they are," murmured Mr. Pottle.

"Oh, Ambrose," she protested with a pout. "How can you say such a thing? Just look at their big eyes, so full of soul. What magnificent animals! So full of understanding and fidelity and—and——"

"Fleas?" suggested Mr. Pottle.

Her glance was glacial.

"Ambrose, you are positively cruel," she said, tiny, injured tears gathering in her wide blue eyes. He was instantly penitent.

"Forgive me, dear," he begged. "I forgot. In the books they don't have 'em, do they? You see, precious, I don't take as much stock in books as I used to. I've been fooled so often."

"They are lovely books," said Mrs. Pottle, somewhat mollified. "You said yourself that you adore dog stories."

"Sure I do, honey," said Mr. Pottle, "but a man can like stories about

271

elephants without wanting to own one, can't he?"

"A dog is not an elephant, Ambrose."

He could not deny it.

"Don't you remember," she pursued rapturously, "that lovely book, 'Hero, the Collie Beautiful,' where a kiddie finds a puppy in an ash barrel, and takes care of it, and later the collie grows up and rescues the kiddie from a fire; or was that the book where the collie flew at the throat of the man who came to murder the kiddie's father, and the father broke down and put his arms around the collie's neck because he had kicked the collie once and the collie used to follow him around with big, hurt eyes and yet when he was in danger Hero saved him because collies are so sensitive and loyal?"

"Uh huh," assented Mr. Pottle.

"And that story we read, 'Almost Human,'" she rippled on fluidly, "about the kiddie who was lost in a snow-storm in the mountains and the brave St. Bernard that came along with bottles of spirits around its neck—St. Bernards always carry them,—and—"

"Do the bottles come with the dogs?" asked Mr. Pottle hopefully.

She elevated disapproving eyebrows.

"Ambrose," she said sternly, "don't always be making jests about alcohol. It's so common. You know when I married you, you promised never even to think of it again."

"Yes, Blossom," said Mr. Pottle, meekly.

She beamed.

"Well, dear, what kind of a dog shall we get?" she asked briskly. He felt that all was lost.

"There are dogs and dogs," he said moodily. "And I don't know anything about any of them."

"I'll read what it says here," she said. Mrs. Pottle was pursuing culture through the encyclopedia, and felt that she would overtake it on almost any page now.

"Dog," she read, "is the English generic term for the quadruped of the domesticated variety of *canis*."

"Well, I'll be darned!" exclaimed her husband. "Is that a fact?"

"Be serious, Ambrose, please. The choice of a dog is no jesting matter," she rebuked him, and then read on, "In the Old and New Testaments the dog is spoken of almost with abhorrence; indeed, it ranks among the unclean beasts—"

"There, Blossom," cried Mr. Pottle, clutching at a straw, "what did

272

I tell you? Would you fly in the face of the Good Book?"

She did not deign to reply verbally; she looked refrigerators at him.

"The Egyptians, on the other hand," she read, a note of triumph in her voice, "venerated the dog, and when a dog died they shaved their heads as a badge of mourning—"

"The Egyptians did, hey?" remarked Mr. Pottle, open disgust on his apple of face. "Shaved their own heads, did they? No wonder they all turned to mummies. You can't tell me it's safe for a man to shave his own head; there ought to be a law against it."

Mr. Pottle was in the barber business.

Unheedful of this digression, Mrs. Pottle read on.

"There are many sorts of dogs. I'll read the list so we can pick out ours. You needn't look cranky, Ambrose; we're going to have one. Let me see. Ah, yes, 'There are Great Danes, mastiffs, collies, dalmatians, chows, Newfoundlands, poodles, setters, pointers, retrievers— Labrador and flat-coated—spaniels, beagles, dachshunds—' I'll admit they are rather nasty; they're the only sort of dog I can't bear—'whippets, otter-hounds, terriers, including Scotch, Irish, Welsh, Skye and fox, and St. Bernards.' St. Bernards, it says, are the largest; 'their ears are small and their foreheads white and dome-shaped, giving them the well known expression of benignity and intelligence.' Oh, Ambrose," —her eyes were full of dreams—"Oh, Ambrose, wouldn't it be just too wonderful for words to have a great big, beautiful dog like that?"

"There isn't any too much room in this bungalow as it is," demurred Mr. Pottle. "Better get a chow."

"You don't seem to realize, Ambrose Pottle," the lady replied with some severity, "that what I want a dog for is protection."

"Protection, my angel? Can't I protect you?"

"Not when you're away on the road selling your shaving cream. Then's when I need some big, loyal creature to protect me."

"From what?"

"Well, burglars."

"Why should they come here?"

"How about all our wedding silver? And then kidnapers might come."

"Kidnapers? What could they kidnap?"

"Me," said Mrs. Pottle. "How would you like to come home from Zanesville or Bucyrus some day and find me gone, Ambrose?" Her lips quivered at the thought.

273

To Mr. Pottle, privately, this contingency seemed remote. His bride was not the sort of woman one might kidnap easily. She was a plentiful lady of a well developed maturity, whose clothes did not conceal her heroic mold, albeit they fitted her as tightly as if her modiste were a taxidermist. However, not for worlds would he have voiced this sacrilegious thought; he was in love; he preferred that she should think of herself as infinitely clinging and helpless; he fancied the role of sturdy oak.

"All right, Blossom," he gave in, patting her cheek. "If my angel wants a dog, she shall have one. That reminds me, Charlie Meacham, the boss barber of the Ohio House, has a nice litter. He offered me one or two or three if I wanted them. The mother is as fine a looking spotted coach dog as ever you laid an eye on and the pups—"

"What was the father?" demanded Mrs. Pottle.

"How should I know? There's a black pup, and a spotted pup, and a yellow pup, and a white pup and a—"

Mrs. Pottle sniffed.

"No mungles for me," she stated flatly. "I hate mungles. I want a thoroughbred, or nothing. One with a pedigree, like that adorably handsome creature there."

She nodded toward the engraving of the giant St. Bernards.

"But, darling," objected Mr. Pottle, "pedigree pups cost money. A dog can bark and bite whether he has a family tree or not, can't he? We can't afford one of these fancy, blue-blooded ones. I've got notes at the bank right now I don't know how the deuce I'm going to pay. My shaving stick needs capital. I can't be blowing in hard-earned dough on pups."

"Oh, Ambrose, I actually believe you—don't—care—whether I'm—kidnaped—or—not!" his wife began, a catch in her voice. A heart of wrought iron would have been melted by the pathos of her tone and face.

"There, there, honey," said Mr. Pottle, hastily, with an appropriate amatory gesture, "you shall have your pup. But remember this, Blossom Pottle. He's yours. You are to have all the responsibility and care of him."

"Oh, Ambrose, you're so good to me," she breathed.

The next evening when Mr. Pottle came home he observed something brown and fuzzy nestling in his Sunday velour hat. With a smothered exclamation of the kind that has no place in a romance, he

274

dumped the thing out and saw it waddle away on unsteady legs, leaving him sadly contemplating the strawberry silk lining of his best hat.

"Isn't he a love? Isn't he just too sweet," cried Mrs. Pottle, emerging from the living room and catching the object up in her arms. "Come to mama, sweetie-pie. Did the nassy man frighten my precious Pershing?"

"Your precious what?"

"Pershing. I named him for a brave man and a fighter. I just know he'll be worthy of it, when he grows up, and starts to protect me."

"In how many years?" inquired Mr. Pottle, cynically.

"The man said he'd be big enough to be a watch dog in a very few months; they grow so fast."

"What man said this?"

"The kennel man. I bought Pershing at the Laddiebrook-Sunshine Kennels today." She paused to kiss the pink muzzle of the little animal; Mr. Pottle winced at this but she noted it not, and rushed on.

"Such an interesting place, Ambrose. Nothing but dogs and dogs and dogs. All kinds, too. They even had one mean, sneaky-looking dachshund there; I just couldn't trust a dog like that. Ugh! Well, I looked at all the dogs. The minute I saw Pershing I knew he was my dog. His little eyes looked up at me as much as to say, 'I'll be yours, mistress, faithful to the death,' and he put out the dearest little pink tongue and licked my hand. The kennel man said, 'Now ain't that wonderful, lady, the way he's taken to you? Usually he growls at strangers. He's a one man dog, all right, all right.'"

"A one man dog?" said Mr. Pottle blankly.

275

"Yes. One that loves his owner, and nobody else. That's just the kind I want."

"Where do I come in?" inquired Mr. Pottle.

"Oh, he'll learn to tolerate you, I guess," she reassured him. Then she rippled on, "I just had to have him then. He was one of five, but he already had a little personality all his own, although he's only three weeks old. I saw his mother—a magnificent creature, Ambrose, big as a Shetland pony and twice as shaggy, and with the most wonderful appealing eyes, that looked at me as if it stabbed her to the heart to have her little ones taken from her. And such a pedigree! It covers pages. Her name is Gloria Audacious Indomitable; the Audacious Indomitables are a very celebrated family of St. Bernards, the kennel man said."

"What about his father?" queried Mr. Pottle, poking the ball of pup with his finger.

"I didn't see him," admitted Mrs. Pottle. "I believe they are not living together now."

She snuggled the pup to her capacious bosom.

"So," she said, "it's whole name is Pershing Audacious Indomitable, isn't it, tweetums?"

"It's a swell name," admitted Mr. Pottle. "Er—Blossom, dear, how much did he cost?"

She brought out the reply quickly, almost timidly.

"Fifty dollars."

"Fif—" his voice stuck in his larynx. "Great Caesar's Ghost!"

"But think of his pedigree," cried his wife.

"Great Caesar's Ghost! Fifty dollars! Great Caesar's Ghost!"

"Why, we can exhibit him at bench shows," she argued, "and win hundreds of dollars in prizes. And his pups will be worth fifty dollars per pup easily, with that pedigree."

"Great Caesar's Ghost!" said Mr. Pottle, despondently. "Fifty dollars! And the shaving stick business all geflooey."

"He'll be worth a thousand to me as a protector," she declared, defiantly. "You wait and see, Ambrose Pottle. Wait till he grows up to be a great, big, handsome, intelligent dog, winning prizes and protecting your wife. He'll be the best investment we ever made, you mark my words."

Had Pershing encountered Mr. Pottle's eye at that moment the marrow of his small canine bones would have congealed.

"All right, Blossom," said her spouse, gloomily. "He's yours. You take care of him. I wonder, I just wonder, that's all."

"What do you wonder, Ambrose?"

"If they'll let him visit us when we're in the poor house."

To this his wife remarked, "Fiddlesticks," and began to feed Pershing from a nursing bottle.

"Grade A milk, I suppose," groaned Mr. Pottle.

"Cream," she corrected calmly. "Pershing is no mungle. Remember that, Ambrose Pottle."

It was a nippy, frosty night, and Mr. Pottle, after much chattering of teeth, had succeeded in getting a place warm in the family bed, and was floating peacefully into a dream in which he got a contract for ten carload lots of Pottle's Edible Shaving Cream, "Just Lather, Shave and Lick. That's All," when his wife's soft knuckles prodded him in the ribs.

"Ambrose, Ambrose, do wake up. Do you hear that?"

He sleepily opened a protesting eye. He heard faint, plaintive, peeping sounds somewhere in the house.

"It's that wretched hound," he said crossly.

"Pershing is not a hound, Ambrose Pottle."

"Oh, all right, Blossom, ALL RIGHT. It's that noble creature. G'night."

But the knuckles tattooed on his drowsy ribs again.

"Ambrose, he's lonesome."

No response.

"Ambrose, little Pershing is lonesome."

"Well, suppose you go and sing him to sleep."

"Ambrose! And us married only a month!"

Mr. Pottle sat up in bed.

"Is he your pup," he demanded oratorically, "or is he not your pup, Mrs. Pottle? And anyhow, why pamper him? He's all right. Didn't I walk six blocks in the cold to a grocery store to get a box for his bed? Didn't you line it with some of my best towels? Isn't it under a nice, warm stove? What more can a hound—"

"Ambrose!"

"—noble creature, expect?"

He dived into his pillow as if it were oblivion.

"Ambrose," said his wife, loudly and firmly, "Pershing is lonesome. Thoroughbreds have such sensitive natures. If he thought we were lying here neglecting him, it wouldn't surprise me a bit if he died of a broken heart before morning. A pedigreed dog like Pershing has the feelings of a delicate child."

Muffled words came from the Pottle pillow.

"Well, whose one man dog is he?"

Mrs. Pottle began to sniffle audibly.

"I d-don't believe you'd c-care if I got up and c-caught my d-death of c-cold," she said. "You know how easily I c-chill, too. But I c-can't leave that poor motherless little fellow cry his heart out in that big, dark, lonely kitchen. I'll just have to get up and—"

She stirred around as if she really intended to. The chivalrous Mr. Pottle heaved up from his pillow like an irate grampus from the depths of a tank.

"I'll go," he grumbled, fumbling around with goose-fleshed limbs for his chilly slippers. "Shall I tell him about Little Red Riding Hood or Goody Two Shoes?"

"Ambrose, if you speak roughly to Pershing, I shall never forgive you. And he won't either. Bring him in here."

"Here?" His tone was aghast; barbers are aseptic souls.

"Yes, of course."

"In bed?"

"Certainly."

"Oh, Blossom!"

"We can't leave him in the cold, can we?"

"But, Blossom, suppose he's—suppose he has—"

The hiatus was expressive.

"He hasn't." Her voice was one of indignant denial. "Pedigreed dogs don't. Why, the kennels were immaculate."

"Humph," said Mr. Pottle dubiously. He strode into the kitchen and

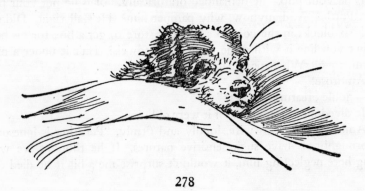

returned with Pershing in his arms; he plumped the small, bushy, whining animal in bed beside his wife.

"I suppose, Mrs. Pottle," he said, "that you are prepared to take the consequences."

She stroked the squirming thing, which emitted small, protesting bleats.

"Don't you mind the nassy man, sweetie-pie," she cooed. "Casting 'spersions on poor lil' lonesome doggie." Then, to her husband, "Ambrose, how can you suggest such a thing? Don't stand there in the cold."

"Nevertheless," said Mr. Pottle, oracularly, as he prepared to seek slumber at a point as remote as possible in the bed from Pershing, "I'll bet a dollar to a doughnut that I'm right."

Mr. Pottle won his doughnut. At three o'clock in the morning, with the mercury flirting with the freezing mark, he suddenly surged up from his pillow, made twitching motions with limbs and shoulders, and stalked out into the living room, where he finished the night on a hard-boiled army cot, used for guests.

As the days hurried by, he had to admit that the kennel man's predictions about the rapid growth of the animal seemed likely of fulfillment. In a very few weeks the offspring of Gloria Audacious Indomitable had attained prodigious proportions.

"But, Blossom," said Mr. Pottle eyeing the animal as it gnawed industriously at the golden oak legs of the player piano, "isn't he growing in a sort of funny way?"

"Funny way, Ambrose?"

"Yes, dear; funny way. Look at his legs."

She contemplated those members.

"Well?"

"They're kinda brief, aren't they, Blossom?"

"Naturally. He's no giraffe, Ambrose. Young thoroughbreds have small legs. Just like babies."

"But he seems so sorta long in proportion to his legs," said Mr. Pottle critically. "He gets to look more like an overgrown caterpillar every day."

"You said yourself, Ambrose, that you know nothing about dogs," his wife reminded him. "The legs always develop fast. Give Pershing a chance to get his growth; then you'll see."

Mr. Pottle shrugged, unconvinced.

279

"It's time to take Pershing out for his airing," Mrs. Pottle observed.

A fretwork of displeasure appeared on the normally bland brow of Mr. Pottle.

"Lotta good that does," he grunted. "Besides, I'm getting tired of leading him around on a string. He's so darn funny looking; the boys are beginning to kid me about him."

"Do you want me to go out," asked Mrs. Pottle, "with this heavy cold?"

"Oh, all right," said Mr. Pottle blackly.

"Now, Pershing, precious, let mamma put on your lil' blanket so you can go for a nice lil' walk with your papa."

"I'm not his papa," growled Mr. Pottle, rebelliously. "I'm no relation of his."

However, the neighbors along Garden Avenue presently spied a short, rotund man, progressing with reluctant step along the street, in his hand a leathern leash at the end of which ambled a pup whose physique was the occasion of some discussion among the dog fanciers who beheld it.

"Blossom," said Mr. Pottle—it was after Pershing had outgrown two boxes and a large wash-basket—"you may say what you like but that dog of yours looks funny to me."

"How can you say that?" she retorted. "Just look at that long heavy coat. Look at that big, handsome head. Look at those knowing eyes, as if he understood every word we're saying."

"But his legs, Blossom, his legs!"

"They are a wee, tiny bit short," she confessed. "But he's still in his infancy. Perhaps we don't feed him often enough."

"No?" said Mr. Pottle with a rising inflection which had the perfume of sarcasm about it, "No? I suppose seven times a day, including once in the middle of the night, isn't often enough?"

"Honestly, Ambrose, you'd think you were an early Christian martyr being devoured by tigers to hear all the fuss you make about getting up just once for five or ten minutes in the night to feed poor, hungry little Pershing."

"It hardly seems worth it," remarked Mr. Pottle, "with him turning out this way."

"What way?"

"Bandy-legged."

"St. Bernards," she said with dignity, "do not run to legs. Mungles

may be all leggy, but not full blooded St. Bernards. He's a baby, remember that, Ambrose Pottle."

"He eats more than a full grown farm hand," said Mr. Pottle. "And
steak at fifty cents a pound!"

"You can't bring up a delicate dog like Pershing on liver," said Mrs.
Pottle, crushingly. "Now run along, Ambrose, and take him for a good
airing, while I get his evening broth ready."

"They extended that note of mine at the bank, Blossom," said Mr.
Pottle.

"Don't let him eat out of ash cans, and don't let him associate with
mungles," said Mrs. Pottle.

Mr. Pottle skulked along sidestreets, now dragging, now being
dragged by the muscular Pershing. It was Mr. Pottle's idea to escape
the attention of his friends, of whom there were many in Granville,
and who, of late, had shown a disposition to make remarks about his
evening promenade that irked his proud spirit. But, as he rounded the
corner of Cottage Row, he encountered Charlie Meacham, tonsorialist,
dog-fancier, wit.

"Evening, Ambrose."

"Evening, Charlie."

Mr. Pottle tried to ignore Pershing, to pretend that there was no connection between them, but Pershing reared up on his stumpy hind legs
and sought to embrace Mr. Meacham.

"Where'd you get the pooch?" inquired Mr. Meacham, with some
interest.

"Wife's," said Mr. Pottle, briefly.

"Where'd she find it?"

"Didn't find him. Bought him at Laddiebrook-Sunshine Kennels."

"Oho," whistled Mr. Meacham.

"Pedigreed," confided Mr. Pottle.

"You don't tell me!"

"Yep. Name's Pershing."

"Name's what?"

"Pershing. In honor of the great general."

Mr. Meacham leaned against a convenient lamp post; he seemed of a
sudden overcome by some powerful emotion.

"What's the joke?" asked Mr. Pottle.

"Pershing!" Mr. Meacham was just able to get out. "Oh, me, oh my.
That's a scream."

281

"Pershing," said Mr. Pottle, stoutly, "Audacious Indomitable. You ought to see his pedigree."

"I'd like to," said Mr. Meacham, "I certainly would like to."

He was studying the architecture of Pershing with the cool appraising eye of the expert. His eye rested for a long time on the short legs and long body.

"Pottle," he said, thoughtfully, "haven't they got a dachshund up at those there kennels?"

Mr. Pottle knitted perplexed brows.

"I believe they have," he said. "Why?"

"Oh, nothing," replied Mr. Meacham, struggling to keep a grip on his emotions which threatened to choke him, "Oh, nothing." And he went off, Mr. Pottle staring at his shoulder blades which titillated oddly as Mr. Meacham walked.

Mr. Pottle, after a series of tugs-of-war, got his charge home. A worry wormed its way into his brain like an auger into a pine plank. The worry became a suspicion. The suspicion became a horrid certainty. Gallant man that he was, and lover, he did not mention it to Blossom.

But after that the evening excursions with Pershing became his cross and his wormwood. He pleaded to be allowed to take Pershing out after dark; Blossom wouldn't hear of it; the night air might injure his pedigreed lungs. In vain did he offer to hire a man—at no matter what cost—to take his place as companion to the creature which daily grew more pronounced and remarkable as to shape. Blossom declared that she would entrust no stranger with her dog; a Pottle, and a Pottle only, could escort him. The nightly pilgrimage became almost unendurable after a total stranger, said to be a Dubuque traveling man, stopped Mr. Pottle on the street one evening and asked, gravely:

"I beg pardon, sir, but isn't that animal a peagle?"

"He is not a beagle," said Mr. Pottle, shortly.

"I didn't say 'beagle,'" the stranger smiled, "I said 'peagle'—p-e-a-g-l-e."

"What's that?"

"A peagle," answered the stranger, "is a cross between a pony and a beagle." It took three men to stop the fight.

Pershing, as Mr. Pottle perceived all too plainly, was growing more curious and ludicrous to the eye every day. He had the enormous head, the heavy body, the shaggy coat, and the benign, intellectual face of

282

his mother; but alas, he had the bandy, caster-like legs of his putative father. He was an anti-climax. Everybody in Granville, save Blossom alone, seemed to realize the stark, the awful truth about Pershing's ancestry. Even he seemed to realize his own sad state; he wore a shame-faced look as he trotted by the side of Ambrose Pottle; Mr. Pottle's own features grew hang-dog. Despite his spouse's hints, Blossom never lost faith in Pershing.

"Just you wait, Ambrose," she said. "One of these fine days you'll wake up and find he has developed a full grown set of limbs."

"Like a tadpole, I suppose," he said grimly.

"Joke all you like, Ambrose. But mark my words: you'll be proud of Pershing. Just look at him there, taking in every word we say. Why, already he can do everything but speak. I just know I could count on him if I was in danger from burglars or kidnapers or anything. I'll feel so much safer with him in the house when you take your trip East next month."

"The burglar that came on him in the dark would be scared to death," mumbled Mr. Pottle. She ignored this aside.

"Now, Ambrose," she said, "take the comb and give him a good combing. I may enter him in a bench show next month."

"You ought to," remarked Mr. Pottle, as he led Pershing away, "he looks like a bench."

It was with a distinct sense of escape that Mr. Pottle some weeks later took a train for Washington where he hoped to have patented and trademarked his edible shaving cream, a discovery he confidently expected to make his fortune.

"Goodbye, Ambrose," said Mrs. Pottle. "I'll write you every day how Pershing is getting along. At the rate he's growing you won't know him when you come back. You needn't worry about me. My one man dog will guard me, won't you, sweetie-pie? There now, give your paw to Papa Pottle."

"I'm not his papa, I tell you," cried Mr. Pottle with some passion as he grabbed up his suit-case and crunched down the gravel path.

In all, his business in Washington kept him away from his home for twenty-four days. While he missed the society of Blossom, somehow he experienced a delicious feeling of freedom from care, shame and responsibility as he took his evening stroll about the capitol. His trip was a success; the patent was secured, the trade-mark duly registered. The patent lawyer, as he pocketed his fee, perhaps to salve his conscience for its size, produced from behind a law book a bottle of an ancient and once honorable fluid and pressed it on Mr. Pottle.

"I promised the wife I'd stay on the sprinkling cart," demurred Mr. Pottle.

"Oh, take it along," urged the patent lawyer. "You may need it for a cold one of these days."

It occurred to Mr. Pottle that if there is one place in the world a man may catch his death of cold it is on a draughty railroad train, and wouldn't it be foolish of him with a fortune in his grasp, so to speak, not to take every precaution against a possibly fatal illness? Besides he knew that Blossom would never permit him to bring the bottle into their home. He preserved it in the only way possible under the circumstances. When the train reached Granville just after midnight, Mr. Pottle skipped blithely from the car, made a sweeping bow to a milk can, cocked his derby over his eye, which was uncommonly bright and playful, and started for home with the meticulous but precarious step of the tight rope walker.

It was his plan, carefully conceived, to steal softly as thistledown falling on velvet, into his bungalow without waking the sleeping Blossom, to spend the night on the guest cot, to spring up, fresh as a dewy daisy in the morn, and wake his wife with a smiling and coherent account of his trip.

Very quietly he tip-toed along the lawn leading to his front door, his latch key out and ready. But as he was about to place a noiseless foot on his porch, something vast, low and dark barred his path, and a bass and hostile growl brought him to an abrupt halt.

284

"Well, well, well, if it isn't lil' Pershin'," said Mr. Pottle, pleasantly, but remembering to pitch his voice in a low key. "Waiting on the porch to welcome Papa Pottle home! Nice lil' Pershin'."

"Grrrrr Grrrrr Grrrrrrrrr," replied Pershing. He continued to bar the path, to growl ominously, to bare strong teeth in the moonlight. In Mr. Pottle's absence he had grown enormously in head and body; but not in leg.

"Pershin'," said Mr. Pottle plaintively, "can it be that you have forgotten Papa Pottle? Have you forgotten nice, kind mans that took you for pretty walks? That fed you pretty steaks? That gave you pretty baths? Nice lil' Pershin', nice lil'—"

Mr. Pottle reached down to pat the shaggy head and drew back his hand with something that would pass as a curse in any language; Pershing had given his finger a whole-hearted nip.

"You low-down, underslung brute," rasped Mr. Pottle. "Get out of my way or I'll kick the pedigree outa you."

Pershing's growl grew louder and more menacing. Mr. Pottle hesitated; he feared Blossom more than Pershing. He tried cajolery.

"Come, come, nice lil' St. Bernard. Great, big, noble St. Bernard. Come for lil' walk with Papa Pottle. Nice Pershin', nice Pershin', you dirty cur—"

This last remark was due to the animal's earnest but only partially successful effort to fasten its teeth in Mr. Pottle's calf. Pershing gave out a sharp, disappointed yelp.

A white, shrouded figure appeared at the window.

"Burglar, go away," it said, shrilly, "or I'll sic my savage St. Bernard on you."

"He's already sicced, Blottom," said a doleful voice. "It's me, Blottom. Your Ambrose."

"Why, Ambrose! How queer your voice sounds! Why don't you come in?"

"Pershing won't let me," cried Mr. Pottle. "Call him in."

"He won't come," she wailed, "and I'm afraid of him at night like this."

"Coax him in."

"He won't coax."

"Bribe him with food."

"You can't bribe a thoroughbred."

Mr. Pottle put his hands on his hips, and standing in the exact center

285

of his lawn, raised a high, sardonic voice.

"Oh, yes," he said, "oh, dear me, yes, I'll live to be proud of Pershing. Oh, yes indeed. I'll live to love the noble creature. I'll be glad I got up on cold nights to pour warm milk into his dear little stummick. Oh, yes. Oh, yes, he'll be worth thousands to me. Here I go down to Washington, and work my head to the bone to keep a roof over us, and when I get back I can't get under it. If you ask me, Mrs. Blottom Pottle née Gallup, if you ask me, that precious animal of yours, that noble creature is the muttiest mutt that ever—"

"Ambrose!" Her edged voice clipped his oration short. "You've been drinking!"

"Well," said Mr. Pottle in a bellowing voice, "I guess a hound like that is enough to drive a person to drink. G'night, Blottom. I'm going to sleep in the flower bed. Frozen petunias will be my pillow. When I'm dead and gone, be kind to little Pershing for my sake."

"Ambrose! Stop. Think of the neighbors. Think of your health. Come into the house this minute."

He tried to obey her frantic command, but the low-lying, far-flung bulk of Pershing blocked the way, a growling, fanged, hairy wall. Mr. Pottle retreated to the flower bed.

"What was it the Belgiums said?" he remarked. "They shall not pash."

"Oh, what'll I do, what'll I do?" came from the window.

"Send for the militia," suggested Mr. Pottle with savage facetiousness.

"I know," cried his wife, inspired, "I'll send for a veterinarian. He'll know what to do."

286

"A veterinarian!" he protested loudly. "Five bones a visit, and us the joke of Granville."

But he could suggest nothing better and presently an automobile discharged a sleepy and disgusted dog-doctor at the Pottle homestead. It took the combined efforts of the two men and the woman to entice Pershing away from the door long enough for Mr. Pottle to slip into his house. During the course of Mrs. Pottle's subsequent remarks, Mr. Pottle said a number of times that he was sorry he hadn't stayed out among the petunias.

In the morning Pershing greeted him with an innocent expression.

"I hope, Mr. Pottle," said his wife, as he sipped black coffee, "that you are now convinced what a splendid watch dog Pershing is."

"I wish I had that fifty back again," he answered. "The bank won't give me another extension on that note, Blossom."

She tossed a bit of bacon to Pershing who muffed it and retrieved it with only slight damage to the pink roses on the rug.

"I can't stand this much longer, Blossom," he burst out.

"What?"

"You used to love me."

"I still do, Ambrose, despite all."

"You conceal it well. That mutt takes all your time."

"Mutt, Ambrose?"

"Mutt," said Mr. Pottle.

"See! He's heard you," she cried. "Look at that hurt expression in his face."

"Bah," said Mr. Pottle. "When do we begin to get fifty dollars per pup. I could use the money. Isn't it about time this great hulking creature did something to earn his keep? He's got the appetite of a lion."

"Don't mind the nassy mans, Pershing. We're not a mutt, are we, Pershing? Ambrose, please don't say such things in his presence. It hurts him dreadfully. Mutt, indeed. Just look at those big, gentle, knowing eyes."

"Look at those legs, woman," said Mr. Pottle.

He despondently sipped his black coffee.

"Blossom," he said, "I'm going to Chicago tonight. Got to have a conference with the men who are dickering with me about manufacturing my shaving cream. I'll be gone three days and I'll be busy every second."

"Yes, Ambrose. Pershing will protect me."

"And when I come back," he went on sternly, "I want to be able to get into my own house, do you understand?"

"I warned you Pershing was a one man dog," she replied. "You'd better come back at noon while he's at lunch. You needn't worry about us."

"I shan't worry about Pershing," promised Mr. Pottle, reaching for his suit-case.

He had not overstated how busy he would be in Chicago. His second day was crowded. After a trip to the factory, he was closeted at his hotel in solemn conference in the evening with the president, a vice-president or two, a couple of assistant vice-presidents and their assistants, and a collection of sales engineers, publicity engineers, production engineers, personnel engineers, employment engineers, and just plain engineers; for a certain large corporation scented profit in his shaving cream. They were putting him through a business third degree and he was enjoying it. They had even reached the point where they were discussing his share in the profits if they decided to manufacture his discovery. Mr. Pottle was expatiating on its merits.

"Gentlemen," he said, "there are some forty million beards every morning in these United States, and forty million breakfasts to be eaten by men in a hurry. Now, my shaving cream being edible, combines——"

"Telegram for Mr. Puddle, Mr. Puddle, Mr. Puddle," droned a bell hop, poking in a head.

"Excuse me, gentlemen," said Mr. Pottle. He hoped they would think it an offer from a rival company. As he read the message his face grew white. Alarming words leaped from the yellow paper.

"Come home. Very serious accident. Blossom."

288

That was all, but to the recently mated Mr. Pottle it was enough. He crumpled the message with quivering fingers.

"Sorry, gentlemen," he said, trying to smile bravely. "Bad news from home. We'll have to continue this discussion later."

"You can just make the 10:10 train," said one of the engineers, sympathetically. "Hard lines, old man."

Granville's lone, asthmatic taxi coughed up Mr. Pottle at the door of his house; it was dark; he did not dare look at the door-knob. His trembling hand twisted the key in the lock.

"Who's that?" called a faint voice. It was Blossom's. He thanked God she was still alive.

He was in her room in an instant, and had switched on the light. She lay in bed, her face, once rosy, now pale; her eyes, once placid, now red-lidded and tear-swollen. He bent over her with tremulous anxiety.

"Honey, what's happened? Tell your Ambrose."

She raised herself feebly in bed. He thanked God she could move.

"Oh, it's too awful," she said with a sob. "Too dreadful for words."

"What? Oh, what? Tell me, Blossom dearest. Tell me. I'll be brave, little woman. I'll try to bear it." He pressed her fevered hands in his.

"I can hardly believe it," she sobbed. "I c-can hardly believe it."

"Believe it? Believe what? Tell me, Blossom darling, in Heaven's name, tell me."

"Pershing," she sobbed in a heartbroken crescendo, "Pershing has become a mother!"

Her sobs shook her.

"And they're all mungles," she cried, "all nine of them."

Thunderclouds festooned the usually mild forehead of Mr. Pottle next morning. He was inclined to be sarcastic.

289

"Fifty dollars per pup, eh?" he said. "Fifty dollars per pup, eh?"

"Don't Ambrose," his wife begged. "I can't stand it. To think with eyes like that Pershing should deceive me."

"Pershing?" snorted Mr. Pottle so violently the toast hopped from the toaster. "Pershing? Not now. Violet! Violet! Violet!"

Mrs. Pottle looked meek.

"The ash man said he'd take the pups away if I gave him two dollars," she said.

"Give him five," said Mr. Pottle, "and maybe he'll take Violet, too."

"I will not, Ambrose Pottle," she returned. "I will not desert her now that she has gotten in trouble. How could she know, having been brought up so carefully? After all, dogs are only human."

"You actually intend to keep that—"

She did not allow him to pronounce the epithet that was forming on his lips, but checked it, with—

"Certainly I'll keep her. She is still a one man dog. She can still protect me from kidnapers and burglars."

He threw up his hands, a despairing gesture.

In the days that followed hard on the heels of Violet's disgrace, Mr. Pottle had little time to think of dogs. More pressing cares weighed on him. The Chicago men, their enthusiasm cooling when no longer under the spell of Mr. Pottle's arguments, wrote that they guessed that at this time, things being as they were, and under the circumstances, they were forced to regret that they could not make his shaving cream, but might at some later date be interested, and they were his very truly. The bank sent him a frank little message saying that it had no desire to go into the barber business, but that it might find that step necessary if Mr. Pottle did not step round rather soon with a little donation for the loan department.

It was thoughts of this cheerless nature that kept Mr. Pottle tossing uneasily in his share of the bed, and with wide-open, worried eyes doing sums on the moonlit ceiling. He waited the morrow with numb pessimism. For, though he had combed the town and borrowed every cent he could squeeze from friend or foe, though he had pawned his favorite case of razors, he was three hundred dollars short of the needed amount. Three hundred dollars is not much compared to all the money in the world, but to Mr. Pottle, on his bed of anxiety, it looked like the Great Wall of China.

He heard the town clock boom a faint two. It occurred to him that

290

there was something singular, odd, about the silence. It took him minutes to decide what it was. Then he puzzled it out. Violet née Pershing was not barking. It was her invariable custom to make harrowing sounds at the moon from ten in the evening till dawn. He had learned to sleep through them, eventually. He pointed out to Blossom that a dog that barks all the time is a deuce of a watch-dog, and she pointed out to him that a dog that barks all the time thus advertising its presence and its ferocity, would be certain to scare off midnight prowlers. He wondered why Violet was so silent. The thought skipped through his brain that perhaps she had run away, or been poisoned, and in all his worry, he permitted himself a faint smile of hope. No, he thought, I was born unlucky. There must be another reason. It was borne into his brain cells what this reason must be.

Slipping from bed without disturbing the dormant Blossom, he crept on wary bare toes from the room and down stairs. Ever so faint chinking sounds came from the dining room. With infinite caution Mr. Pottle slid open the sliding door an inch. He caught his breath.

There, in a patch of moonlight, squatted a chunky figure of a masked man, and he was engaged in industriously wrapping up the Pottle silver in bits of cloth. Now and then he paused in his labors to pat caressingly the head of Violet who stood beside him watching with fascinated interest, and wagging a pleased tail. Mr. Pottle was clamped to his observation post by a freezing fear. The busy burglar did not see him, but Violet did, and pointing her bushel of busy head at him, she let slip a deep "Grrrrrrrrrr." The burglar turned quickly, and a moonbeam rebounded from the polished steel of his revolver as he leveled it at a place where Mr. Pottle's heart would have been if it had not at that precise second been in his throat, a quarter of an inch south of his Adam's apple.

"Keep 'em up," said the burglar, "or I'll drill you like you was an oil-well."

Mr. Pottle's hands went up and his heart went down. The ultimate straw had been added; the wedding silver was neatly packed in the burglar's bag. Mr. Pottle cast an appealing look at Violet and breathed a prayer that in his dire emergency her blue-blood would tell and she would fling herself with one last heroic fling at the throat of the robber. Violet returned his look with a stony stare, and licked the free hand of the thief.

A thought wave rippled over Mr. Pottle's brain.

291

"You might as well take the dog with you, too," he said.

"Your dog?" asked the burglar, gruffly.

"Whose else would it be?"

"Where'd you get her?"

"Raised her from a pup up."

"From a pup up?"

"Yes, from a pup up."

The robber appeared to be thinking.

"She's some dog," he remarked. "I never seen one just like her."

For the first time in the existence of either of them, Mr. Pottle felt a faint glow of pride in Violet.

"She's the only one of her kind in the world," he said.

"I believe you," said the burglar. "And I know a thing or two about dogs, too."

"Really?" said Mr. Pottle, politely.

"Yes, I do," said the burglar, and a sad note had softened the gruffness of his voice. "I used to be a dog trainer."

"You don't tell me?" said Mr. Pottle.

"Yes," said the burglar, with a touch of pride, "I had the swellest dog and pony act in big time vaudeville once."

"Where is it now?" Mr. Pottle was interested.

"Mashed to bologny," said the burglar, sadly. "Train wreck. Lost every single animal. Like that." He snapped melancholy fingers to illustrate the sudden demise of his troupe. "That's why I took to this," he added. "I ain't a regular crook. Honest. I just want to get together enough capital to start another show. Another job or two and I'll have enough."

Mr. Pottle looked his sympathy. The burglar was studying Violet with eyes that brightened visibly.

"If," he said, slowly, "I only had a trick dog like her, I could start again. She's the funniest looking hound I ever seen, bar none. I can just hear the audiences roaring with laughter." He sighed reminiscently.

"Take her," said Mr. Pottle, handsomely. "She's yours."

The burglar impaled him with the gimlet eye of suspicion.

"Oh, yes," he said, "I could get away with a dog like that, couldn't I? You couldn't put the cops on my trail if I had a dog like that with me, oh no. Why, I could just as easy get away with Pike's Peak or a flock of Masonic Temples as with a dog as different looking as her.

No, stranger, I wasn't born yesterday."

"I won't have you pinched, I swear I won't," said Mr. Pottle earnestly. "Take her. She's yours."

The burglar resumed the pose of thinker.

"Look here, stranger," he said at length. "Tell you what I'll do. Just to make the whole thing fair and square and no questions asked, I'll buy that dog from you."

"You'll what?" Mr. Pottle articulated.

"I'll buy her," repeated the burglar.

Mr. Pottle was incapable of replying.

"Well," said the burglar, "will you take a hundred for her?"

Mr. Pottle could not get out a syllable.

"Two hundred, then?" said the burglar.

"Make it three hundred and she's yours," said Mr. Pottle.

"Sold!" said the burglar.

When morning came to Granville, Mr. Pottle waked his wife by gently, playfully, fanning her pink and white cheek with three bills of a large denomination.

"Blossom," he said, and the smile of his early courting days had come back, "you were right. Violet was a one man dog. I just found the man."

293

THE CHRISTMAS OF THE FUTURE

FRANK SULLIVAN

THERE is every reason to believe that the old haphazard and unscientific methods of celebrating Christmas are slowly dying out and that the Christmas of the future will be observed with a maximum of efficiency and a minimum loss of energy.

In the past Christmas as a holiday has often been fraught with danger to life and limb, but science is making rapid strides in the direction of making the Yuletide safe for democracy. An example of this: I heard only the other day of the admirable work a prominent inventor is doing to combat the holly menace. There are few of us who at one time or another have not received flesh wounds—not serious, to be sure, but none the less painful—as a result of sitting unawares on barbed holly left in chairs by frenzied Christmas tree trimmers. Such lesions will soon be a thing of the past. I am not authorized to give details but I understand that within the year this inventor I speak of will have a serviceable and cheap rubber holly on the market, guaranteed not to puncture.

Other time-honored Christmas features seem to have outlived their day. You no longer find Christmas trees festooned with ropes of popcorn. Those of us who are in our forties can remember when days were spent popping corn and stringing it into yards of trimming for the Christmas tree. By the time the tree was taken down at Twelfth Night the popcorn had hung long enough to acquire an attractively gamey tang, with a flavor of tinsel dust, lint and dried evergreen needles. It was considered quite a delicacy by the small fry of those times. For years hot buttered popcorn seemed quite tame to me by comparison. This eating of mummified popcorn, and the wholesale consumption by tots of Christmas tree candles were probably, with the recent depression, the main factors in producing the dyspepsia which is so marked a characteristic of the generation of the present writer. Popcorn and wax candles have joined the dodo and the Yule log. The children of today must find some other means of acquiring acute indi, gestion. They are resourceful and ingenious, and will no doubt have little trouble doing so.

Another Christmas reform impends. I am told that within a year or two science will have stripped the kiss under the mistletoe of its terrors. For some time past experiments have been proceeding with a new automatic antiseptic mistletoe. The leaves are of sterilized green satin and the berries are made of indurated milk. It will function on the principle of the automatic sprinkler, in this manner: two kissers approach the mistletoe in a spirit of holiday lust. As they square off under the mistletoe the heat generated by their fondness for each other releases hundreds of tiny sprinklers concealed in the mistletoe "berries" and a spray of healing formaldehyde sifts gently down upon them like a benison, destroying all coryza, grippe, influenza, pneumonia or tetanus germs that may be lurking about the kissers' kissers.

Of course, the antiseptic mistletoc is only a temporary measure. Eventually the kiss under the mistletoe must go, bag and baggage. It is unhygienic, sloppy and sentimental; and it breeds unscientific thinking. It has no place in our modern life.

The Christmas of the future will be a triumph of science over waste. Energy now frittered away in futile holiday pursuits will be conserved for more constructive purposes. For one thing, Christmas will be made to end immediately after dinner on Christmas Day, thus eliminating the demoralizing Christmas afternoon, the most depressing few hours in the Christian calendar. I refer to the period from about three o'clock on, when reaction from the hysteria of trimming the tree and opening the presents has set in and all the world seems dark and dreary; when the fruit cake is irrevocably inside the celebrant and has made unmistakably clear its determination not to merge with the port wine, walnuts, oyster stuffing, cranberry sauce and the rest of the Christmas viands. It is the time when the kiddies begin to do battle for the possession of the few toys that remain unbroken; and it is the time when Daddy, called upon to fix the electric train, trips over the track—or the baby—and plunges headlong into the Christmas tree, ripping off the electrical trimmings and causing a short circuit. Christmas afternoon must go.

In the Christmas of the future the gift problem, with its associated problems of shopping, mailing, wrapping, exchanging, etc., will cease to be the *bête noire* it is today. Everyone will cooperate. Christmas cards will be mailed earlier and earlier until the bulk of them will have been delivered about the time the second income tax installments begin to clog the mails. Parcels will be wrapped more and more securely as the years go by until he will be a fast worker indeed who gets his presents all unwrapped by the second Sunday after Epiphany.

Shopping will not be the bedlam it is today. It will be controlled. The energies of American women will be harnessed. There will be national leagues of shoppers. Teams from stores like Macy's, Lord & Taylor, Marshall Field, Filene's and Wanamaker's will compete with each other in shopping bouts under the rules now governing wrestling. It will be no time at all before controlled Christmas shopping has developed a hardy, buxom race of American woman shoppers which might well serve as a first line of national defense in case of emergency. Perhaps it may eventually be said of the United States that our victories were won on the notion counters of Gimbel's.

One of the worst psychological effects of Christmas on people is the rage that follows when a person gives a friend a gift and the friend fails to reciprocate. This will be eliminated in the Christmas of the future by the Declaration of Gift. This will simply be a public notice of every citizen's Christmas intentions. Early in the fall everyone will be required by law to file a list with the Collector of Internal Revenue of the persons to whom he proposes to give Christmas presents, with the nature and the planned cost of each gift.

These lists will be tacked up at the post office and department stores of each city for public scrutiny. Each person can examine the lists, find out what his friends are doing, and act accordingly. If I have you on my list for a necktie or a compact and I find from the public list that you have not put me down for anything, I can just cross you off my list. Or, if a citizen thinks he has a right to expect a present from a friend who has failed to declare to that effect, the injured party shall have the legal right to apply to the courts for a writ of mandamus compelling the defendant, or recalcitrant donor, to show cause why the aforesaid present should not be given to the plaintiff, or piqued donee.

Two people who find that they are giving each other presents of equal value can pair off like Senators voting at Washington and cancel both gifts, taking the will for the deed. This practice will be called phantom giving.

As Christmas becomes more and more scientific and less encumbered

296

with sentimental flubdub children will play less and less part in its celebration. The heaviest burden of the Christmas celebration has always fallen on the tots, for it is the season of the year when parents have to be coddled and humored more than at any other time. The child has to simulate an unfelt curiosity in mysterious packages that arrive during December and are whisked furtively to the attic. Children have to compose letters to Santa Claus to placate Christmas-crazed parents, and they are hauled off to department stores where they are expected to display glee at the sight of a Santa Claus in palpably fake whiskers.

All this is too much of a strain to place on their little libidos. It fills their subconsciousnesses with impressions that pop out twenty or thirty years later in the most bloodcurdling manifestations. In the future it is probable that Santa Claus will be required to be cleanshaven and that only Dr. Freud will be allowed to continue wearing a beard.

So it will go. As we progress scientifically we shall slough off the antiquated customs and leave off saying "Merry Christmas" or drinking wassail (of slight nutritive value and totally lacking in the essential vitamins). The celebration of Christmas will become more and more efficient until it will at last be so efficient that it will become unnecessary to keep Christmas at all.

The elimination of New Year, Thanksgiving and Halloween will follow as a matter of course and those who have chanced to read this glance into the future may live to see the day when we will just skip from Labor Day to Lent.

VERSES FOR A GREETING CARD

PHYLLIS MC GINLEY

How often and how sweetly wends
This fancy toward my distant friends.
No knife can cut our love in twain
So long as distant they remain.

297

BEAUTY'S SISTER

OWEN JOHNSON

His hair it is a faded white,
His eye a watery blue;
He had no buttons on his coat,
No shoe-strings in his shoe.

"BEAUTY" SAWTELLE, or Chesterton V. Sawtelle, as it was pronounced when each Monday the master of the form read the bi-weekly absences from bath, sat adjusting his skate on the edge of the pond, with a look of ponderous responsibility on the freckled face, crowned by a sheaf of tow hair, like the wisp of a Japanese doll. Presently he drew from his pocket a dance-card, glanced over it for the twentieth time, and replaced it with a sigh.

"Cracky!" he said, in despair. "Sixteen regulars and eight extras; sixteen and eight, twenty-four. Gee!"

Beauty's heart was heavy, and his hope faint, for the sinister finger of the Prom had cast its shadow over the lighthearted democracy of boyhood. Into this free republic, where no thoughts of the outside society should penetrate, the demoralizing swish of coming petticoats had suddenly intruded its ominous significance of a world without, where such tyrannies as money and birth stand ready to divide the unsuspecting hosts.

Now Beauty's woes were manifold: He was only a second former, and the Prom was the property of the lords of the school, the majestic fourth formers, who lived in the Upper House, and governed themselves according to the catalogue and a benevolent tempering of the exact theory of independence.

A few rash under-formers with pretty sisters were admitted on sufferance, and robbed of their partners if the chance arose. Beauty, scrubby boy of fourteen, with a like aversion to girls and stiff collars in his ugly little body, had been horrified to learn that his sister, at the invitation of

298

Rogers, the housemaster, was coming to the Prom. On his shoulders devolved the herculean task of filling a card from the upper class, only a handful of whom he knew, at a moment when the cards had been circulated for weeks. So he stood dejectedly, calculating how to fill the twenty-four spaces that were so blank and interminable. Twenty-four dances to fill, and the Prom only two weeks off!

In the middle of the pond boys were darting and swaying in a furious game of hockey. Beauty lingered, biding his opportunity, searching the crowd for a familiar face, until presently, Wash Simmons, emerging from the melee, darted to his side, grinding his skates and coming to a halt for breath, with a swift: "Hello, Venus! How's the Dickinson these days?" [The Dickinson was a dormitory.]

Beauty, murmuring an inaudible reply, stood turning and twisting, desperately seeking to frame a demand.

"What's the secret sorrow, Beauty?" continued Wash, with a glance of surprise.

"I say, Wash," said Beauty, plunging—"I say, have you got any dances left?"

"I? Oh, Lord, no!" said the pitcher of the school nine, with a quick glance. "Gone long ago."

He drew the strap tight, dug his hands into his gloves again, and with a nod flashed back into the crowd. Beauty, gulping down something that rose in his throat, started aimlessly to skirt the edge of the pond. He had understood the look that Wash had given him in that swift moment.

In this abstracted mood, he suddenly came against something angular and small that accompanied him to the ice with a resounding whack.

"Clumsy beast!" said a sharp voice.

From his embarrassed position, Beauty recognized the Red Dog.

"Excuse me, Red Dog," he said hastily; "I didn't see you."

"Why, it's Beauty," said the Red Dog, rubbing himself. "Blast you! all the same."

"I say, Red Dog," said Beauty, "have you any dances left?"

"All gone, Beauty," answered Red Dog, stooping suddenly to recover his skate.

"Nothing left?"

"Nope—filled the last extra to-day," said Red Dog, with the shining face of prevarication. Then he added, "Why Venus, are *you* going to the Prom?"

299

"No," said Sawtelle; "it's my sister."

"Oh, I'm sorry. I'd like to oblige you, but you see how it is," said Red Dog, lamely.

"I see."

"Ta, ta, Beauty! So long!"

Sawtelle shut his lips, struck a valiant blow at an imaginary puck, and began to whistle.

> *'Tis a jolly life we lead*
> *Care and sorrow we defy—*

After piping forth this inspiring chorus with vigorous notes, the will gave way. He began another:

> *To Lawrenceville my father sent me,*
> *Where for college I should prepare;*
> *And so I settled down,*
> *In this queer, forsaken town,*
> *About five miles away from anywhere.*

The bellows gave out. Overcome by the mournfulness of the last verse, he dropped wearily on the bank, continuing doggedly:

> *About five miles from anywhere, my boys,*
> *Where old Lawrenceville evermore shall stand;*
> *For has she not stood,*
> *Since the time of the flood—*

Whether the accuracy of the last statement or the forced rhyme displeased him, he broke off, heaved a sigh, and said viciously: "They lied, both of 'em."

"Well, how's the boy?" said a familiar voice.

Beauty came out of the vale of bitterness to perceive at his side the great form of Turkey Reiter, preparing to adjust his skates.

"Oh, Turkey," said Beauty, clutching at the straw, "I've been looking everywhere—"

"What's the matter?"

"Turkey, I'm in an awful hole."

"Out with it."

300

"I say, Turkey," said Sawtelle, stumbling and blushing—"I say, you know, my sister's coming to the Prom, and I thought if you'd like—that is, I wanted to know if—you wouldn't take her dance-card and get it filled for me." Then he added abjectly: "I'm awfully sorry."

Turkey looked thoughtful. This was a commission he did not relish. Beauty looked particularly unattractive that afternoon, in a red tobogganing toque that swore at his faded white hair, and the orange freckles that stared out from every point of vantage.

"Why, Beauty," he began hesitatingly, "the way it is, you see, my card's already filled, and I'm afraid, honestly, that's about the case with all the others."

"She's an awfully nice girl," said Sawtelle, looking down in a desperate endeavour to control his voice.

"Nice girl," thought Turkey, "ahem! Yes; must be a good-looker, too, something on Venus's particular line of beauty."

He glanced at his companion, and mentally pictured a lanky girl, with sandy hair, a little upstart nose, and a mass of orange freckles. But between Turkey and Sawtelle relations had been peculiar. There had been many moments in the last year at the Dickinson when the ordinary luxuries of life would have been difficult had it not been for the superior financial standing of Chesterton V. Sawtelle. The account had

301

been a long one, and there was a slight haziness in Turkey's mind as to the exact status of the balance. Also, Turkey was genuinely grateful, with that sense of gratitude which is described as a lively looking forward to favours to come.

"Oh, well, young un," he said with rough good humour, "give us the card. I'll do what I can. But, mind you, I can't take any myself. My card's full, and it wouldn't do for me to cut dances."

Jumping up, he started to escape the effusive thanks of the overjoyed Sawtelle, but suddenly wheeled and came skating back.

"Hello, Beauty!" he called out, "I say, what's your sister's name?"

"Sally—that is, Sarah," came the timid answer.

"Heavens!" said Turkey to himself as he flashed over the ice. "That settles it. Sally—Sally! A nice pickle I'm in! Wonder if she sports spectacles and old-fashioned frocks. A nice pickle—I'll be the laughing-stock of the whole school. Guess I won't have much trouble recognizing Beauty's sister. Whew! That comes from having a kind heart!"

With these and similar pleasant reflections he threaded his way among the crowd of skaters until at length he perceived Hickey skimming over the ice, stealing the puck from a bunch of scrambling players, until, his progress checked, and the puck vanishing into a distant melee, he came to a stop for breath. Turkey, profiting by the occasion, descended on his victim.

"Whoa there, Hickey!"

"Who it is!"

"How's your dance-card?"

"A dazzling galaxy of beauty, a symposium of grace, a feast of—"

"Got anything left? I have a wonder for you if you have."

"Sure; twelfth regular and sixth extra—but the duchess will be awfully cut up."

"Twelfth and sixth," said Turkey, with a nod; "that's a go."

"Who's the heart-smasher?" asked Hickey, with an eye on the approaching puck.

"A wonder, Hickey; a screamer. There'll be nothing to it. Ta, ta! Much obliged."

"What's her name?"

"Sawtelle—some distant relative of the Beauty's, I believe. I'm filling out her card. Obliged for the dance. Ta, ta!"

"Hold up!" said Hickey, quickly. "Hold up! Jiminy! I almost forgot—why, I do believe I went and promised those two to Hasbrouck.

302

Isn't that a shame! Sorry. To think of my forgetting that! Try to give you some other. Confound it! I have no luck." With the most mournful look in the world he waved his hand and sped ostentatiously toward the bunch of players.

"Hickey's on to me," thought Turkey as he watched him disengage himself from the crowd and skate off with Sawtelle; "no hope in that quarter."

Finally, after an hour's persistent work, during which he pleaded and argued, commanded and threatened, he succeeded in filling exactly six of the necessary twenty-four dances. Indeed, he would have had no difficulty in completing the card if he could have passed over that fatal name. But each time, just as he was congratulating himself on another conquest, his victim would ask, "By the way, what name shall I put down?"

"Oh—er—Miss Sawtelle," he would answer nonchalantly; "a distant relative of the Beauty—though nothing like him—ha! ha!"

Then each would suddenly remember that the dances in question were already half-promised,—a sort of an understanding; but of course he would have to look it up,—but of course, if he found they were free, why, then of course, he wanted, above all things in the world, to dance with Miss Sawtelle.

"Well, anyhow," said Turkey to himself, recapitulating, "I've got six, provided they don't all back out. Let me see. I can make the Kid take three—that's nine—and Snookers will have to take three—that's twelve,—and, hang it! Butcher and Egghead have got to take two each—that would make sixteen. The other eight I can fill up with some harmless freaks: some will snap at anything."

That night at the supper-table Turkey had to face the music.

"You're a nice one, you are," said Hickey, starting in immediately, "you arch deceiver. You are a fine friend; I have my opinion of you. 'Handsome girl,' 'a wonder,' 'fine talker,' 'a screamer'—that's the sort of game you try on your friends, is it? Who is she? Oh—ah, yes, a *distant* relative of the Beauty."

"What's up now?" said the Kid, editor of the "Lawrence," and partner of Turkey's secrets, joys, and debts.

"Hasn't he tried to deceive you yet?" continued Hickey, with an accusing look at Turkey. "No? That's a wonder! What do you think of a fellow who tries to pass off on his friends such a girl as the Beauty's sister?"

"No!" said Butcher Stevens.

"What!" exclaimed Macnooder, laying down his knife with a thud.

"Beauty's sister," said the Egghead, gaping with astonishment.

"Well, why not?" said Turkey, defiantly.

"Listen to that!" continued Hickey. "The brazenness of it!"

The four graduates of the Dickinson, after a moment of stupefied examination of Hickey and Reiter, suddenly burst into roars of laughter that produced a craning of necks and a storm of inquiries from the adjoining tables.

When the hilarity had been somewhat checked, Hickey returned to the persecution of the blushing Turkey.

"Bet you three to one she's a mass of freckles," he said. "Bet you even she wears glasses; bet you one to three she's cross-eyed; bet you four to one she won't open her mouth."

"Hang you, Hickey!" said Turkey, flushing, "I won't have her talked about so."

"Did you take any dances?" said the Kid to Hickey.

"Me?" exclaimed the latter, in great dudgeon. "Me! Well, I guess not! I wouldn't touch any of that tribe with a ten-foot pole."

"Look here, you fellows have got to shut up," said Turkey, forced at last into a virtuous attitude by the exigency of the situation. "I promised the Beauty I'd fill his sister's card for him, and I'm going to do it. The girl can't help her looks. You talk like a lot of cads. What you fellows ought to do is to join in and give her a treat. The girl is probably from the backwoods, and this ought to be made the time of her life."

MILK
YOUNGREN

304

"Turkey," said the malicious Hickey, "how many dances have you eagerly appropriated?"

Turkey stopped point-blank, greeted by derisive jeers.

"Oho!"

"That's it, is it?"

"Fake!"

"Humbug!"

"Not at all," said Turkey, indignantly. "What do you think I am?"

"Pass over your list and let's see the company you're going to introduce her to," said Hickey, stretching out his hand for the dance-card. "Ah, I must congratulate you, my boy; your selection is magnificent; the young lady will be charmed." He flipped the card disdainfully to the Egghead, saying, "A bunch of freaks!"

"Hang it all!" said the Egghead, "that's too hard on any girl. A fine opinion she'll have of Lawrenceville fellows! We can't stand for that."

"Look here," said the Kid, suddenly. "Turkey is at fault, and has got to be punished. Here's what we'll do, though: let's each take a dance on condition that Turkey takes her out to supper."

"Oh, I say!" protested Turkey, who had other plans.

The others acclaimed the plan gleefully rejoicing in his discomfiture, until Turkey, driven to a corner, was forced to capitulate.

That evening on the esplanade he called Snookers to him, and resting his hand affectionately on the little fellow's shoulder said, "Old man, do you want to do me a favour?"

"Sure."

"I'm filling up a girl's card for the Prom, and I want you to help me out."

"Certainly; give me a couple, if the girl's the real thing."

"Much obliged. I'll put your name down."

"Second and fifth. Say, who is she?"

"Oh, some relative of Sawtelle's—remember you used to go with him a good deal in the Dickinson. It's his sister."

"Whew!" said Snookers, with a long-drawn whistle. "Say, give me three more, will you?"

"Hardly," answered Turkey, with a laugh; "but I'll spare you another."

"I didn't think it quite fair to the girl," he explained later, "to give her too big a dose of Snookers. Queer, though, how eager the little brute was!"

305

The last week dragged interminably in multiplied preparations for the great event. In the evenings the war of strings resounded across the campus from the "gym," where the Banjo and Mandolin clubs strove desperately to perfect themselves for the concert. The Dramatic Club, in sudden fear, crowded the day with rehearsals, while from the window of Room 65, Upper, the voice of Biddy Hampton, soloist of the Glee Club, was heard chanting "The Pride of the House is Papa's Baby" behind doors stout enough to resist the assaults of his neighbours.

Oil-stoves and flatirons immediately came into demand, cushions were rolled back from window-seats, and trousers that were limp and discouraged, grew smooth and well-creased under the pressure of the hot iron. Turkey and Doc Macnooder, who from their long experience in the Dickinson had become expert tailors, advertised on the bulletin board:

REITER AND MacNOODER

Bon Ton Tailors

Trousers neatly pressed, at fifteen cents per pair; all payments strictly cash—IN ADVANCE.

Each night the dining-room of the Upper was cleared, and the extraordinary spectacle was seen of boys of all sizes in sweaters and jerseys, clasping each other desperately around the waist, spinning and bumping their way about the reeling room to the chorus of:

"Get off my feet!"

"Reverse, you lubber!"

"Now, *one*, two, three—"

"A fine lady you are!"

"Do you expect me to carry you around the room?"

"Darn you, fatty!"

"Hold tight!"

"Let 'er rip now!"

From the end of the room the cynics and misogynists, roosting on the piled-up tables and chairs, croaked forth their contempt:

"Oh, you fussers!"

"You lady-killers!"

"Dance, my darling, dance!"

306

"Squeeze her tight, Bill!"

"That's the way!"

"Look at Skinny!"

"Keep a-hoppin', Skinny!"

"Look at him spin!"

"For heaven's sake, someone stop Skinny!"

Of evenings certain of the boys would wander in pairs to the edge of the woods and confide to each other the secret attachments and dark, forlorn hopes that were wasting them away. Turkey and the Kid, who were going as stags, opened their hearts to each other and spoke of the girl, the one distant girl, whose image not all the fair faces that would come could for a moment dim.

"Kid," said Turkey, in solemn conclusion, speaking from the experience of eighteen years, "I am going to make that little girl—my wife."

"Turkey, old man, God bless you!" answered the confidant, with nice regard for old precedents. Then he added, a little choked, "Turkey, I, too—I—"

"I understand, Kid," said Turkey, gravely clapping his shoulder; "I've known it all along."

"Dear old boy!"

They walked in silence.

307

"What's her name?" asked Turkey, slowly.

"Lucille. And hers?"

"Marie Louise."

Another silence.

"Kid, is it all right?"

The romanticist considered a moment, and then shook his head.

"No, Turk."

"Dear old boy, you'll win out."

"I must. And you, does she care?"

A heavy sigh was the answer. They walked back arm in arm, each fully believing in the other's sorrow, and almost convinced of his own. At the esplanade of the Upper they stopped and listened to the thumping of the piano and the systematic beat from the dancers.

"I wish it were all over," said Turkey, gloomily. "This can mean nothing to me."

"Nor to me," said the Kid, staring at the melancholy moon.

On the fateful day the school arose, so to speak, as one boy, shaved, and put on a clean collar. Every boot was blacked, every pair of trousers creased to a cutting edge. The array of neckties that suddenly appeared in gigantic puffs or fluttering wings was like the turn of autumn in a single night.

Chapel and the first two recitations over, the esplanade of the Upper was crowded with fourth formers, circulating critically in the dandified throng, chattering excitedly of the coming event. Perish the memory of the fashion there displayed! It seemed magnificent then: let that be the epitaph.

The bell called, and the group slowly departed to the last recitation. From each house a stream of boys came pouring out and made their lagging way around the campus toward Memorial. Slower and slower rang the bell, and faster came the unwilling slaves—those in front with dignity; those behind with despatch, and so on down the line to the last scattered stragglers, who came racing over the lawns. The last peal sounded, the last laggard tore up Memorial steps, and vanished within. A moment later the gong in the hall clanged, and the next recitation was on. The circle, a moment before alive with figures, was quiet and deserted. A group of seven or eight lounging on the esplanade were chatting indolently, tossing a ball back and forth with the occupant of a third-story window.

308

At this moment Turkey emerged from the doorway in shining russets, a Gladstone collar, a tie of robin's-egg-blue, and a suit of red and green plaids, such as the innocent curiosity of a boy on his allowance goes to with the thirst of possession.

"Hurrah for Turkey!" cried the Kid. "He looks like a regular fashion-plate."

In an instant he was surrounded, punched, examined, and complimented.

"Well, fellows, it's time to give ourselves them finishing touches," said the Egghead, with a glance of envy. "Turkey is trying to steal a march on us. The girls are coming."

"Hello!" cried the Kid, suddenly. "Who's this?"

All turned. From behind Foundation House came a carriage. It drove on briskly until nearly opposite the group on the steps, when the driver reined in, and some one within looked out dubiously.

"Turkey, you're in luck," said the Gutter Pup. "You're the only one with rouge on. Go down gracefully and see what the lady wants."

So down went Turkey to his duty. They watched him approach the carriage and speak to some one inside. Then he closed the door and spoke to the driver, evidently pointing out his destination, for the cab continued around the circle.

Then Turkey made a jump for the esplanade, and, deaf to all inquiries, seized upon his roommate and dragged him aside.

"Great guns! Kid," he exclaimed, "I've seen her—Beauty's sister! She isn't like Beauty at all. She's a stunner, a dream! Look here! Get

309

that dance-card. Get it, if you have to lie and steal. He's in recitation now. You've got to catch him when he comes out. For heaven's sake don't let any one get ahead of you! Tell him two girls have backed out, and I want five more dances. Tell him I'm to take her to the debate to-night, and the Dramatic Club to-morrow. Kid, get that card!"

Releasing his astounded roommate, he went tearing across the campus to meet the carriage.

"What's happened to our staid and dignified president?" cried the Gutter Pup in wonder. "Is he crazy?"

"Oh, say, fellows," exclaimed the Kid, overcome by the humour of the situation, "who do you think that was?"

The carriage had now stopped before the Dickinson, and Turkey, arrived in time, was helping out a tall, slender figure in black. A light flashed over the group.

"Beauty's sister."

"No!"

"Yes."

"Impossible!"

"Beauty's sister it is," cried the Kid; "and the joke is, she's a stunner, a dream!"

"A dream!" piped up the inevitable Snookers. "Well, I guess! She's an all-around A-No. 1. Gee! I just got a glimpse of her at a theater, and I tell you, boys, she's a paralyzer."

But his remark ended on the air, for all, with a common impulse had disappeared. Snookers, struck with the same thought, hastened to his room.

Ten minutes later they reappeared. Hickey, in a suit of pronounced checks, his trousers carefully turned up à l'Anglais, glanced approvingly at the array of manly fashion.

"And now, fellows," he said, pointing to the Chapel, which Turkey was entering with Miss Sawtelle, "that traitor shall be punished. We'll guard every entrance to Memorial, capture our friend, 'Chesterton V. Sawtelle (absent from bath),' relieve him of that little dance-card, and then, Romans, to the victors belong the spoils!"

The Kid having delayed over the choice between a red-and-yellow necktie or one of simple purple, did not appear until Hickey had stationed his forces. Taking in the situation at a glance, he chuckled to himself, and picking up a couple of books, started for the entrance.

"Lucky it's Hungry and the Egghead," he said to himself as he passed them and entered the Lower Hall. "Hickey would have guessed the game."

He called Sawtelle from the second form, and, slipping his arm through his, drew him down the corridor.

"Sawtelle," he said, "I want your sister's dance-card. There's some mistake, and Turkey wants to fix it up. Thanks; that's all. Oh, no, it isn't either. Turkey said he'd be over after supper to take your sister to the debate, and that he had seats for the Dramatic Club to-morrow. Don't forget all that. So long! See you later."

In high feather at the success of this stratagem, he skipped downstairs, and, avoiding Hickey, went to meet Turkey in the Chapel, where he was duly presented.

When Sawtelle emerged at length from the study-room, he was amazed at the spontaneity of his reception. He was no longer "Beauty" or "Apollo" or "Venus."

"Sawtelle, old man," they said to him, "I want to see you a moment."

"Chesterton, where have you been?"

"Old man, have you anything to do?"

Each strove to draw him away from the others, and failing in this, accompanied him to the jiggershop, where he was plied with substantial flattery, until, having disposed of jiggers, soda, and eclairs, he cast one lingering glance at the tempting counters, and said with a twinkle in ugly little eyes:

"And now, fellows, I guess my sister must be over at the house. Come around this afternoon, why don't you, and meet her?"—an invitation which was received with enthusiasm and much evident surprise.

When the Prom opened that evening, Beauty's sister made her entree flanked by the smitten Turkey and the languishing Hasbrouck, while the stricken Kid brought up the rear, consoled by the responsibility of her fan. Five stags who had been lingering miserably in the shadow searching for something daring and imaginative to lay at her feet, crowded forward only to be stricken dumb at the splendour of her toilette.

Beauty's sister, fresh from a Continental season, was quite overwhelmed by the subtle adoration of the famous Wash Simmons and of Egghead, that pattern of elegance and *savoir-faire*—overwhelmed, but not at all confused. Gradually under her deft manipulation the power of speech returned to the stricken. Then the rout began. The young ladies from city and country finishing-schools, still struggling

311

with their teens, were quite eclipsed by the gorgeous Parisian toilette and the science of movement displayed by the sister of Chesterton V. Sawtelle. The ordinary ethics of fair play were thrown to the winds. Before the eyes of every one, Turkey held up the worthless dance-card, and tore it into shreds. Only the brave should deserve the fair. Little Smeed, Poler Fox, and Snorky Green struggled in vain for recognition, and retired crestfallen and defrauded, to watch the scramble for each succeeding dance, which had to be portioned among three and often four clamourers.

In fact, it became epidemic. They fell in love by blocks of five, even as they had sought the privileges of the measles. Each implored a memento to fix imperishably on his wall. The roses she wore consoled a dozen. The Gutter Pup obtained her fan; the Kid her handkerchief, a wonderful scented transparency. Glendenning and Hasbrouck brazenly divided the gloves, while Turkey, trembling at his own blurting audacity, was blown to the stars by permission to express in a letter certain delicate thoughts which stifle in the vulgar scramble of the ballroom.

When the last dance had been fought for, divided, and re-divided, and the lights peremptorily suppressed, the stags *en masse* accompanied Beauty's sister to the Dickinson, where each separately pressed her hand and strove to give his "Good-night" an accent which would be understood by her alone.

On that next morning that somehow always arises, Turkey and the Kid, envied by all, drove her to the station, listening mutely to her gay chatter, each plunged in melancholy, secretly wondering how she managed to conceal her feeling so well.

They escorted her to the car, and loaded her with magazines and candies and flowers, and each succeeded in whispering in her ear a rapid, daring sentence, which she received from each with just the proper encouragement. Then, imaginary Lucilles and Marie Louises forgot, they drove back, heavy of heart, and uncomprehending, viewing the landscape without joy or hope, suffering stoically as men of eighteen should. Not a word was spoken until from the last hill they caught the first glimmer of the school. Then Turkey hoarsely, flickering the air with the last of the whip, said:

"Kid—"

"What?"

"That *was* a woman."

"A woman of the world, Turkey."

They left the carriage at the stable, and strolled up to the jiggershop, joining the group, all intent on the coming baseball season; and gradually the agony eased a bit. Presently a familiar little figure, freckled and tow-headed, sidled into the shop, and stood with fists jammed in empty pockets, sniffing the air for succor.

"Oh, you Beauty! oh, you astonishing Venus!" cried the inevitable persecutor. Then from the crowd Macnooder began to intone the familiar lines:

> "His hair, it is a faded white,
> His eye a watery blue;
> He has no buttons on his coat, .
> No shoe-strings in his shoe."

"Doc," said the Beauty, blushing sheepishly, "set me up to a jigger, will you? Go on, now!"

Then Macnooder, roaring, shouted back: "Not this year; next year—Sister!"

313

A ROMAN GUIDE

MARK TWAIN

I WISH to say one word about Michael Angelo Buonarotti. I used to
worship the mighty genius of Michael Angelo—that man who was
great in poetry, painting, sculpture, architecture—great in everything
he undertook. But I do not want Michael Angelo for breakfast—for
luncheon—for dinner—for tea—for supper—for between meals. I like
a change, occasionally. In Genoa, he designed everything; in Milan
he or his pupils designed everything; he designed the Lake of Como;
in Padua, Verona, Venice, Bologna, who did we ever hear of, from
guides, but Michael Angelo? In Florence, he painted everything, designed everything, nearly, and what he did not design he used to sit
on a favorite stone and look at, and they showed us the stone. In Pisa
he designed everything but the old shot-tower, and they would have
attributed that to him if it had not been so awfully out of the perpen-
dicular. He designed the piers of Leghorn and the custom-house regulations of Civita Vecchia. But, here—here it is frightful. He designed
St. Peter's; he designed the Pope; he designed the Pantheon, the uniform of the Pope's soldiers, the Tiber, the Vatican, the Coliseum, the
Capitol, the Tarpeian Rock, the Barberini Palace, St. John Lateran, the
Campagna, the Appian Way, the Seven Hills, the Baths of Caracalla,
the Claudian Aqueduct, the Cloaca Maxima—the eternal bore designed
the Eternal City, and unless all men and books do lie, he painted everything in it! Dan said the other day to the guide, "Enough, enough,
enough! Say no more! Lump the whole thing! Say that the Creator
made Italy from designs by Michael Angelo!"

I never felt so fervently thankful, so soothed, so tranquil, so filled
with a blessed peace, as I did yesterday when I learned that Michael
Angelo was dead.

But we have taken it out of this guide. He has marched us through
miles of pictures and sculpture in the vast corridors of the Vatican;
and through miles of pictures and sculpture in twenty other palaces;

314

he has shown us the great picture in the Sistine Chapel, and frescoes enough to fresco the heavens—pretty much all done by Michael Angelo. So with him we have played that game which has vanquished so many guides for us—imbecility and idiotic questions. These creatures never suspect—they have no idea of a sarcasm.

He shows us a figure and says: "Statoo brunzo." (Bronze Statue.)

We look at it indifferently and the doctor asks: "By Michael Angelo?"

"No—not know who."

Then he shows us the ancient Roman Forum. The doctor asks: "Michael Angelo?"

A stare from the guide. "No—a thousan' year before he is born."

Then an Egyptian obelisk. Again: "Michael Angelo?"

"Oh, *mon dieu*, genteelmen! Zis is *two* thousan' year before he is born!"

He grows so tired of that unceasing question sometimes, that he dreads to show us anything at all. The wretch has tried all the ways he can think of to make us comprehend that Michael Angelo is only responsible for the creation of a *part* of the world, but somehow he has not succeeded yet. Relief for overtasked eyes and brain from study and sightseeing is necessary, or we shall become idiotic sure enough. Therefore this guide must continue to suffer. If he does not enjoy it, so much the worse for him. We do.

In this place I may as well jot down a chapter concerning those necessary nuisances, European guides. Many a man has wished in his heart he could do without his guide; but knowing he could not, has wished he could get some amusement out of him as a remuneration for the affliction of his society. We accomplished this latter matter, and if our experience can be made useful to others they are welcome to it.

Guides know about enough English to tangle everything up so that a man can make neither head nor tail of it. They know their story by heart—the history of every statue, painting, cathedral, or other wonder they show you. They know it and tell it as a parrot would—and if you interrupt, and throw them off the track, they have to go back and begin over again. All their lives long, they are employed in showing strange things to foreigners and listening to their bursts of admiration. It is human nature to take delight in exciting admiration. It is what prompts children to say "smart" things, and do absurd ones, and in other ways "show off" when company is present. It is what makes gossips turn out in rain and storm to go and be the first to tell a startling bit of news. Think, then, what a passion it becomes with a guide, whose privilege it is, every day, to show to strangers wonders that throw them into perfect ecstasies of admiration! He gets so that he could not by any possibility live in a soberer atmosphere. After we discovered this, we *never* went into ecstasies any more—we never admired anything—we never showed any but impassive faces and stupid indifference in the presence of the sublimest wonders a guide had to display. We had found their weak point. We have made good use of it ever since. We have made some of those people savage, at times, but we have never lost our own serenity.

The doctor asks the questions, generally, because he can keep his countenance, and look more like an inspired idiot, and throw more imbecility into the tone of his voice than any man that lives. It comes natural to him.

The guides in Genoa are delighted to secure an American party, because Americans so much wonder, and deal so much in sentiment and emotion before any relic of Columbus. Our guide there fidgeted about as if he had swallowed a spring mattress. He was full of animation—full of impatience. He said:

"Come wis me, genteelmen!—come! I show you ze letter writing by Christopher Colombo!—write it himself!—write it wis his own hand!—come!"

He took us to the municipal palace. After much impressive fumbling of keys and opening of locks, the stained and aged document was spread before us. The guide's eyes sparkled. He danced about us and tapped the parchment with his finger:

"What I tell you, genteelmen! Is it not so? See! handwriting Christopher Colombo!—write it himself!"

We looked indifferent—unconcerned. The doctor examined the document very deliberately, during a painful pause. Then he said, without any show of interest:

"Ah—Ferguson—what—what did you say was the name of the party who wrote this?"

"Christopher Colombo! ze great Christopher Colombo!"

Another deliberate examination.

"Ah—did he write it himself, or—or how?"

"He write it himself!—Christopher Colombo! he's own handwriting,

316

write by himself!"

Then the doctor laid the document down and said:

"Why, I have seen boys in America only fourteen years old that could write better than that."

"But zis is ze great Christo——"

"I don't care who it is! It's the worst writing I ever saw. Now you mustn't think you can impose on us because we are strangers. We are not fools, by a good deal. If you have got any specimens of penmanship of real merit, trot them out!—and if you haven't, drive on!"

We drove on. The guide was considerably shaken up, but he made one more venture. He had something which he thought would overcome us. He said:

"Ah, genteelmen, you come wis me! I show you beautiful, oh, magnificent bust Christopher Colombo!—splendid, grand, magnificent!"

He brought us before the beautiful bust—for it *was* beautiful—and sprang back and struck an attitude:

"Ah, look, genteelmen!—beautiful, grand,—bust Christopher Colombo!—beautiful bust, beautiful pedestal!"

The doctor put up his eyeglass—procured for such occasions:

"Ah—what did you say this gentleman's name was?"

"Christopher Colombo!—ze great Christopher Colombo!"

"Christopher Colombo—the great Christopher Colombo. Well, what did *he* do?"

"Discover America!—discover America, oh, ze devil!"

"Discover America. No—that statement will hardly wash. We are just from America ourselves. We heard nothing about it. Christopher Colombo—pleasant name—is—is he dead?"

"Oh, corpo di Baccho!—three hundred year!"

"What did he die of?"

"I do not know!—I cannot tell."

"Small-pox, think?"

"I do not know, genteelmen!—I do not know *what* he die of!"

"Measles, likely?"

"May be—may be—I do *not* know—I think he die of somethings."

"Parents living?"

"Im-posseeble!"

"Ah—which is the bust and which is the pedestal?"

"Santa Maria!—*zis* ze bust!—*zis* ze pedestal!"

"Ah—I see, I see—happy combination—very happy combination, indeed. Is—is this the first time this gentleman was ever on a bust?"

That joke was lost on the foreigner—guides cannot master the subtleties of the American joke.

We have made it interesting for this Roman guide. Yesterday we spent three or four hours in the Vatican again, that wonderful world of curiosities. We came very near expressing interest, sometimes— even admiration—it was very hard to keep from it. We succeeded though. Nobody else ever did, in the Vatican museums. The guide was bewildered—nonplussed. He walked his legs off, nearly, hunting up extraordinary things, and exhausted all his ingenuity on us, but it was a failure; we never showed any interest in anything. He had reserved what he considered to be his greatest wonder till the last— a royal Egyptian mummy, the best-preserved in the world, perhaps. He took us there. He felt so sure, this time, that some of his old enthusiasm came back to him:

"See, genteelmen!—Mummy! Mummy!"

The eyeglass came up as calmly, as deliberately as ever.

"Ah—Ferguson—what did I understand you to say the gentleman's name was?"

"Name?—he got no name!—Mummy!—'Gyptian mummy!"

"Yes, yes. Born here?"

"No! 'Gyptian mummy!"

"Ah, just so. Frenchman, I presume?"

"No!—not Frenchman, not Roman!—born in Egypta!"

"Born in Egypta. Never heard of Egypta before. Foreign locality, likely. Mummy—mummy. How calm he is—how self-possessed. Is, ah—is he dead?"

"Oh, sacré bleu, been dead three thousan' year!"

The doctor turned on him savagely:

"Here, now, what do you mean by such conduct as this! Playing us for Chinamen because we are strangers and trying to learn! Trying to impose your vile second-hand carcasses on us!—thunder and lightning, I've a notion to—to—if you've got a nice fresh corpse, fetch him out!—or, by George, we'll brain you!"

We make it exceedingly interesting for this Frenchman. However, he has paid us back, partly, without knowing it. He came to the hotel this morning to ask if we were up, and he endeavored as well as he could to describe us, so that the landlord would know which persons

318

he meant. He finished with the casual remark that we were lunatics. The obversation was so innocent and so honest that it amounted to a very good thing for a guide to say.

There is one remark (already mentioned) which never yet has failed to disgust these guides. We use it always, when we can think of nothing else to say. After they have exhausted their enthusiasm pointing out to us and praising the beauties of some ancient bronze image or broken-legged statue, we look at it stupidly and in silence for five, ten, fifteen minutes—as long as we can hold out, in fact— and then ask:

"Is—is he dead?"

That conquers the serenest of them. It is not what they are looking for—especially a new guide. Our Roman Ferguson is the most patient, unsuspecting, long-suffering subject we have had yet. We shall be sorry to part with him. We have enjoyed his society very much. We trust he has enjoyed ours, but we are harassed with doubts.

"Do that ventriloquist call again. You're driving him crazy!"

319

RING OUT, WILD BELLS

WOLCOTT GIBBS

When I finally got around to seeing Max Reinhardt's cinema version of "A Midsummer-Night's Dream," and saw a child called Mickey Rooney playing Puck, I remembered suddenly that long ago I had taken the same part.

Our production was given on the open-air stage at the Riverdale Country School, shortly before the war. The scenery was only the natural scenery of that suburban dell, and the cast was exclusively male, ranging in age from eleven to perhaps seventeen. While we had thus preserved the pure, Elizabethan note of the original, it must be admitted that our version had its drawbacks. The costumes were probably the worst things we had to bear, and even Penrod, tragically arrayed as Launcelot in his sister's stockings and his father's drawers, might have been embarrassed for us. Like Penrod, we were costumed by our parents, and like the Schofields, they seemed on the whole a little weak historically. Half of the ladies were inclined to favor the Elizabethan, and they had constructed rather bunchy ruffs and farthingales for their offspring; others, who had read as far as the stage directions and learned that the action took place in an Athenian wood, had produced something vaguely Athenian, usually beginning with a sheet. Only the fairies had a certain uniformity. For some reason their parents had all decided on cheesecloth, with here and there a little ill-advised trimming with tinsel.

My own costume was mysterious, but spectacular. As nearly as I have ever been able to figure things out, my mother found her inspiration for it in a Maxfield Parrish picture of a court jester. Beginning at the top, there was a cap with three stuffed horns; then, for the main part, a pair of tights that covered me to my wrists and ankles; and finally slippers with stuffed toes that curled up at the ends. The whole thing was made out of silk in alternate green and red stripes, and (unquestionably my poor mother's most demented stroke) it was covered from head to foot with a thousand tiny bells. Because all our costumes were obviously perishable, we never wore them in rehearsal, and naturally nobody knew that I was invested with these peculiar sound effects until I made my entrance at the beginning of the second act.

Our director was a man who had strong opinions about how Shakespeare should be played, and Puck was one of his favorite characters. It was his theory that Puck, being "the incarnation of mischief," never ought to be still a minute, so I had been coached to bound onto the stage, and once there to dance up and down, cocking my head and waving my arms.

"I want you to be a little whirlwind," this man said.

Even as I prepared to bound onto the stage, I had my own misgivings about those dangerously abundant gestures, and their probable effect on my bells. It was too late, however, to invent another technique for playing Puck, even if there had been room for anything but horror in my mind. I bounded onto the stage.

The effect, in its way, must have been superb. With every leap I rang like a thousand children's sleighs, my melodies foretelling God knows what worlds of merriment to the enchanted spectators. It was even worse when I came to the middle of the stage and went into my gestures. The other ringing had been loud but sporadic. This was persistent, varying only slightly in volume and pitch with the vehemence of my gestures. To a blind man, it must have sounded as though I had recklessly decided to accompany myself on a xylophone. A maturer actor would probably have made up his mind that an emergency existed, and abandoned his gestures as impracticable under the circumstances. I was thirteen, and incapable of innovations. I had been told by responsible authorities that gestures went with this part, and I continued to make them. I also continued to ring—a silvery music, festive and horrible.

If the bells were hard on my nerves, they were even worse for the rest of the cast, who were totally unprepared for my new interpretation. Puck's first remark is addressed to one of the fairies, and it is mercifully brief.

I said, "How now, spirit! Whither wander you?"

This unhappy child, already embarrassed by a public appearance in cheesecloth and tinsel, was also burdened with an opening speech of sixteen lines in verse. He began bravely:

321

"Over hill, over dale,
　Thorough bush, thorough brier,
Over park, over pale,
　Thorough flood, thorough fire . . ."

At the word "fire," my instructions were to bring my hands up
from the ground in a long, wavery sweep, intended to represent fire.
The bells pealed. To my startled ears, it sounded more as if they exploded. The fairy stopped in his lines and looked at me sharply. The
jingling, however, had diminished; it was no more than as if a faint
wind stirred my bells, and he went on:

"I do wander every where,
　Swifter than the moone's sphere . . ."

Here again I had another cue, for a sort of swoop and dip indicating
the swiftness of the moone's sphere. Again the bells rang out, and
again the performance stopped in its tracks. The fairy was clearly
troubled by these interruptions. He had, however, a child's strange
acceptance of the inscrutable, and was even able to regard my bells as
a last-minute adult addition to the program, nerve-racking but not to
be questioned. I'm sure it was only this that got him through that first
speech.

My turn, when it came, was even worse. By this time the audience
had succumbed to a helpless gaiety. Every time my bells rang, laughter
swept the spectators, and this mounted and mingled with the bells until
everything else was practically inaudible. I began my speech, another
long one, and full of incomprehensible references to Titania's change-
ling.

"Louder!" said somebody in the wings. "You'll have to talk louder."
It was the director, and he seemed to be in a dangerous state.
"And for heaven's sake, stop that jingling!" he said.
I talked louder, and I tried to stop the jingling, but it was no use. By
the time I got to the end of my speech, I was shouting and so was the
audience. It appeared that I had very little control over the bells, which
continued to jingle in spite of my passionate efforts to keep them quiet.
All this had a very bad effect on the fairy, who by this time had many
symptoms of a complete nervous collapse. However, he began his next
speech:

322

"Either I mistake your shape and making quite,
Or else you are that shrewd and knavish sprite
Call'd Robin Goodfellow: are you not he
That . . ."

At this point I forgot that the rules had been changed and I was supposed to leave out the gestures. There was a furious jingling, and the fairly gulped.

"Are you not he that, that . . ."

He looked miserably at the wings, and the director supplied the next line, but the tumult was too much for him. The unhappy child simply shook his head.

"Say anything!" shouted the director desperately. "Anything at all!" The fairy only shut his eyes and shuddered.

"All right!" shouted the director. "All right, Puck. *You* begin *your* next speech."

By some miracle, I actually did remember my next lines, and had opened my mouth to begin on them when suddenly the fairy spoke. His voice was a high, thin monotone, and there seemed to be madness in it, but it was perfectly clear.

"Fourscore and seven years ago," he began, "our fathers brought forth on this continent a new nation, conceived . . ."

He said it right through to the end, and it was certainly the most successful speech ever made on that stage, and probably one of the most successful speeches ever made on any stage. I don't remember, if I ever knew, how the rest of us ever picked up the dull, normal thread of the play after that extraordinary performance, but we must have, because I know it went on. I only remember that in the next intermission the director cut off my bells with his penknife, and after that things quieted down and got dull.

323

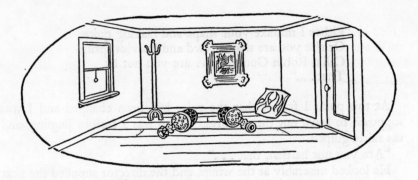

THE KENNEL AND THE CAT COOP

ELLIS PARKER BUTLER

LITTLE JANE was sitting on the second-from-the-lowest brownstone step of Mrs. Hale's boarding house this June evening and she was weeping gently and silently, because she was homesick and tired and had no home to be homesick for. She had been in New York a year now and that was long enough to learn that working as a stenographer for Wilson, Dickett and Company was absolutely no beer and hardly any skittles. It was work.

It was dusk and presently Ned Norton came out of the boarding house. He stood a moment or two at the top of the stoop whistling softly a jazz tune, the words of which were something like "Oh, mammy! My true-oo blue-oo ma-ha-my! My ma-ha—ha-ha—ma-ha—me-he-ma-ha-my!" He wore a straw hat with a noisy ribbon band and the hat was pushed on one side of his head. He had a cane hung over on his wrist just below where his wrist watch glittered.

Looking down at what he had first thought was a shadow he saw it was Little Jane and he noticed that her shoulders had a despondent droop. He put the cigarette in his mouth and lighted it, cast the match from him with a flip of his fingers and walked down to Little Jane's step.

He seated himself beside her, looked sideways into her face and saw a tear, and quite in his florid style put a comforting hand under her elbow. Little Jane drew the elbow out of his hand.

"Please don't!" she said.

324

Ned Norton held out the offending hand and slapped it sharply.

"Down, Fido!" he said to it reprovingly. "Bad dog! Go and lie down!" He said, "Aowr! Aowr! Aowr!" imitating a dog that has been slapped. He said, "Well, don't come annoying ladies then, you worthless hound; the next time you do that I'll take you over to the river and drown you. The idea! You great big lumbering cur! you miserable cheese-hound! You—"

He continued to scold the unfortunate dog and Little Jane continued to look across the street at nothing.

"I'm sorry!" she said presently. "I—I just feel so mean tonight. You —I didn't mean—"

"Yeep! Yeep!" said Ned Norton, imitating a happy dog. He said, "Good dog! Good Fido! Nice old fellow!" and Little Jane smiled.

"You—you like dogs?" she said.

Ned Norton bent down and stroked the head of the imaginary dog.

"He's a nice old doggie; yes, he is!" he said. "He's a good old doggie!" He snapped his fingers. "Up! Up!" he said. "Shake hands with the lady. That's a dog! Nice old Fido!"

"What—what kind of dog is he?" asked Little Jane, and she felt one thousand per cent better already.

"Collie," said Ned Norton promptly. "Soft brown with a white saddle and white forepaws. That dog—what do you suppose I paid for that dog? As a pup. One—thousand—dollars! Absolutely thoroughbred. Here! Fido! Roll over! Roll over! How's that?" He bent down and patted the head of the imaginary Fido. "Don't you want to pat him?" he asked anxiously. "He'd like you to pat him."

Little Jane laughed.

Every evening after dinner they took Fido for a walk. The walk was almost invariably the same, westward to Mount Tom, which is— as everyone ought to know—on the edge of the Hudson. Here they took the leash from Fido and let him run a while. He was a good dog and had a special permit from the mayor permitting him to run at large without a muzzle. While he ran about playing with the children or chasing imaginary rabbits, Little Jane and Ned Norton sat on a bench and talked. Little Jane was diffident and inclined to periods of shyness, and when these came Fido would come running to them to be petted. Ned Norton would pet him and then Little Jane would pet him and laugh. Ned Norton would hold out his cane and Fido would jump over it. Sometimes half a dozen children—real children—would be

325

grouped at a respectful distance watching Fido go through his whole set of tricks.

"Over!" Ned Norton would say, and over the cane Fido would go, each time higher until Ned held the cane as high as his head. Sometimes Fido missed this high jump and had to try it again. Or, with Ned Norton holding the cane as a baton and walking backward, Fido would walk on his hind legs. He rolled over. He played dead. He was a "lame dog." The children could almost see the dog. They asked for him when Ned Norton and Little Jane came to Mount Tom.

"Make Fido do some tricks," they begged.

Sometimes, going to Mount Tom or returning from there, Ned Norton let Little Jane hold the leash at which Fido pulled so strenuously.

"Just hold him while I light a cigarette," Ned Norton would say. Fido became quite a famous dog among the younger set of Mount Tom.

One evening—that was in July, the twenty-eighth or twenty-ninth —Ned Norton and Little Jane were bringing Fido back to Mrs. Hale's boarding house when suddenly Little Jane stooped down.

"Oh, the dear little kitten!" she exclaimed. "The sweet little thing! Look, Ned, the poor little thing has hurt its paw!"

She gathered the imaginary kitten into her cupped hands. She stroked its soft fur.

"It's hungry," Ned said. "You ought to take it home and give it some milk."

"I don't believe it belongs to anyone," said Jane, holding her cupped hands to her face. "I believe it's a stray kitten. I'm going to keep it!"

"That's no stray cat, Jane," Ned said. "Not a cat like that. Look at it—that's a pedigreed cat. Look at the ribbon around its neck."

"I don't care," Jane said, "I'm going to keep it anyway. It's a lost kitten and if I don't take it some dog will kill it, poor little thing! Hadn't I better keep it, Ned?"

"Well, Fido likes it," Ned said. "It's a nice cat. Kitty, want some milk?"

"Miau!" said Jane very softly.

"Hear him purr," Ned said. "All right, keep him if you want to. What are you going to call him?"

"I think I'll call him Alexander," Jane said. "I had a cat named Alexander when I was a little bit of a girl back in Iddlesborough, Ohio, long before Father and Mother died."

After that Fido and Alexander were great friends.

Mrs. Hale had a hooked nose and suffered from repressed emotions and acute indigestion but she was a good woman for all that and she insisted that, as her present, she be allowed to give the wedding, so the invitations went out reading, "Mrs. Nathan Vince Hale requests your presence at the—" and the ceremony was to be in the back parlor. There was to be a wedding dinner and dancing, and Effie Wills volunteered to play the piano and manage the phonograph.

The wedding presents began arriving as soon as the invitations were mailed and nearly every time Ned and Jane returned from their work or from hunting the apartment, there were more pickle forks. Some weddings run to one thing and some to another but this one ran to pickle forks. The pickle forks were a source of much merriment; everything that looked even remotely like a pickle fork became one— marshmallow forks, fish forks, and dinner forks—and for convenience and joy Ned called all the presents that had a deep and unfathomable purpose, as so many wedding presents have, "pickle forks."

The truth is that the presents were not much. Wilson, Dickett and Company sent a small case of plated table silver and that topped the list until Branch and Glare, Ned's employers, sent another small case of plated table silver exacty like it. But if you have ever seen one of the arrays of wedding gifts that have to have detectives standing around, Jane's gifts would have looked rather pitifully paltry. They ran, in general, to the ninety-eight-cent variety. But that made no difference to Jane—she loved them all. Ned, of course, had to make fun of some of them. There was an affair of ash, stained to resemble walnut, that was a straight high post with square pegs at the top and four silly legs at the bottom. It was to hang things on, but if you hung a cap on one of the pegs without hanging a cap of equal weight on the opposite peg, the thing fell right over flat on the floor. There was a photogravure picture in a gilt frame that Ned immediately entitled "Diaphanoos Bobbling at the Brook." It looked as much like that as like anything, and was pretty terrible, especially the frame. There was one sofa pillow that looked like the worst stage of a fire in an egg packery.

That evening before the wedding night Ned came home from work and ran up the stairs, taking three steps at a jump, knowing he would find Jane in the second floor back parlor, which Mrs. Hale had set aside for the gift display. He called, "Here, Fido! Here, Fido," as soon as he entered and he heard Jane's "Miau!" in answer, but there was no dog and cat waste of time when Ned went into the room. Jane flew at him and had her arms around him in an instant and kissed him tremendously.

"Ned! Ned!" she cried. "It's something wonderful—wonderful—wonderful! What do you think I've got? You can't guess!"

"A pickle fork," he guessed.

"Look!" she exulted and held a slip of paper so close to his eyes that he had to bend his head back to see it.

"Oh, laddie! Oh, sonny! Oh, boy!" he exclaimed.

"One—thousand—dollars!" cried Jane. "It's a check from Aunt Jane—she was here. I didn't see her; I hadn't come in, but she saw Mrs. Hale and she gave it to her. She said she felt she must bring it herself because it would seem so cold and everything just to send it and—"

"I didn't know you had an Aunt Jane," Ned said.

"I haven't," Jane said. "At least, not hardly. I mean she isn't a real aunt—not quite. Mother's sister married Mr. Elfus and Mother's sister died, Ned, and Mr. Elfus married Aunt Jane—"

"Then she was really your aunt—"

"No, she wasn't anybody. I mean not until. She was from Detroit. But, you see, I was named for her. She was visiting in Iddlesborough when I was born, and she really was sort of aunt. She was Mr. Elfus' wife in place of the wife who was my aunt—well, anyway!"

"Anyway," said Ned, "she's a dear old thing."

"No," said Jane hesitantly. "No, she isn't, Ned. I—of course, we'll see her sometime, and I don't want you to get a wrong idea. She's haughty, Ned. Haughty and—well, stiff, I guess, and easily upset."

"Like the clothespole," said Ned, and he hung his hat on it and it fell over on the floor with a bang. He picked the thing up and set it on its legs. "My dear Aunt Jane," he said, bowing low to it. "I do beg your pardon. You must excuse my familiarity. But I will say, on behalf of all, that you are a darling."

"Oh, you'd never say that to her!" cried Jane. "Not to Aunt Jane."

It seemed, from what Mrs. Hale had said, that Aunt Jane had been in California when the invitation reached Detroit, and Aunt Jane had only put a foot in Detroit and then was out again, hurrying to New York because she had to catch a steamer for France. The steamer left the next morning, Aunt Jane had told Mrs. Hale, and Aunt Jane had to go to East Orange, but she was sorry she could only give money—

328

she wished she had known in advance so she could have given a gift. Something Japanese, Mrs. Hale said. "Because if there is anything I do know," Mrs. Hale had said Aunt Jane had said, "It is Japanese art."

"Japanese art!" scoffed Jane. "Just think, Ned—a thousand dollars! And I know exactly what I'm going to do with it."

"You're going to do exactly what you want to with it," said Ned.

"I'm going to buy things for our apartment," declared Jane. "I'm going to have the loveliest furniture we can get with this money."

"And I can sit on the couch," said Ned triumphantly, "but you can't, Fido. Fido, get down off that couch! How dare you! Go to the kitchen!"

Even Mrs. Hale was excited by the size of the box that came just after dinner that night. She let her husband open it in the front hall, begging him to be careful with the hatchet, and all the boarders stood around, eager to see what had come from Toshikawa and Company.

After leaving the boarding house that afternoon Aunt Jane had stepped into the taxi she had kept waiting at the door.

"And now," she said, "the ferry for East Orange, New Jersey. Do you know how to get there?"

"Yes, ma'am,' was the reply, but that taxi never did take Aunt Jane to the ferry. The taxi was speeding nicely down the avenue when Aunt Jane, looking out of the window, saw the two big windows of Toshikawa and Company.

"Driver! Driver!" she called, tapping on the glass that separated him from her. "Stop here! This is far enough! Stop here!"

Aunt Jane knew Toshikawa and Company and she knew they were honest and reliable, but that did not concern her at the moment. In Detroit was a lady named May Ann Washington, of mahogany-brown hue and vastly girth, and she had been cook for Aunt Jane for just eight months. During those eight months Aunt Jane had been at home not over seven weeks, but, none the less, May Ann had been faithful and she was a good-natured cook and if she left to get married it was an entirely reasonable leaving.

"I want," said Aunt Jane to the clerk, who approached her when she entered the shop, "a pair of vases. I know just what I want, so don't try to sell me anything else. I want vases about this high, and I want them with a lot of red and yellow on them, and plenty of gold. The more hideous they are the more she'll be pleased. My cook," she said in explanation.

He led her straight to the monstrosities.

"Very beaut'ful vase, yes," said the clerk. "Ten dollar."

"A pair?" asked Aunt Jane.

"Ten dollar, two," said the clerk cheerfully.

"I'll take them," said Aunt Jane. "You wouldn't believe any human being could make anything so hideous, would you?"

"Yes, ma'am. Very beaut'ful vase."

"Here's where I want them sent," said Aunt Jane, writing on the back of one of her cards. "Find out for me what the express will be; I want to pay it."

She followed the clerk, but presently she stopped him. She was standing before a noble chest or box of red and gold enamel, a box perhaps three feet long and two feet high. She bent down to study the workmanship and the design, and opened the lid to look inside.

"And what do you want for this?" she asked.

"Two hunner dollar," said the clerk. "Very beaut'ful. Old Japanese box."

The box was superb. It was enameled inside with all the beauty of the outside and the bronze lock was engraved most delightfully.

"One hundred and fifty dollars," said Aunt Jane.

"Two hunner dollar," the clerk insisted. It was a bargain at that price, Aunt Jane knew.

"Well," she said, "I'll take it. And I want it sent to this address this

330

evening. You understand? Send it right away."

"Yes, ma'am. Right away," the clerk said, and he took Aunt Jane's card, on which she had written Jane's name and "with love" and Mrs. Hale's address.

Then she paid for her purchases and, it is to be supposed, went to East Orange, New Jersey.

When Mr. Hale had pulled the last of the creaking boards of the lid of the case to an upright position, Mrs. Hale carefully removed the excelsior shavings, which had been thoughtfully wrapped in paper. Jane herself was allowed to reach into the case and draw out the vases, separately wrapped. She read the card.

"Oh! from Aunt Jane!" she cried. "Ned, this will be something wonderful!"

Then she unwrapped the first vase. She looked at it with doubt. She stood it on the floor and unwrapped the second vase. No one said anything. Mrs. Hale had some things that were bad enough but she had nothing nearly so bad as these. No one there had seen anything quite so awful as these. Jane looked at Ned.

"To tell you the honest truth, Jane," said Ned, "I don't know a thing about Japanese art."

It was quite impossible to allow the two vases to be in any of the rooms they meant to use. Fortunately enough the thousand dollars Aunt Jane had given Jane sufficed only to outfit the rooms that were really needed and the extra room—the one that had to be rented with the rest because no other apartment quite suited—had nothing in it but Aunt Jane (which was what they had come to call the hatrack thing), the picture of "Diaphanoos Bobbling at the Brook," the "fire in the egg packery" sofa pillow, and the kennel and the cat coop.

Jane had made of the apartment a really charming little home. The

331

woodwork had been done in a flat white, rubbed, and the mantels were in good Adam style, and Jane let this set the note. She took the advice of Effie Wills, who was taking a course in interior decoration and furnishing, and what there was was good, and there was not too much of it.

"Absolutely not!" Effie Wills said in regard to the two vases. "They're hideous. You can't have them anywhere."

"But they must be something," urged Jane, "Aunt Jane knows about Japanese art."

"They're the cheapest stuff made in Japan for the trashiest American trade. At the top price they're not worth over ten dollars a pair, and as art they're not worth a cent. They are hideous, Jane. They're simply terrible. If you don't think I'm right, try one of them somewhere."

Jane tried one. No matter where she put it the vase was a blatant shriek of ugliness.

"No use," Ned said. "We've got to put it in Aunt Jane's room. But I tell you what, Jane—we can use one for a kennel for Fido and the other for a cat coop for Alexander."

"I thought Fido was a collie," suggested Effie Wills.

"He is," said Ned, "but he shrinks when he goes near those vases. Any self-respecting dog would."

"Ned!" cried Jane reprovingly.

So the two vases became the kennel and the cat coop and they were laid on their sides in "Aunt Jane's room." On one wall hung Diaphanoos, in one corner was the pillow known as the "egg packery conflagration" and in the corner stood "Aunt Jane." The door was always kept closed but there were supposed to be two holes cut in it—a big one for Fido to enter and exit by, and a little one for Alexander.

The egg packery conflagration was the most trouble, it having been the gift of Dot Langham who had worked at Wilson, Dickett and Company with Jane. Dot came to see Jane now and then and when she did the egg packery conflagration had to be somewhere pretty quick. Luckily the bedroom was across the narrow hall from Aunt Jane's room and with Dot in the living room Jane could step into Aunt Jane's room and throw the sofa pillow across the hall into the bedroom and onto a chair. "Diaphanoos Bobbling at the Brook" gave no one any trouble at all, having come from an old schoolmate of Jane's in Iddlesborough, Ohio. "Aunt Jane," standing in the corner of the unused room, was even less trouble. She had been given by one of

332

Ned's male friends and, although he came to see Ned now and then, he had so little sense of what was meet that he believed a vacant room was the place to keep an Aunt Jane. Ned let him hang his hat on the Aunt Jane, or his overcoat if he was wearing one.

"Hang it on the side toward the wall, Henry," Ned would say. "If you don't the old lady will topple over."

The kennel and the cat coop did not bother Jane at all during the first summer of her married life. Aunt Jane was safely in Europe and there was not much chance that she would return until autumn, if she returned then, and she might not be home for years. She said so on the post cards she sent Jane from time to time. It seemed she had an address in Paris, and Jane wrote her there.

"I can never thank you enough," Jane wrote, "for the wonderful things I have been able to do with the check you gave me. We have just the dearest little apartment home you ever saw, and Ned and I are so happy in it. And then to think of you sending us something else on top of that! We were so delighted and thrilled by your beautiful present; we both love Japanese things."

"I know good Japanese things when I see them," Aunt Jane wrote across the end of a post card from Switzerland.

Nearly every evening the Ned Nortons had a dinner party. Fido sat patiently on his haunches, waiting for Ned to toss him imaginary bits of meat, and Alexander dozed somewhere on a chair, but Mr. Diaphanoos and Aunt Jane sat at the table.

"Have you ever been in Greece?" Mr. Diaphanoos would ask Aunt Jane.

"No, not in Greece," Aunt Jane would answer, perhaps.

"You ought to go there," Mr. Diaphanoos would say. "You'd enjoy Greece. We have some swell dancers, down by the brooks there—bare-legged in mosquito netting. I hang out around the brooks mostly, when I'm at home in Greece."

"I care very little for dances," Aunt Jane would reply. "I go in more for Japanese art. That's one thing I do know about."

"Yes," Mr. Diaphanoos would say, "I've seen some swell Japanese art myself. Dog kennels of the early Stung Period and cat coops of the late Whang Period."

A little later, a year or so later, when Jane hired the little maid whose name was Marjatta, that amazed-eyed youngster never quite knew whether Ned and Jane were crazy or merely in earnest.

333

"Vud I mak place for Meest'r Daphnoos an' Aun' Chane t'night, Mees No'ton?" she would ask.

She took it all quite solemnly. Sometimes she would stand for ten minutes with a dish in her hand watching Ned put Fido through his tricks. She could not quite understand these Americans. She learned to hurry "ekks," the sofa pillow, into the bedroom when Dot called and to recognize invisible cats and dogs, and to pretend to serve invisible Mr. Diaphnooses and Aunt Janes, but she had half a notion that Ned was the crazy one. The invisibles seldom appeared when Ned was not at home. It was when the door opened and let him in that his call, "Here, Fido! Here, Fido!" rang through the apartment and Mrs. Norton said, "Miau!" It was then they began to talk about Aunt Jane—"How's Aunt Jane's rheumatism?" "Diaphy hasn't been flirting with you while I was away?" "Up, Fido, up! That's the dog!"

"Ned," Mrs. Norton said, "if ever Aunt Jane comes unexpectedly, you see these two places on the mantel? I'll try to get her into the bedroom to take off her hat and you put the kennel and the coop in these places."

"Let's have a fire drill," Ned suggested, so they firedrilled amazingly.

"Why, my dear Aunt Jane!" Jane cried at the door and Ned dashed for the vacant room. Jane stood at the bedroom door and Ned, on his hands and knees, with the kennel under one arm and the coop under the other, crept to the living room. By the time Jane led Aunt Jane to the living room the kennel was on one end of the mantel and the coop on the other. "Ned, this is Aunt Jane."

"Well! well! well!" cried Ned, jumping out of his chair. "You dear old soul!"

"Only, not quite so affectionate," said Jane. "Otherwise O.K."

The trouble was that Aunt Jane had been for many years in Iddlesborough the Family Hope. There was no reason for thinking Aunt Jane would ever really do anything for anyone, the connection being

334

so slight, but everyone knows how Family Hopes behave. They won't perish, and they will keep alive. Little Jane had certainly been named for Aunt Jane, and Aunt Jane had no one else. Of Aunt Jane's money Jane had the vaguest possible idea; she knew it was in automobiles and in Detroit. If Aunt Jane was a poor deluded creature who did not know art, even Japanese, there was no use being unpleasant about it.

"Marjatta," Jane said now and then, "this morning take some soap and water and wash the kennel and the cat coop. And don't break them!"

"Yes'm; no'm," Marjatta would say.

One Sunday afternoon Ned and Jane took Fido to Mount Tom for a run. It was a delightful day and they went immediately after noon dinner, leaving Marjatta to do the dishes, after doing which Marjatta was to have the rest of the afternoon and the evening off. She had finished the dishes and straightened the dining room and was giving the kitchen a last touch when the bell rang. The little maid removed her work apron and went to the door, her broad face beaming good will to all mankind. When she opened the door she saw a tall woman, very straight and imposing, with hair only slightly flecked with gray. She more nearly fitted Marjatta's idea of a queen or an empress than anyone Marjatta had ever seen.

"Yez'm," said Marjatta.

"Is this where the Nortons live?" asked Aunt Jane.

"Yez'm," said Marjatta.

"Are they in?" asked Aunt Jane.

"No'm," said Marjatta. "They go out with Fido."

"Is no one here, then?" asked Aunt Jane.

Marjatta considered this.

"Yez'm," she said when she had given the matter thought. "Aun' Jane an' Meest'r Daphnoos. An' Alexander."

"Oh!" said Aunt Jane with some surprise, for she certainly had no way of knowing that Aunt Jane and Mr. Diaphanoos and Fido and Alexander were well known to all the Norton's friends. "Aunt Jane is here, is she? Well, I'll come in. When are the Nortons to be back?"

"Don' know," said Marjatta cheerfully.

"Which way do I go? Straight through there?" asked Aunt Jane, and she walked straight through into the living room. She stood a moment looking about her. "Well, this is all very nice; Jane has done herself well," she said. "I say this is all very pretty and nice," she repeated to

335

Marjatta, who stood smiling her broad innocent smile. "I suppose Mr. Daphnoos is a boarder? Sounds Greek to me. Who is Aunt Jane?"

"Steek," said Marjatta. "Putting hats on."

"Never heard of her," said Aunt Jane. "A milliner? Well, no matter. You needn't bother Mrs. Steek, girl. I'll wait for the young folks."

She removed her hat and placed it on the back of a chair. Marjatta immediately took it and hurried away with it, placing it on the bed in the bedroom, and Aunt Jane walked here and there, looking at the few pictures on the walls.

"All very nice; they have good taste," she said. "And clean, too." Marjatta returned. "They must have a decent dog," Aunt Jane said; "not a hair anywhere. What kind of dog?"

"Collie dog," said Marjatta.

"Does it have fleas?"

"Yez'm, soomtimes fleas," said Marjatta, grinning broadly as she remembered Ned's scoldings of the imaginary dog.

"I like dogs," said Aunt Jane, looking into the dining room. "Do they have a cat?"

"Yez'm; Alexander," said Marjatta.

"I don't like cats," said Aunt Jane, who was now in the dining room and giving it her minute approval. "This the kitchen? Very nice. I don't suppose they'll mind my looking about a little. I'm Mrs. Elfus."

"Yez'm," said Marjatta.

"That's your room? Very nice! Where do they sleep?"

"Coom!" said Marjatta cheerfully, and she led the way to the bedroom, where Aunt Jane saw her hat on the bed and approved of the wall paper, the furniture, everything.

"Nice!" she said. "And where do this Mr. Daphnoos and Aunt Jane stay?"

"Here," said Marjatta, and she put her hand on the door of the extra room.

"No, no!" exclaimed Aunt Jane. "I won't bother them; they're nothing to me. What's the cat like?"

Marjatta opened the door of the spare room.

"My word!" exclaimed Aunt Jane. What she saw was the conflagration in the egg packery lying on the floor, the amazing picture of Mr. Diaphanoos bobbling at the brook on the wall, and the kennel and the cat coop lying on their sides in one corner.

"Kennel," said Marjatta, bending down to look in the first vase.

336

"Cat coop," she said, looking into the other. "Coom, keety, keety!" She picked up the imaginary cat and showed it to Aunt Jane.

"My word!" exclaimed Aunt Jane again. "Is the child insane?"

Marjatta put the cat on the floor, and, presumably, the cat went back into the cat coop. She turned to the photogravure.

"Meest' Daphnoos," she said with deep admiration, for, except for the kennel and the cat coop, she thought Mr. Diaphanoos the most beautiful thing in the world. And she liked this queenly visitor; she was eager to be of the utmost service to her.

"Ekks on fire," she said, picking up the mad sofa pillow and patting it.

"My absolute word!" exclaimed Aunt Jane. "Child, I will see this Aunt Jane after all. Where is she?"

"Aun' Jane," said Marjatta, and she pointed a stubby finger at the clothes-stick. She did more. She went into the hall and got a cap of Ned's and hung it on one of Aunt Jane's pegs and Aunt Jane immediately fell down flat on the floor. Marjatta grinned her deep appreciation of this fine athletic ability. "Aun' Jane seets down standing oop," she said proudly.

"Yes," said the other Aunt Jane hastily. "Yes, so I see. And I suppose these are wedding presents too hideous to be seen. Well! And what did you call these?"

"Kennel for dog; cat coop for cat," said Marjatta.

"And whoever gave them these hideous things?"

"Aun' Jane, where the ottermobiles are making," said Marjatta.

"Oh!" exclaimed Aunt Jane. "So that's it! Well—what's your name?"

"Marjatta."

"Well, I won't wait, Marjatta; I'll come back. My hat, if you please."

Marjatta was gone when Ned opened the door with a "There you are, home again, old fellow!" and threw off Fido's leash. It was not late

337

in the afternoon and Ned hung his hat on the rack in the hall and went straight through to the living room. He dropped into his easy chair and took up the section of the morning paper he had not read. Jane was putting her best hat in the flowered bandbox in the little closet in the bedroom when the bell rang.

"I'll go," she called to Ned, and she went. She cried out with joy as she saw the Family Hope standing there. "Oh, Aunt Jane!" she cried and kissed her. Ned sat suddenly straight in his chair. For a moment he stared at nothing with startled eyes, listening to Jane's eager words of welcome; then he got down on his hands and knees cautiously. He peered from behind the big chair until Jane had taken Aunt Jane into the bedroom. Hunched down he hurried down the hall and into the monstrosity room. He tucked the kennel under one of his arms, and the coop under the other.

"And just look at the view from this window," Jane was urging.

"Yes," said Aunt Jane, but she caught a glimpse of red and yellow and gold, and of an elbow, and of two legs. She turned to the window. "Yes," she said, "a very nice view. You can see almost an inch of the river, can't you?"

"And this, of course, is our hall," said Jane, putting out a hand to latch the door of the spare room, "and then here is our living room, and you haven't met my husband, have you? Ned, this is Aunt Jane."

"Well, well, well!" cried Ned Norton. "So this is Aunt Jane! I was beginning to think I would never see—"

But Aunt Jane's eyes were on the mantel. On either corner of the dainty white Adam mantel stood a vase. The vases glared like whanging brass. They dwarfed the mantel, they dwarfed the room, they dwarfed everything. They were hideous.

"Ah, the vases!" said Ned. "Jane thanked you, but I haven't thanked you." He went to the kennel and touched it with his finger, gently, lovingly. "They're wonderful things. The design—the Japanese know how to do these things. There's a touch—know what I mean—a feeling—"

He stood back and looked from the kennel to the coop, admiringly, his head on one side.

"Yes, they're lovely," said Jane hastily. "I was showing Aunt Jane the apartment—"

"Superb things," insisted Ned.

"I suppose you keep them there all the time?" said Aunt Jane.

Ned hesitated.

"Well, no!" he said at last frankly. "No, we don't. We move them around. We try to see where they look best. One place and another, you know. But here—I do think, Jane, that where we have them now—"

"Yes," said Aunt Jane, "but how does the dog get into it when it is up there?"

"The dog?"

"I can see how the cat can get in one," said Aunt Jane, "but I don't see how a dog can get up there. Not and get in it without breaking it. Not a big dog like a collie."

For a moment Ned looked at Aunt Jane and his face changed expression a dozen times. Then he saw something in Aunt Jane's eyes. He held out his left hand and slapped it smartly with his right.

"Down, Fido! Bad dog!" he said.

"We love—loved to have you give them to us, Aunt Jane," she said, "but they did not seem to fit in with our other things—"

Then Aunt Jane proved that she was indeed the Family Hope. She walked to the mantel and took down the two vases.

"Is the cat in the coop?" she asked. "No? Then—"

She bumped the two vases together and the pieces fell crisply jangling to the tiles before the mantel.

"My dear child!" she cried and she threw both arms around Little Jane and kissed her.

Ned Norton slipped quietly out of the room. He went to the spare room and opened the window and, looking down the air shaft to see that a falling object would harm no one, he dropped out of the window the most unuseful article of furniture ever made. He was merely reducing the number of Aunt Janes.

TO A SMALL BOY
STANDING ON MY SHOES
WHILE I AM WEARING THEM

OGDEN NASH

Let's straighten this out, my little man,
And reach an agreement if we can.
I entered your door as an honored guest.
My shoes are shined and my trousers are pressed,
And I won't stretch out and read you the funnies
And I won't pretend that we're Easter bunnies.
If you must get somebody down on the floor,
What in the hell are your parents for?
I do not like the things that you say
And I hate the games that you want to play.
No matter how frightfully hard you try,
We've little in common, you and I.

340

The interest I take in my neighbor's nursery
Would have to grow, to be even cursory,
And I would that performing sons and nephews
Were carted away with the daily refuse,
And I hold that frolicsome daughters and nieces
Are ample excuse for breaking leases.
You may take a sock at your daddy's tummy
Or climb all over your doting mummy,
But keep your attentions to me in check
Or, sonny boy, I will wring your neck.
A happier man today I'd be
Had a visiting adult done it to me.

THE TERMITE

OGDEN NASH

Some primal termite knocked on wood
And tasted it, and found it good,
And that is why your Cousin May
Fell through the parlor floor today.

THE PENSIVE PEN

KEITH PRESTON

I wish I were the Hottentot,
  Not polyglot nor pensive;
His native spot is nice and hot;
  His wardrobe inextensive.
He never lacks a leafy cot,
Some coals on which his pot is sot,
A cache concealed in some cool grot
Of liquor for his nightly tot,
  (That's strong but inexpensive.)
He pays his grocer scot and lot;
His guests get gratis what he's got;
All politics, says he, are rot;
  He is not apprehensive.
So, polyglot and pensive, I
  Admire the Hottentot,
Who lives where mercury is high
  And other things are not.

THE TRANSFERRED GHOST

FRANK R. STOCKTON

THE country residence of Mr. John Hinckman was a delightful place to me, for many reasons. It was the abode of a genial, though somewhat impulsive, hospitality. It had broad, smooth-shaven lawns and towering oaks and elms; there were bosky shades at several points, and not far from the house there was a little rill spanned by a rustic bridge with the bark on; there were fruits and flowers, pleasant people, chess, billiards, rides, walks, and fishing. These were great attractions, but none of them, nor all of them together, would have been sufficient to hold me to the place very long. I had been invited for the trout season, but should probably have finished my visit early in the summer had it not been that upon fair days, when the grass was dry, and the sun was not too hot, and there was but little wind, there strolled beneath the lofty elms, or passed lightly through the bosky shades, the form of my Madeline.

This lady was not, in very truth, my Madeline. She had never given herself to me, nor had I, in any way, acquired possession of her. But, as I considered her possession the only sufficient reason for the continuance of my existence, I called her, in my reveries, mine. It may have been that I would not have been obliged to confine the use of this possessive pronoun to my reveries had I confessed the state of my feelings to the lady.

But this was an unusually difficult thing to do. Not only did I dread, as almost all lovers dread, taking the step which would in an instant put an end to that delightful season which may be termed the ante-interrogatory period of love, and which might at the same time terminate all intercourse or connection with the object of my passion, but I was also dreadfully afraid of John Hinckman. This gentleman was a good friend of mine, but it would have required a bolder man than I was at that time to ask him for the gift of his niece, who was the head of his household, and, according to his own frequent statement, the main

343

prop of his declining years. Had Madeline acquiesced in my general views on the subject, I might have felt encouraged to open the matter to Mr. Hinckman; but, as I said before, I had never asked her whether or not she would be mine. I thought of these things at all hours of the day and night, particularly the latter.

I was lying awake one night, in the great bed in my spacious chamber, when, by the dim light of the new moon, which partially filled the room, I saw John Hinckman standing by a large chair near the door. I was very much surprised at this, for two reasons: in the first place, my host had never before come into my room, and, in the second place, he had gone from home that morning, and had not expected to return for several days. Therefore it was that I had been able that evening to sit much later than usual with Madeline on the moonlit porch. The figure was certainly that of John Hinckman in his ordinary dress, but there was a vagueness and indistinctness about it which presently assured me that it was a ghost. Had the good old man been murdered, and had his spirit come to tell me of the deed, and to confide to me the protection of his dear—? My heart fluttered, but I felt that I must speak. "Sir," said I.

"Do you know," interrupted the figure, with a countenance that indicated anxiety, "whether or not Mr. Hinckman will return to-night?"

I thought it well to maintain a calm exterior, and I answered:

"We do not expect him."

"I am glad of that," said he, sinking into the chair by which he stood. "During the two years and a half that I have inhabited this house, that man has never before been away for a single night. You can't imagine the relief it gives me."

As he spoke he stretched out his legs and leaned back in the chair. His form became less vague, and the colors of his garments more distinct and evident, while an expression of gratified relief succeeded to the anxiety of his countenance.

"Two years and a half!" I exclaimed. "I don't understand you."

"It is fully that length of time," said the ghost, "since I first came here. Mine is not an ordinary case. But before I say anything more about it, let me ask you again if you are sure Mr. Hinckman will not return to-night."

"I am as sure of it as I can be of anything," I answered. "He left to-day for Bristol, two hundred miles away."

"Then I will go on," said the ghost, "for I am glad to have the oppor-

344

tunity of talking to some one who will listen to me. But if John Hinckman should come in and catch me here, I should be frightened out of my wits."

"This is all very strange," I said, greatly puzzled by what I had heard. "Are you the ghost of Mr. Hinckman?"

This was a bold question, but my mind was so full of other emotions that there seemed to be no room for that of fear.

"Yes, I am his ghost," my companion replied, "and yet I have no right to be. And this is what makes me so uneasy and so much afraid of him. It is a strange story, and, I truly believe, without precedent. Two years and a half ago, John Hinckman was dangerously ill in this very room. At one time he was so far gone that he was really believed to be dead. It was in consequence of too precipitate a report in regard to this matter that I was, at that time, appointed to be his ghost. Imagine my surprise and horror, sir, when, after I had accepted the position and assumed its responsibilities, that old man revived, became convalescent, and eventually regained his usual health. My situation was now one of extreme delicacy and embarrassment. I had no power to return to my original unembodiment, and I had no right to be the ghost of a man who was not dead. I was advised by my friends to quietly maintain my position, and was assured, that, as John Hinckman was an elderly man, it could not be long before I could rightfully assume the position for which I had been selected. But I tell you, sir," he continued with animation, "the old fellow seems as vigorous as ever, and I have no idea how much longer this annoying state of things will continue. I spend my time trying to get out of that old man's way. I must not leave this house, and he seems to follow me everywhere. I tell you, sir, he haunts me."

"That is truly a queer state of things," I remarked. "But why are you afraid of him? He couldn't hurt you."

345

"Of course he couldn't," said the ghost. "But his very presence is a shock and terror to me. Imagine, sir, how you would feel if my case were yours."

I could not imagine such a thing at all. I simply shuddered.

"And if one must be a wrongful ghost at all," the apparition continued, "it would be much pleasanter to be the ghost of some man other than John Hinckman. There is in him an irascibility of temper, accompanied by a facility of invective, which is seldom met with; and what would happen if he were to see me, and find out, as I am sure he would, how long and why I had inhabited his house, I can scarcely conceive. I have seen him in his bursts of passion, and although he did not hurt the people he stormed at any more than he would hurt me, they seemed to shrink before him."

All this I knew to be very true. Had it not been for this peculiarity of Mr. Hinckman, I might have been more willing to talk to him about his niece.

"I feel sorry for you," I said, for I really began to have a sympathetic feeling toward this unfortunate apparition. "Your case is indeed a hard one. It reminds me of those persons who have had doubles; and I suppose a man would often be very angry indeed when he found that there was another being who was personating himself."

"Oh, the cases are not similar at all," said the ghost. "A double, or doppelgänger, lives on the earth with a man, and being exactly like him, he makes all sorts of trouble, of course. It is very different with me. I am not here to live with Mr. Hinckman. I am here to take his place. Now, it would make John Hinckman very angry if he knew that. Don't you know it would?"

I assented promptly.

"Now that he is away, I can be easy for a little while," continued the ghost, "and I am so glad to have an opportunity of talking to you. I have frequently come into your room and watched you while you slept, but did not dare to speak to you for fear that if you talked with me Mr. Hinckman would hear you, and come into the room to know why you were talking to yourself."

"But would he not hear you?" I asked.

"Oh, no!" said the other. "There are times when any one may see me, but no one hears me except the person to whom I address myself."

"But why did you wish to speak to me?" I asked.

"Because," replied the ghost, "I like occasionally to talk to people, and

346

especially to some one like yourself, whose mind is so troubled and perturbed that you are not likely to be frightened by a visit from one of us. But I particularly want to ask you to do me a favor. There is every probability, so far as I can see, that John Hinckman will live a long time, and my situation is becoming insupportable. My great object at present is to get myself transferred, and I think that you may, perhaps, be of use to me."

"Transferred!" I exclaimed. "What do you mean by that?"

"What I mean," said the other, "is this: now that I have started on my career, I have got to be the ghost of somebody, and I want to be the ghost of a man who is really dead."

"I should think that would be easy enough," I said. "Opportunities must continually occur."

"Not at all! not at all!" said my companion, quickly. "You have no idea what a rush and pressure there is for situations of this kind. Whenever a vacancy occurs, if I may express myself in that way, there are crowds of applications for the ghostship."

"I had no idea that such a state of things existed," I said, becoming quite interested in the matter. "There ought to be some regular system, or order of precedence, by which you could all take your turns, like customers in a barber's shop."

"Oh, dear, that would never do at all!" said the other. "Some of us would have to wait forever. There is always a great rush whenever a good ghostship offers itself—while, as you know, there are some positions that no one would care for. It was in consequence of my being in too great a hurry on an occasion of the kind that I got myself into my present disagreeable predicament, and I have thought that it might be possible that you would help me out of it. You might know of a case where an opportunity for a ghostship was not generally expected, but which might present itself at any moment. If you would give me a short notice, I know I could arrange for a transfer."

"What do you mean?" I exclaimed. "Do you want me to commit suicide or to undertake a murder for your benefit?"

"Oh, no, no, no!" said the other, with a vapory smile. "I mean nothing of that kind. To be sure, there are lovers who are watched with considerable interest, such persons having been known, in moments of depression, to offer very desirable ghostships, but I did not think of anything of that kind in connection with you. You were the only person I cared to speak to, and I hope that you might give me some infor-

347

mation that would be of use; and, in return, I shall be very glad to help you in your love affair."

"You seem to know that I have such an affair," I said.

"Oh, yes!" replied the other, with a little yawn. "I could not be here so much as I have been without knowing all about that."

There was something horrible in the idea of Madeline and myself having been watched by a ghost, even, perhaps, when we wandered together in the most delightful and bosky places. But then, this was quite an exceptional ghost, and I could not have the objections to him which would ordinarily arise in regard to beings of his class.

"I must go now," said the ghost, rising, "but I will see you somewhere to-morrow night; and remember—you help me, and I'll help you."

I had doubts the next morning as to the propriety of telling Madeline anything about this interview, and soon convinced myself that I must keep silent on the subject. If she knew there was a ghost about the house, she would probably leave the place instantly. I did not mention the matter, and so regulated my demeanor that I am quite sure Madeline never suspected what had taken place.

For some time I had wished that Mr. Hinckman would absent himself, for a day at least, from the premises. In such case I thought I might more easily nerve myself up to the point of speaking to Madeline on the subject of our future collateral existence. But now that the opportunity for such speech had really occurred, I did not feel ready to avail myself of it. What would become of me if she refused me?

I had an idea, however, that the lady thought that if I were going to speak at all, this was the time. She must have known that certain sentiments were afloat within me, and she was not unreasonable in her wish to see the matter settled one way or the other. But I did not feel like taking a bold step in the dark. If she wished me to ask her to give herself to me, she ought to offer me some reason to suppose that she would make the gift. If I saw no probability of such generosity, I would prefer that things should remain as they were.

That evening I was sitting with Madeline on the moonlit porch. It was nearly ten o'clock, and ever since supper-time I had been working myself up to the point of making an avowal of my sentiments. I had not positively determined to do this, but wished gradually to reach the proper point when, if the prospect looked bright, I might speak. My

348

companion appeared to understand the situation—at least, I imagined that the nearer I came to a proposal the more she seemed to expect it. It was certainly a very critical and important epoch in my life. If I spoke, I should make myself happy or miserable forever; and if I did not speak, I had every reason to believe that the lady would not give me another chance to do so.

Sitting thus with Madeline, talking a little, and thinking very hard over these momentous matters, I looked up and saw the ghost, not a dozen feet away from us. He was sitting on the railing of the porch, one leg thrown up before him, the other dangling down as he leaned against a post. He was behind Madeline, but almost in front of me, as I sat facing the lady. It was fortunate that Madeline was looking out over the landscape, for I must have appeared very much startled. The ghost had told me that he would see me some time this night, but I did not think he would make his appearance when I was in the company of Madeline. If she should see the spirit of her uncle, I could not answer for the consequences. I made no exclamation, but the ghost evidently saw that I was troubled.

"Don't be afraid," he said; "I shall not let her see me, and she cannot hear me speak unless I address myself to her, which I do not intend to do."

I suppose I looked grateful.

"So you need not trouble yourself about that," the ghost continued. "But it seems to me that you are not getting along very well with your affair. If I were you, I should speak out without waiting any longer. You will never have a better chance. You are not likely to be interrupted, and, so far as I can judge, the lady seems disposed to listen to you favorably—that is, if she ever intends to do so. There is no knowing when John Hinckman will go away again; certainly not this summer. If I were in your place, I shall never dare to make love to Hinckman's niece if he were anywhere about the place. If he should catch any one offering himself to Miss Madeline, he would then be a terrible man to encounter."

I agreed perfectly to all this.

"I cannot bear to think of him!" I ejaculated aloud.

"Think of whom?" asked Madeline, turning quickly toward me.

Here was an awkward situation. The long speech of the ghost, to which Madeline paid no attention, but which I heard with perfect distinctness, had made me forget myself.

349

It was necessary to explain quickly. Of course, it would not do to admit that it was of her dear uncle that I was speaking, and so I mentioned hastily the first name I thought of.

"Mr. Vilars," I said.

This statement was entirely correct, for I never could bear to think of Mr. Vilars, who was a gentleman who had, at various times, paid much attention to Madeline.

"It is wrong for you to speak in that way of Mr. Vilars," she said. "He is a remarkably well educated and sensible young man, and has very pleasant manners. He expects to be elected to the legislature this fall, and I should not be surprised if he made his mark. He will do well in a legislative body, for whenever Mr. Vilars has anything to say he knows just how and when to say it."

This was spoken very quietly, and without any show of resentment, which was all very natural, for if Madeline thought at all favorably of me she could not feel displeased that I should have disagreeable emotions in regard to a possible rival. The concluding words contained a hint which I was not slow to understand. I felt very sure that if Mr. Vilars were in my present position he would speak quickly enough.

"I know it is wrong to have such ideas about a person," I said, "but I cannot help it."

The lady did not chide me, and after this she seemed even in a softer mood. As for me, I felt considerably annoyed, for I had not wished to admit that any thought of Mr. Vilars had ever occupied my mind.

"You should not speak aloud that way," said the ghost, "or you may get yourself into trouble. I want to see everything go well with you, because then you may be disposed to help me, especially if I should chance to be of any assistance to you, which I hope I shall be."

I longed to tell him that there was no way in which he could help

me so much as by taking his instant departure. To make love to a young lady with a ghost sitting on the railing near by, and that ghost the apparition of a much-dreaded uncle, the very idea of whom in such a position and at such a time made me tremble, was a difficult, if not an impossible, thing to do. But I forbore to speak, although I may have looked my mind.

"I suppose," continued the ghost, "that you have not heard anything that might be of advantage to me. Of course, I am very anxious to hear, but if you have anything to tell me, I can wait until you are alone. I will come to you to-night in your room, or I will stay here until the lady goes away."

"You need not wait here," I said; "I have nothing at all to say to you."

Madeline sprang to her feet, her face flushed and her eyes ablaze.

"Wait here!" she cried. "What do you suppose I am waiting for? Nothing to say to me, indeed! I should think so! What should you have to say to me?"

"Madeline," I exclaimed, stepping toward her, "let me explain."

But she had gone.

Here was the end of the world for me! I turned fiercely to the ghost.

"Wretched existence!" I cried, "you have ruined everything. You have blackened my whole life! Had it not been for you—"

But here my voice faltered. I could say no more.

"You wrong me," said the ghost. "I have not injured you. I have tried only to encourage and assist you, and it is your own folly that has done this mischief. But do not despair. Such mistakes as these can be explained. Keep up a brave heart. Good-by."

And he vanished from the railing like a bursting soap-bubble.

I went gloomily to bed, but I saw no apparitions that night except those of despair and misery which my wretched thoughts called up. The words I had uttered had sounded to Madeline like the basest insult. Of course, there was only one interpretation she could put upon them.

As to explaining my ejaculations, that was impossible. I thought the matter over and over again as I lay awake that night, and I determined that I would never tell Madeline the facts of the case. It would be better for me to suffer all my life than for her to know that the ghost of her uncle haunted the house. Mr. Hinckman was away, and if she knew of his ghost she could not be made to believe that he was not dead. She might not survive the shock! No, my heart might bleed, but I would never tell her.

351

The next day was fine, neither too cool nor too warm. The breezes were gentle, and nature smiled. But there were no walks or rides with Madeline. She seemed to be much engaged during the day, and I saw but little of her. When we met at meals she was polite, but very quiet and reserved. She had evidently determined on a course of conduct, and had resolved to assume that, although I had been very rude to her, she did not understand the import of my words. It would be quite proper, of course, for her not to know what I meant by my expressions of the night before.

I was downcast and wretched, and said but little, and the only bright streak across the black horizon of my woe was the fact that she did not appear to be happy, although she affected an air of unconcern. The moonlit porch was deserted that evening, but wandering about the house, I found Madeline in the library alone. She was reading, but I went in and sat down near her. I felt that, although I could not do so fully, I must in a measure explain my conduct of the night before. She listened quietly to a somewhat labored apology I made for the words I had used.

"I have not the slightest idea what you meant," she said, "but you were very rude."

I earnestly disclaimed any intention of rudeness, and assured her, with a warmth of speech that must have made some impression upon her, that rudeness to her would be an action impossible to me. I said a great deal upon the subject, and implored her to believe that if it were not for a certain obstacle I could speak to her so plainly that she would understand everything.

She was silent for a time, and then she said, rather more kindly, I thought, than she had spoken before:

"Is that obstacle in any way connected with my uncle?"

"Yes," I answered, after a little hesitation, "it is, in a measure, connected with him."

She made no answer to this, and sat looking at her book, but not reading. From the expression of her face, I thought she was somewhat softened toward me. She knew her uncle as well as I did, and she may have been thinking that if he were the obstacle that prevented my speaking (and there were many ways in which he might be that obstacle), my position would be such a hard one that it would excuse some wildness of speech and eccentricity of manner. I saw, too, that the warmth of my partial explanations had had some effect on her, and

352

I began to believe that it might be a good thing for me to speak my mind without delay. No matter how she should receive my proposition, my relations with her could not be worse than they had been the previous night and day, and there was something in her face which encouraged me to hope that she might forget my foolish exclamations of the evening before if I began to tell her my tale of love.

I drew my chair a little nearer to her, and as I did so the ghost burst into the room from the doorway behind her. I say burst, although no door flew open and he made no noise. He was wildly excited, and waved his arms above his head. The moment I saw him, my heart fell within me. With the entrance of that impertinent apparition, every hope fled from me. I could not speak while he was in the room.

I must have turned pale, and I gazed steadfastly at the ghost, almost without seeing Madeline, who sat between us.

"Do you know," he cried, "that John Hinckman is coming up the hill? He will be here in fifteen minutes and if you are doing anything in the way of lovemaking, you had better hurry it up. But this is not what I came to tell you. I have glorious news! At last I am transferred! Not forty minutes ago a Russian nobleman was murdered by the Nihilists. Nobody ever thought of him in connection with an immediate ghostship. My friends instantly applied for the situation for me, and obtained my transfer. I am off before that horried Hinckman comes up the hill. The moment I reach my new position, I shall put off this hated semblance. Good-by! You can't imagine how glad I am to be, at last, the real ghost of somebody."

"Oh!" I cried, rising to my feet and stretching out my arms in utter wretchedness, "I would to Heaven you were mine!"

"I *am* yours," said Madeline, raising to me her tearful eyes.

"They ran me through with the flatwork this week!"

353

MOMENT MUSICALE

MARGARET FISHBACK

I want to vegetate and read,
And joyously repair to seed. . . .
This burning itch to Get Ahead
Leaves much too little time for bed.

*"Has this apartment any mice?
We must have lots of them!"*

ANECDOTAGE

RICHARD ARMOUR

Some anecdotes are dull and old,
But some, I think, are swell.
The former are the ones I'm told,
The latter, those I tell.

UNCLE PODGER HANGS A PICTURE

JEROME K. JEROME

You never saw such a commotion up and down a house, in all your life, as when my Uncle Podger undertook to do a job. A picture would have come home from the frame-maker's and be standing in the dining-room, waiting to be put up; and Aunt Podger would ask what was to be done with it, and Uncle Podger would say:

"Oh, you leave that to *me*. Don't you, any of you, worry yourselves about that. *I'll* do all that." And then he would take off his coat and begin.

First he would send the girl out for sixpen'orth of nails, and then one of the boys after her to tell her what size to get; and, from that, he would gradually work down, and start the whole house.

"Now you go and get me my hammer, Will," he would shout; "and you bring me the rule, Tom; and I shall want the step-ladder, and I had better have a kitchen-chair, too; and, Jim! you run round to Mr. Goggles, and tell him, 'Pa's kind regards, and hopes his leg's better; and will he lend him his spirit-level?' And don't you go, Maria, because I shall want somebody to hold me the light; and when the girl comes back, she must go out again for a bit of picture-cord; and Tom—where's Tom?—Tom, you come here; I shall want you to hand me up the picture."

And then he would lift up the picture, and drop it, and it would come out of the frame, and he would try to save the glass, and cut himself; and then he would spring round the room, looking for his handkerchief.

He could not find his handkerchief, because it was in the pocket of the coat he had taken off, and he did not know where he had put the coat, and all the house had to leave off looking for his tools, and start looking for his coat; while he would dance around and hinder them.

"Doesn't anybody in the whole house know where my coat is? I never came across such a set in all my life—upon my word I didn't.

355.

Six of you!—and you can't find a coat that I put down not five minutes ago! Well, of all the—"

Then he'd get up, and find that he had been sitting on it, and would call out:

"Oh, you can give it up! I've found it myself now. Might just as well ask the cat to find anything as expect you people to find it."

And, when half an hour had been spent in tying up his finger, and a new glass had been got, and the tools, and the ladder, and the chair, and the candle had been brought, he would have another go, the whole family, including the girl and the charwoman, standing round in a semicircle, ready to help. Two people would have to hold the chair, and a third would help him up on it, and hold him there, and a fourth would hand him a nail, and then a fifth would pass him up the hammer, and he would take hold of the nail, and drop it.

"There!" he would say, in an injured tone, "now the nail's gone."

And we would all have to go down on our knees and grovel for it, while he would stand on the chair, and grunt, and want to know if he was to be kept there all the evening.

The nail would be found at last, and by that time he would have lost the hammer.

"Where's the hammer? What did I do with the hammer? Great heavens! Seven of you, gaping round there, and you don't know what I did with the hammer!"

We would find the hammer for him, and then he would have lost sight of the mark he had made on the wall, where the nail was to go in.

At last, Uncle Podger would get the spot fixed again, and put the point of the nail on it with his left hand, and take the hammer in his right hand. And, with the first blow, he would smash his thumb, and drop the hammer, with a yell, on somebody's toes.

Aunt Maria would mildly observe that, next time Uncle Podger was going to hammer a nail into the wall, she hoped he'd let her know in time, so that she could make arrangements to go and spend a week with her mother while it was being done.

"Oh! you women, you make such a fuss over everything," Uncle Podger would reply, picking himself up. "Why I *like* doing a little job of this sort."

A CHANGE OF TREATMENT

W. W. JACOBS

"Yes, I've sailed under some 'cute skippers in my time," said the night-watchman; "them that go down in big ships see the wonders o' the deep, you know," added with a sudden chuckle, "but the one I'm going to tell you about ought never to have been trusted out without 'is ma. A good many o' my skippers had fads, but this one was the worse I ever sailed under.

"It's some few years ago now; I'd shipped on his barque, the *John Elliott*, as slow-going an old tub as ever I was aboard of, when I wasn't in quite a fit an' proper state to know what I was doing, an' I hadn't been in her two days afore I found out his 'obby through overhearing a few remarks made by the second mate, who came up from dinner in a hurry to make 'em. 'I don't mind saws an' knives hung round the cabin,' he ses to the fust mate, 'but when a chap has a 'uman 'and alongside 'is plate, studying it while folks is at their food, it's more than a Christian man can stand.'

" 'That's nothing,' ses the fust mate, who had sailed with the barque afore. 'He's half crazy on doctoring. We nearly had a mutiny aboard once owing to his wanting to hold a *post-mortem* on a man what fell from the mast-head. Wanted to see what the poor feller died of.'

357

" 'I call it unwholesome,' ses the second mate very savage. 'He offered me a pill at breakfast the size of a small marble; quite put me off my feed, it did.'

"Of course, the skipper's fad soon got known for'ard. But I didn't think much about it, till one day I seed old Dan'l Dennis sitting on a locker reading. Every now and then he'd shut the book, an' look up, closing 'is eyes, an' moving his lips like a hen drinking, an' then look down at the book again.

" 'Why, Dan,' I ses, 'what's up? You ain't larning lessons at your time o' life?'

" 'Yes, I am,' ses Dan very soft. 'You might hear me say it; it's this one about heart disease.'

"He hands over the book, which was stuck full o' all kinds o' diseases, and winks at me 'ard.

" 'Picked it up on a bookstall,' he ses; then he shuts 'is eyes an' said his piece wonderful. It made me quite queer to listen to 'im. 'That's how I feel,' ses he, when he'd finished. 'Just strength enough to get to bed. Lend a hand, Bill, an' go an' fetch the doctor.'

"Then I see his little game, but I wasn't going to run any risks, so I just mentioned, permiscous like, to the cook as old Dan seemed rather queer, an' went back an' tried to borrer the book, being always fond of reading. Old Dan pretended he was too ill to hear what I was saying, an' afore I could take it away from him, the skipper comes hurrying down with a bag in his 'and.

" 'What's the matter, my man?' ses he.

" 'I'm all right, sir,' ses old Dan, ' 'cept that I've been swoonding away a little.'

" 'Tell me exactly how you feel,' ses the skipper, feeling his pulse.

"Then old Dan said his piece over to him, an' the skipper shook his head an' looked very solemn.

" 'How long have you been like this?' he ses.

" 'Four or five years, sir,' ses Dan. 'It ain't nothing serious, sir, is it?'

" 'You lie quite still,' ses the skipper, putting a little trumpet thing to his chest an' then listening. 'Um! The prognotice is very bad.'

" 'Prog what, sir?' ses Dan, staring.

" 'Prognotice,' ses the skipper. At least, I think that's the word he said. 'You keep perfectly still, an' I'll go an' mix you up a draught, and tell the cook to get some strong beef-tea on.'

"Well, the skipper 'ad no sooner gone, than Cornish Harry, a great

358

big lumbering chap o' six feet two, goes up to old Dan, an' he ses, 'Gimme that book.'

" 'Go away,' ses Dan, 'don't come worrying 'ere; you 'eard the skipper say how bad my prognotice was.'

" 'You lend me the book,' ses Harry, ketching hold of him, 'or else I'll bang you first, and split to the skipper arterwards. I believe I'm a bit consumptive.'

"He dragged the book away from the old man, and began to study. There was so many complaints in it he was almost tempted to have something else instead of consumption, but he decided on that at last, an' he got a cough that worried the fo'c'sle all night long, an' the next day, when the skipper came down to see Dan he could 'ardly 'ear hisself speak.

" 'That's a nasty cough you've got, my man,' ses he.

" 'Oh, it's nothing, sir,' ses Harry, careless like. 'I've 'ad it for months now off and on. I think it's perspiring so of a night does it.'

" 'What?' ses the skipper. 'You perspire nights?'

" 'Dredful,' ses Harry. 'You could wring the clo'es out. I s'pose it's healthy for me, ain't it, sir?'

" 'Undo your shirt,' ses the skipper, going over to him an' sticking the trumpet agin him. 'Now take a deep breath. Don't cough.'

" 'I can't help it, sir,' ses Harry, 'it will come. Seems to tear me to pieces.'

359

" 'You get to bed at once,' says the skipper, taking away the trumpet, an' shaking his 'ed. 'It's a fortunate thing for you, my lad, you're in skilled hands. With care, I believe I can pull you round. How does that medicine suit you, Dan?'

" 'Beautiful, sir,' says Dan. 'It's wonderful soothing, I slep' like a new-born babe arter it.'

" 'I'll send you some more,' ses the skipper. 'You're not to get up, mind, either of you.'

" 'All right, sir,' ses the two in very faint voices, an' the skipper went away arter telling us to be careful not to make a noise.

"We all thought it a fine joke at first, but the airs them two chaps give themselves was something sickening. Being in bed all day, they was naturally wakeful of a night, and they used to call across the fo'c'sle inquiring arter each other's healths, an' waking us other chaps up. An' they'd swop beef-tea an' jellies with each other, an' Dan 'ud try an' coax a little port wine out o' Harry, which he 'ad to make blood with, but Harry 'ud say he hadn't made enough that day, an' he'd drink to the better health of old Dan's prognotice, an' smack his lips until it drove us a'most crazy.

"Arter these chaps had been ill two days, the other fellers began to put their heads together, an' said they was going to be ill too, and both the invalids got into a fearful state of excitement.

" 'You'll only spoil it for all of us,' ses Harry, 'and you don't know what to have without the book.'

" 'It's all very well doing your work as well as our own,' ses one of the men. 'It's our turn now. It's time you two got well.'

" '*Well?*' ses Harry, '*well?* Why, you silly, iggernerant chaps, we shan't never get well; people with our complaints never do. You ought to know that.'

" 'Well, I shall split,' ses one of them.

" 'You do!' ses Harry, 'you do, an' I'll put a 'ed on you that all the port wine and jellies in the world wouldn't cure. 'Sides, don't you think the skipper knows what's the matter with us?'

"Afore the other chap could reply, the skipper hisself comes down, accompanied by the fust mate, with a look on his face which made Harry give the deepest and hollowest cough he'd ever done.

" 'What they reely want,' ses the skipper, turning to the mate, 'is keer-ful nussing.'

" 'I wish you'd let *me* nuss 'em,' ses the fust mate, 'only ten minutes— I'd put 'em both on their legs, an' running for their lives into the bargain, in ten minutes.'

" 'Hold your tongue, sir,' ses the skipper; 'what you say is unfeeling, besides being an insult to me. Do you think I studied medicine all these years without knowing when a man's ill?'

"The fust mate growled something and went on deck, and the skipper started examining of 'em again. He said they was wonderfully patient lying in bed so long, an' he had 'em wrapped up in their bedclo'es and carried on deck, so the pure air could have a go at 'em. *We* had to do the carrying, an' there they sat, breathing the pure air, and looking at the fust mate out of the corners of their eyes. If they wanted anything from below, one of us had to go an' fetch it, an' by the time they was taken down to bed again, we all resolved to be took ill too.

"Only two of 'em did it, though, for Harry, who was a powerful, ugly-tempered chap, swore he'd do all sorts o' dreadful things to us if we didn't keep well and hearty, an' all 'cept these two did. One of 'em, Mike Rafferty, laid up with a swelling on his ribs, which I knew myself he 'ad 'ad for fifteen years, and the other chap had paralysis. I never saw a man so reely happy as the skipper was. He was up an' down with 'is medicines and his instruments all day long, and used to make notes of the cases in his big pocket-book, and read 'em to the second mate at meal-times.

"The fo'c'sle had been turned into a hospital about a week, an' I was on deck doing some odd job or the other, when the cook comes up to me.

" " 'Nother invalid,' ses he, 'fust mate's gone mad!'

" 'Mad?' ses I.

" 'Yes,' ses he. 'He's got a big basin in the galley, an' he's laughing like

361

a hyener an' mixing bilge-water an' ink an' paraffin an' butter an' soap an'
all sorts o' things up together. The smell's enough to kill a man.'

"Curious-like, I jest walked up to the galley an' puts my 'ead in, an'
there was the mate as the cook said, smiling all over his face, and ladling
some thick sticky stuff into a stone bottle.

" 'How's the pore sufferers, sir?' ses he, stepping out of the galley jest
as the skipper was going by.

" 'They're very bad; but I hope for the best,' ses the skipper, looking
at him hard. 'I'm glad to see you've turned a bit more feeling.'

" 'Yes, sir,' ses the mate. 'I didn't think so at fust, but I can see now
them chaps is all very ill. You'll s'cuse me saying it, but I don't quite
approve of your treatment.'

"I thought the skipper would ha' bust.

" 'My treatment?' ses he. 'My treatment? What do you know about
it?'

" 'You're treating 'em wrong, sir,' ses the mate. 'I have here' (patting
the jar) 'a remedy which 'ud cure them all if you'd only let me try it.'

" 'Pooh!' ses the skipper. 'One medicine cure all diseases! What is it?
Where'd you get it?'

" 'I brought the ingredients aboard with me,' ses the mate. 'It's a wonderful medicine discovered by my grandmother, an' it'll surely cure
them pore chaps.'

" 'Rubbish!' ses the skipper.

" 'Very well, sir,' ses the mate, shrugging his shoulders. 'O' course, if
you won't let me, you won't. Still I tell you, if you'd let me try I'd cure
'em all in two days. That's a fair challenge.'

"Well, they talked, and talked, and talked, until at last the skipper give way and went down below with the mate, and told the chaps they was to take the new medicine for two days, jest to prove the mate was wrong.

" 'Let pore old Dan try it first, sir,' ses Harry, starting up, an' sniffing as the mate took the cork out; 'he's been awful bad since you've been away.'

" 'Harry's worse than I am, sir,' ses Dan; 'it's only his kind heart that makes him say that.'

" 'It don't matter which is fust,' ses the mate, filling a tablespoon with it, 'there's plenty for all. Now, Harry.'

" 'Take it,' ses the skipper.

"Harry took it, an' the fuss he made you'd ha' thought he was swallering a football. It stuck all round his mouth, and he carried on so dredful that the other invalids was half sick afore it came to them.

"By the time the other three 'ad 'ad theirs it was as good as a pantermime, an' the mate corked the bottle up, and went an' sat down on a locker while they tried to rinse their mouths out with the luxuries which had been given 'em.

" 'How do you feel?' ses the skipper.

" 'I'm dying,' ses Dan.

" 'So'm I,' ses Harry; 'the mate's p'isoned us.'

"The skipper looks over at the mate very stern and shakes his 'ead slowly.

" 'It's all right,' ses the mate. "It's always like that the first dozen or so doses.'

" 'Dozen or so doses!' ses old Dan, in a far-away voice.

" 'It has to be taken every twenty minutes,' ses the mate; an' the four men groaned all together.

" 'I can't allow it,' ses the skipper, 'I can't allow it. Men's lives mustn't be sacrificed for an experiment.'

" ' 'Tain't a experiment,' ses the mate very indignant, 'it's an old family medicine.'

" 'Well, they sha'n't have any more,' ses the skipper.

" 'Look here,' ses the mate. 'If I kill any one o' these men I'll give you twenty pound, I will.'

" 'Make it twenty-five,' ses the skipper, considering.

" 'Very good,' ses the mate. 'Twenty-five; I can't say no fairer than that, can I? It's about time for another dose now.'

"He gave 'em another tablespoonful all round as the skipper left, an' the chaps that wasn't invalids nearly bust with joy. He wouldn't let 'em have anything to take the taste out, 'cos he said it didn't give the medicine a chance, an' he told us other chaps to remove the temptation, an' you bet we did.

"After the fifth dose, the invalids began to get desperate, an' when they heard they'd got to be woke up every twenty minutes through the night to take the stuff, they sort o' give up. Old Dan said he felt a gentle glow stealing over him and strengthening him, and Harry said that it felt like a healing balm to his lungs. All of 'em agreed it was a wonderful sort o' medicine, an' arter the sixth dose the man with paralysis dashed up on deck, and ran up the rigging like a cat. He sat there for hours spitting, an' swore he'd brain anybody who interrupted him, an' arter a little while Mike Rafferty went up an j'ined him, an' if the fust mate's ears didn't burn by reason of the things them two pore sufferers said about 'im, they ought to.

"They was all doing full work next day, an' though, o' course, the skipper saw how he'd been done, he didn't allude to it. Not in words, that is; but when a man tries to make four chaps do the work of eight, an' hits 'em when they don't, it's a easy job to see where the shoe pinches."

CALLING DR. KILDARE!
CALLING DR. PASTURE!

ARTHUR KOBER

THE male members of the Excelsior Social Club assembled in a corner of the Grosses' living room, leaving the girls sitting around the table. Bella Gross, the hostess, passed a dish of chocolates around the group in the corner, then took her place at the table. "Gee whiz!" she said, frowning anxiously. "Too bad about Sarah Fineman!"

"What'sa matter?" asked Nettie Portnow, a new member.

"It's her sister's baby, little Ruthie," Bella said. "She's laid up with an infection and they think maybe the poor thing's got a temprachure."

"Y'know something?" Blonde Francey Frompkin closely inspected her teeth in a hand mirror she held before her. "I hope Sarah's sister got a good baby specialist fa a doctor. Otherwise I wouldn't wanna be responsible fa what happens."

"Fa haven's sake, waddeya mean?" Nettie Portnow asked.

"I mean, you take a plain, neighborhood doctor. O.K. So you come to him with a cold; you got maybe an earache; you got this, that, and the other thing. But with a baby doctor, it's a very delicate matter." She buried her mirror in her handbag and snapped it shut. "Such things, you gotta call in a baby specialist. Correct, Billie?"

"Oh, nachelly," Bella said. "A little baby's sickness is very highly complicated. If it was me, I wouldn't bother with nobody else but a specialist fomm such cases."

Jennie Gershkorn sat staring vacantly ahead, her fingers idly drumming on the table. "Speaking fomm medical men," she said in a voice that seemed far away, "you know what?"

"What?" asked Bella.

"I was thinking just now, spose something should happen to me, God fabbid. I would care oney one thing about the doctor—how old is he? I mean, I don't want no young doctor, even if he's a specialist. With

.365

me they'd hafta be an elderly type physician with lotsa experience along the medical line."

"Well, certainey," Bella agreed.

"Listen," Jennie went on. "I'm not saying a young doctor's no good. But with an elderly doctor, I dunno—at lease a person got some confidence in a gray-haired type man."

"Oh, emphatically," said Bella.

"That's why so far as I'm concerned, you can keep your Lew Ayreses. I want no part of them, thank you."

Francey Frompkin, her thoughts lost in a maze of mental traffic, now came to life. "Fa heaven's sake, listen to her! Lew Ayres isn't a doctor, Jennie. He happens to be in the moompickcha game."

"I know that, Francey," said Jennie, a touch of petulance in her manner. "That's exactly what I'm talking about—his pickchas. In the movies, Lew Ayres is constantly taking off a young doctor all the time—Dr. Kildare."

"Oh, I think he's simply wunnaful!" declared Nettie Portnow. "He's so true to life, that Lew Ayres—right down to a T."

"I dunno." Jennie wagged her head sadly and continued to beat the table with her fingers. "A young and good-looking doctor zammining me—I dunno." She squirmed in her chair. "I'd get kinda—well, I'd get kinda embarrassed like. Besides, I simply haven't got the same fate in Lew Ayres like I got in—well, say, in Dr. Gillespie."

"And who, pray, is Dr. Gillespie?" Miss Frompkin wanted to know.

"My God, Francey, where you been all your life? Evveybody knows Dr. Gillespie. It's so obvious like the nose on your face, if you'll excuse me. Dr. Gillespie is Lionel Barrymore, of course!"

"Now, there's a real actor!" Bella cried. "My goodness gracious me, when he gets up there and starts talking to that jury and he says, 'Gentlemen of the jury, sure my client is guilty. But hommany people in this room wouldn't of done the same thing in the same circumstances? Look me in the eye and tell me that!' And when he stands there talking to them and waving his head all the time, honestly, I—I—well, I don't know what!"

"Say, when it comes to taking off a professional man, there's nobody like Lionel, irregardless of what anybody says." Justice compelled Jennie to agree with Bella, but she remained firm in her loyalty to medicine. "Still in all, I like him better when he's a doctor." She rose to her feet, pushed back her chair, and posed dramatically. "There he

366

is, see, all dressed up in white. On his face he's got on a mask like—you know, to keep away the germs fomm the operation. Then he starts in washing his hands." She rolled up her sleeves and illustrated by making big, scooping gestures. "First one arm—that's so he should be sterilized—and then the next arm. And then the nurse comes along to put on the special rubber gloves he's gotta wear to the operation. Oh, he's simply movvelous, that Lionel!"

"Y'know, I once saw a pickcha about a doctor—I can't think of the exact name." Nettie gazed up as if she were looking for an answer in the air and were confident of its quick appearance. She presently shook her head and turned helplessly to Bella. " 'The Sit-something,' I think it was."

" 'The Citadel.' I saw that. With that Robert Donut fella. This was way before he became 'Goodbye, Mr. Chips.' "

"Robert Donut!" Francey Frompkin's features assumed an ecstatic expression as she released her breath in a soft and gurgling sigh. "Boy, oh, boy—some doctor, that Robert! Now there's a fella who can take my pulse any time—and twice on Sundays!"

"Listen," said Jennie, frowning. "He's an English fella, that Robert Donut."

"So what?"

"So by the time you sent away fa a passport and you got to Europe and you waited arounn he should give you an appointment, you'd be a gonner awreddy. Besides," Jennie added, clinging to her argument, "he's a *young* doctor. Say, y'know who's more my type—I mean along the elderly line?"

"Who?" asked Bella.

"Edward G. Robinson."

"Edward G. Robinson—that gangster!" Bella Gross eyed her friend in horror and disgust. "Honestly, Jen, I simply can't unnastann a remark like that. Next thing you know, spose you got gallstones or something like that, God fabbid, you'll be saying to me, 'Howz about I should go to Jimmy Cagney?' at that rate! Why not have the 'Dead End' kids handle your gallstones and be done with it?"

"Wait a minute, Billie, before you jump to any unnecessary conclusions." Jennie compressed her lips, threw back her head and in her most regal tones said, "I happen to be referring *not* to Edward G. Robinson's gangster pickchas, where I admit he's a crook and a dirty rotten thief, I don't care what happens to him. The pickcha I got

367

strickly in my mind is where he's a movvelous elderly type doctor."

"Finstance?" said Bella.

"Finstance a pickcha where he is a mature doctor with a beard on his face. Finstance the pickcha 'Dr. Pasture,' where he takes off a doctor, the biggest in his line. I suppose you gonna sit here and tell me he's not movvelous, that Dr. Pasture?"

"Oh, sure, sure," Bella hastily agreed. "I was thinking you meant Edward G. Robinson where he's a racketeer. Believe me, I wouldn't want that type fella to operate on me for love nor money. That's all I'm saying."

"Parm me fa conterdicting, Jen," said Francey, "but it seems to me that Pul Muni and not Edward G. Robinson played in 'Doctor Pasture.' Am I correct?"

Jennie dug her forefinger into her cheek and stared vacantly at Francey. "You know something? I think you're correct. Still in all, I remember Edward G. Robinson with whiskers on his face and evvey-body called him Doctor. Now lemme think. What pickcha did Edward have whiskers on? I remember it—'The Magic Bullets'!"

"Listen," Bella said, "you just now said he's a doctor and not a gangster. Seems ta me, Jen, that 'Magic Bullets' is more like the type pickcha where people are shooting off pistols and they're excaping fomm prison."

Before Jennie could enlighten her hostess, Francey clapped her hands together. "Ronald Colman!" she murmured, a beatific smile on her face. "Ronald Colman! Gee, I remember when he was Dr. Arrow-smith in the pickcha fomm the same name. Oh, he was a simply movvelous physician!"

"But that's ancient history," insisted Jennie. "O.K., Francey, spose he was a wunnaful doctor then. You know hommany years have passed since that time? Plenty! I bet if you make Ronald Colman a doctor today, it'd be goodbye patient."

Nettie Portnow eyed Jennie sharply, studying her for several seconds before speaking. "I think I got the hundritt-per-cent perfeck doctor fa you Jen," she said. "He's elderly, he's got lotsa medical experience—oh, he's your type positively!"

"Who's that?" Jenny asked.

"Jean Hersholt."

"I remember Jean Hersholt," Bella said. "He took off that doctor fomm way up north—what's his name? Yeah, Dr. Dafoe!"

368

"What'sa matter, Nettie?" said Francey, giggling. "You want Jennie should be Mrs. Dionne the Second and give out with quintuplets yet?"

"Sh-h-h, Francey." Bella turned around to see whether this question had been overheard by the men. "Honestly," she said, "that type vulgarity is extremely unnecessary, specially with the fellas in the same room."

"Dr. Dafoe." Jennie considered the name. "Y'know, right now he would be a very good doctor fa Sarah Fineman's sister's baby. But where do I come to him?"

"I din mean Dr. Dafoe for you," Nettie said. "I'm thinking of Jean Hersholt where he takes off another elderly gentleman—y'know, the one with the religious name. Lemme see now. Dr. Christian. That's the name."

"Well, I—" Jennie began, but further discussion was interrupted by the breaking up of the group in the corner.

"O.K." said Max Fine, taking his place at the head of the table. "If evveybody will kindly occupy a chair, I think we'll commence the meeting and proceed with the aggender." He picked up his gavel, looked slowly around the room, struck the table several times, and said, "In the name of the Excelsior Social Club, I hereby call this meeting to order."

TO A LADY TROUBLED BY INSOMNIA

FRANKLIN P. ADAMS

Let the waves of slumber billow
Gently, softly o'er thy pillow;
Let the darkness wrap thee round
Till in slumber thou art drowned;
Let my tenderest lullabies
Guard the closing of thine eyes;
If *these* fail to make thee weary,
Then I cannot help thee, dearie.

369

AWAKE, AWAKE!

ROBERT BENCHLEY

THE art of awakening people out of a sound sleep is one which needs a little refining. There is too much cruelty abroad. Being awakened at all is bad enough without having it done by a gorilla.

I don't suppose we should blame the Pullman porter because he gives those four vicious tugs at the bottom of your blanket. When it happens, I could leap from my berth and strangle him with my bare hands, but, as I lie there determining to go back to sleep just to spite him, I realize that of all people, Pullman porters have a right to be peremptory in their signals that it is time to get up. With a whole carful of sleepers to whip into shape, they must have a pretty tough time of it.

Sometime I would like to read an article by a Pullman porter detailing the responses—and percentage of direct successes—he gets on his morning rounds. There is a man who sees human nature at its worst.

But, granting the porter's right to make a beast of himself at awakening his charges, who else is justified in being uncharitable about the act? Certainly not friends or relatives of the sleeper. And yet among these we find the worst offenders.

370

There are some people who undergo a complete change of nature when it comes time to get someone else out of bed. Ordinarily they may be sweet-natured, considerate Christians, loath to offend and slow to command. But when the time comes to awaken somebody, a fiendish gleam comes into their eyes and their hands twitch in anticipation.

"Let me get him up," they sometimes beg. "I'll do it." Two fangs appear over their under lips and a hump on their backs, and they tiptoe to the bedroom where the unsuspecting victim is lying, like vampires on some grisly errand.

"Come on, come on!" they shout with glee. "Time to get up!" With this, and before the sleeper has a chance to scowl and gag himself into consciousness, they yank the covers back or shake him violently by the shoulder. The late Jack Pickford had a little whimsey of firing a revolver off in the room of the sleeper. This I do not consider one-tenth as despicable as the personal attacks of those who pretend that they are doing only their duty. A revolver fired to awaken a man is definitely a violation of all codes, a thing so horrendous as almost to be funny. There is no pretense of being anything but a cad of the first water, and I am not so sure that, if awakening has got to be performed, a good revolver shot by the ear is not the kindest method to adopt. At any rate, the sleeper doesn't have those first awful seconds when he thinks that maybe, if he were to pretend to be dead, he would eventually be let alone. He knows that he is dead.

But the hypocrites who, already being awake, cannot bear to see anyone else sleeping, and yet have not the nerve to shoot a gun off, but must pretend that they are doing it for your own good—these are the abominations. As they leer down at you, after their vicious "Come on!" so smug in their superiority and so sure that they are "doing the right thing," they represent the worst element in our civilization—the Brother's Keeper.

If anyone feels that he has to awaken me, I would suggest that he purchase a set of those mellifluous dinner chimes or a small harp, and walk slowly up and down beside my bed, playing something that he knows how to play. It may take a few minutes to bring me to, or it may take a couple of hours, but he will at least have the consolation of knowing that he has behaved like a gentleman and not an unconscionable boor.

And, besides, why does anyone feel that he has to awaken me at all? Did I ever ask to be awakened?

371

THE NEED OF CHANGE

JULIAN STREET

It was in a little pink inn, sticking tenaciously to a Tyrolese mountain-side, that we first met the Denbeighs. They sat facing us at table, an extremely British couple in everything save a disposition to be friendly. On our second day they greeted us with a pleasant "Good morning," and that evening, as Janet and I were sipping coffee on the terrace, Mr. Denbeigh offered me his cigar case, saying, with rapid crisp inflection, a word that sounded like "Smilk?"

I accepted a cigar, and Janet asked Mrs. Denbeigh to show her her crocheting. So we became acquainted.

They were a tall rawboned pair, suggesting—as human beings often do suggest other animals—upstanding Irish hunters. Their clothing was invariably black, Mrs. Denbeigh wearing a short serge skirt that hinted at home amputation, and her husband the reversed collar and notched coat that proclaim the clergyman. Temperature and altitude made no difference. Even on our mountain jaunts their costume was the same. If, in its natural urban environment, the uniform ecclesiastical whispers a scanty purse, among the mountain tops it fairly bellows one. That the Denbeighs were in very modest circumstances we considered evident, and we liked them the more for the grace with which they accepted their condition.

Much as we enjoyed the Tyrol and our new-found friends, Janet and I could not forget that we had never been abroad before and might never come again. Europe is a long way from Canal Dover, Ohio. We had only one month left, and a month is none too much time in which to see Venice, Florence, Rome, Switzerland, and France—unless one is willing to rush about like a mere tourist. When the day of parting came, our regret was mitigated by a cordial invitation from the Denbeighs to visit them at their home in Eastherst, an hour's journey out of London. As we were to sail from England, we accepted eagerly. Not only did we wish to see our friends again, but we felt that a visit to a simple little English household would prove interesting.

On reaching London we wrote to them, announcing our arrival, and early the next morning received a telegraphic invitation to come to them for the week-end.

Saturday afternoon found us on the train bound for Eastherst. A guidebook which we had purchased at the station helped us to enjoy the brief journey by reading of the places we passed. The name of the book is "Picturesque Kent," and its author is the Rev. Adelbert G. de P. Crocks, M.A., F.R.H.S., Rector of Biddlington-on-Blye. We had barely reached Mr. Crocks' descriptions of the charms of Eastherst, when the train stopped there and we alighted. Carrying our two bags and followed by Janet I moved toward the station, wondering if I should find a cab. The only person in sight was a little man, very trim in chauffeur's livery. He came running up and touched his cap.

"Mr. and Mrs. Wooley, sir?"

I admitted it.

"Thenk-you-sir," he said telegraphically. "Boxes in the van, sir?"

Boxes in the van? I must have shown my perplexity, for Janet pinched my arm and murmured: "Trunks," while the man said: " 'Eavy leggage, sir."

"Oh, of course, trunks," I said. "No, I have no trunks. Just these two pieces."

He shot me a quick glance, as if surprised.

"Thenk-you-sir. This way, if you please, sir." Seizing our bags he waddled off.

Following him up the station steps, we found a large limousine awaiting us. The chauffeur, sitting at the wheel, touched his hat as we came up, and I, a little dazed by this unexpected grandeur, touched mine. The little man who had met us on the platform, evidently a footman, opened the car door for us, stowed our bags in the trunk behind, and leaped to the seat beside the driver.

"For heaven's sake!" exclaimed Janet as we moved off. I thought she was going to reprove me for having touched my hat to the chauffeur, but apparently she had not noticed, for she continued: "This can't possibly be the Denbeighs' car, can it?"

I too had been thinking about that.

"Of course not. It must belong to one of Denbeigh's rich parishioners. Rich parishioners are sometimes very good to clergymen, you know."

We were slipping along a sweet, winding lane. To the right was a row of thatched cottages, to the left a high stone wall, behind which stood a row of fine old oaks, their branches spreading out above the road.

After following the wall for some distance we turned in through a gateway, passed a stone lodge, the keeper of which saluted, and proceeded up a drive which wound through ancient woods.

Presently we came to a broad reach of turf. In the foreground a flock of sheep was grazing; in the distance men were playing cricket.

"It seems to be some sort of park," I said. "Let's look it up in the book."

When I say to Janet, "Let's look it up," I always mean, "You look it up."

She produced the little guidebook and ran swiftly through the pages.

"Yes, here it is. Eastherst Park ... Eastherst Hall," and she began to read.

"There is an air of feudal magnificence and solitary grandeur about the castle which neither the ravages of time nor the spoiling hand of man has been able to destroy. Its walls, richly tinted by the tender hand of nature, thrown into relief by magnificent ivy, its beautiful Elizabethan gardens, its imposing façade, its—"

"Ah," I said, "the Denbeighs probably thought we'd enjoy driving through the place on our way."

"Yes, I wonder if we'll see the castle."

"Does anybody live in it?" I asked, craning my neck in search of walls richly tinted by the tender hand of nature, but seeing only trees— for we had left the lawn behind, crossed a stone bridge, and were again winding through thick woods. During this progress Janet had not looked up; she was reading busily.

"There it is!" I cried suddenly as we emerged from the trees.

Without so much as a glance at the splendid building, she leaned toward me, marking with her finger a place in the book:

"Look!"

"But *you* look!" I exclaimed. "The dickens with the book. There's the *castle!*"

"Yes," cried Janet, still pointing to the print, "and *there's* the name of the *people!*"

Her tone startled me. I looked——

". . . seat of the eighth and last Earl of Vibart . . . occupied by his widow until death without issue . . . title became extinct . . . estates reverted to Lady Vibart's niece, Miss Prebyn, who married . . ."

"Go on!" cried Janet, watching me.

". . . who married the Reverend John Arthur Frederick Denbeigh, second son of the Right Honourable Sir Richard Denbeigh, K.C.M.G., M.P., of Denbeigh Court, Stoke-Wetherington, Haversham, Herts."

I had a quick impulse to leap from the car and make a run for it—nevermind my baggage. But there was Janet—I couldn't leave her to face it out alone.

"Joseph!"

"What?"

"*Did you bring evening clothes?*"

"Yes! Did you bring—?"

"My black net and my—"

The motor was stopping before the "imposing façade." The footman leaped to earth and opened the door. I had the sensation of a rat about to be shaken from a wire trap.

The Reverend Mr. Crocks gives nine paragraphs to the principal entrance to Eastherst Hall, "a great, Gothic arch, crowned by the Vibart wolf-dog carved in stone. . . ." I shall not quote him further. Read his book. You will find that a stone bridge, replacing the drawbridge of earlier times, crosses the old moat, now a sunken garden. Great doors have, likewise, superseded the portcullis. One of these doors swung open as we alighted, and two retainers made a rush at us. One took our bags, the other bowed us through the portal. I hoped he did not notice that my legs were shaking. Janet said *she* did.

The hall inside was cool and half dark. I got a vague impression of great space; of huge portraits, massive furnishings—among the latter a large, solemn gentleman in a dress suit, who approached with slow, majestic tread, stopped within six feet of us, bowed splendidly and made a proclamation:

"The Rector and Mrs. Denbeigh's compliments, Sir and Madam, and tea will be served in the blue drawing-room at five o'clock, if you

375

please." Then, turning to a footman: "Tate, you will show Mr. and Mrs. Wooley to their apartments."

Without a word, we followed Tate. The floor was slippery, which made me take short shuffling steps, in place of the stately stride that would have suited the surroundings. At the head of a vast stairway two maids awaited us. They joined the procession, escorting us along the corridor.

First we came to Janet's sleeping chamber. It was blue and white throughout—blue satin paneled walls, white furniture and woodwork. The tennis court in our back yard at home could have been placed in one corner of it and still leave ample room for the patent clothes-driers at either end. Passing through our two dressing rooms, cosy chambers, each covering about an acre, we reached my bedroom. If Janet's was large, what, oh what, was mine! Its area was that of a parade ground. A dark green tapestry hung from the ceiling to the top of a high oak wainscot, and the furniture was also of oak, heavily carved. The bed in particular commanded my attention. It was a four-poster as big as a log cabin and it had an ornamental wooden roof that somehow made me think of a cathedral.

While the servants remained, Janet and I tried to appear barely satisfied with our accommodations. When they departed Janet locked the door, crossed the room and stood for a moment gazing at me. Then, suddenly, we fell into each other's arms.

"A castle!" she cried. "A castle! Oh, these bedrooms! Mine was made for a French marquise with millions and millions of lovers, and yours is a room for a king to die in, surrounded by weeping courtiers and a regiment or two of cavalry!" She pointed at my bed. "You'll never be able to sleep—never! It looks like a safe-deposit vault! Think of walking right into a castle without having your cane and kodak seized and checked by a uniformed attendant! Think of wandering about a castle without narrow strips of canvas and rope railings!"

"For my part," I said, "I rather prefer strips of canvas—they save one from slipping." I was serious, but Janet laughed until tears ran down her cheeks.

"Well," I suggested, "we'd better be unpacking."

"Yes," said Janet, moving toward her room, "and I feel like unwinding a thread so I can find my way back."

My bag was almost empty when there came a rap at the hall door. Outside was a manservant, with a long, equine face, solemn as the grave,

376

and short-cropped hair, sprinkled with gray. He stood as though expecting to come in. "I am to valet you, sir." (He pronounced it val'-et, not val-ay'.)

"Do you wish to—ah—do it now?"

"May I unpack you, sir?"

Ah! so he wished to unpack me. I was unpacked already, but I knew, at once, it wouldn't do to let him find me out.

"You might come back in a few minutes," I said, with an easy, authoritative air.

"Thank you, sir. Very good, sir." He closed the door. I locked it. There was something austere about him that I didn't like. I was glad he hadn't caught me napping. I repacked hurriedly, and had just locked my bag when he knocked again. This time I let him enter.

A dim memory of a story I had read in which the hero "tossed his keys lightly to the valet," made me feel that I ought to toss this valet mine, but something in his solemn face forbade it. I compromised by handing him the keys with a careless gesture. But it was too careless. The keys fell to the floor. We both stooped to pick them up and bumped our heads together.

"Beg pardon, sir," he said. But I knew *he* knew I should have left the picking up to him. It was stupid of me. I felt angry; angry with myself, angry with the valet, angry with the Denbeighs for letting us believe them simple people like ourselves. By what right had they dressed so plainly? It was deceitful. And Denbeigh a minister!

While the valet attacked my bag, I strolled about the room whistling, trying to appear unconscious of his presence; but I watched from the corners of my eyes, for I was anxious to profit by the chance to see a valet in the act of valeting.

He produced my Tuxedo, smoothed it, put it on a hanger, and took it to the closet. As he opened the closet door, a sudden horror gripped me. There, hanging limp upon a hook, was my own bathrobe!

He took it down.

Despite my consternation, my brain worked rapidly. If I said it was not mine he could take it. If I said it was, he would see that I had soiled my lily hands with the menial labor of unpacking and, worse yet, packing up again. I decided on the former course.

"There's a bathgown here, sir."

I looked at it and shook my head indifferently. "Some one must have left it."

"I failed to find your bathgown in your bag, sir."

"H-m, that's odd—very odd."

He examined the robe.

"This is not Lord Wolfendale's bathgown, sir. That I know. His lordship occupied these quarters last week, sir. I recall his lordship's bathgown well, sir. It was of lavender brocade."

"He probably had two," I suggested, looking out of the window.

"This bathgown has the name of an American maker in it, sir," he continued with polite tenacity. "There has been no other American gentleman in Eastherst Hall since I've been here, sir." I distinctly fancied his tone implied: "The old place is going to the dogs."

"Let's see it." I gave up.

He handed me the robe. I turned it over, thoughtfully.

"Well, by Jove!" I exclaimed. "It *is* mine, after all. It's an old one I'd forgotten. Well, well! How in the world do you suppose it got there?" This was intended merely as an ejaculation but the valet chose to take it as a question.

"Really, sir, I can't say, sir." Something in his manner seemed to add: "Civility forbids."

In a last effort to pass the matter off, I mumbled incoherently—I don't know just what—about "Mrs. Wooley" and "neuralgia." I purposed to end the matter there, leaving everything in vagueness. The valet, however, had a disconcerting way of standing at attention when I spoke, thus attaching undue importance to every word I uttered, and this made my final hesitating soliloquy sound altogether idiotic. After waiting to make sure that my maunderings had ceased, he said: "Yes, sir. Thank you, sir," and picking up my shoes, moved toward the door.

378

"What time shall I return, sir?"

I wondered what he meant. He talked of coming before he'd even gone.

"What time should *you* say?" I ventured, as a feeler.

"Four, sir?"

"Yes, four—yes, that's a good idea; four. Of course. Four will do very nicely."

"Very good, sir. Thank you, sir. Four."

"Four; yes."

He went out and closed the four—the door, I mean. I locked it. One soon acquires the habit of locking doors on valets. I was extremely nervous. By way of working off my agitation I danced a little, singing in a low voice:

> "The door at four;
> At four, the door."

In the midst of this performance Janet entered. She was alarmed at first, but I explained. She had been maided, so to speak, while I was being valeted, but had not found the service trying. Women never do. They take to ladies' maids more readily than men do—I mean more readily than men take to valets. No able-bodied, self-respecting man can get used to a valet in a single generation. There must be a hereditary taint. But in spite of the inconvenience, it is the duty of every self-made millionaire to have a valet, consoling himself, meantime, with the thought that by doing so he is building up a family—leaving his sons and grandsons not alone mere money but the nucleus of that taste for laziness and luxury which is recognized as the hallmark of caste. The son will like a valet; the grandson will positively need one. His nurse will give him over to his governess, his governess to his tutor, his tutor to his valet, who will remain in charge until succeeded by a keeper. You see I'm bitter on the subject. *Why* was my valet coming back at four? And was it four P.M or four A.M.?

I asked Janet.

"You mean what four and what for?"

"Yes, dear. I'll be awfully obliged for any help."

Janet, I may say, spent three years at an expensive finishing school in the East, and her prompt reply proved to my satisfaction that the money was well spent.

"He's coming back at four this afternoon to dress you for tea," she said.

"To *dress* me! How will he do it? Where do I stop and where does he begin? Am I to lie upon the bed and let him tuck me into my things, or can I help a little by raising an arm or a leg?"

"I don't know, exactly," she replied. "We didn't learn about valets at Miss Spink's. Think of stories and plays. Didn't the valet in that lovely English play we saw last year tie his master's necktie, and turn up his trousers, and—"

"But my pants are turned up already," I protested. "He can't turn them up any further. I won't allow him to—to go mussing round my pants!"

"Well, you'll have to manage the best you can, dear. I must go and dress," she said, and left me to my fate.

Feeling that it would be awkward to have the valet wash me, I repaired at once to the dressing room, and went through my ablutions. For that, at least, he would be too late. I was clean, dry, and partially arrayed when, at four o'clock precisely, I heard his knock.

Donning the disputed bathgown, I let him in. He bore my shoes and a tall pitcher of hot water. I had understood that the English never use hot water; perhaps he had understood that Americans never use cold.

"Your hot water, sir," he said.

"Thanks, I don't use it," I lied, wishing to show him that, although an alien, I was not unlike the British.

"Thank you, sir. Very good, sir." He put down the pitcher and seized the shirt which I had cast aside. After removing the buttons, he placed them in a fresh garment, extracted from the pitifully small supply the bureau drawer contained. Meantime I strolled about, humming and scrutinizing him cautiously. He brushed the suit I had been wearing and laid it on a chair. This told me that I was not expected to wear another suit to tea.

"Will you dress, sir?" he asked, taking up the shirt and coming at me. I didn't move, merely replying, "Oh, yes."

He advanced and, stepping behind me took hold of the collar of the bathgown. I stood limp and let him slip the garment off. He then raised the shirt. I helped him by lifting my arms and fumbling for the sleeves. The shirt on, we buttoned it together. I had not meant to help him with the buttons, but having raised my own arms I fell into the

380

swing of habit. Our hands interfered most awkwardly.

"Too many cooks spoil the broth," I said, wishing to pass the matter off in jest.

"The broth, sir? You wish some broth?"

"No. I was quoting an old saying."

"Yes, sir. Thank you, sir." He thanked me for everything—and nothing. It was maddening.

Selecting a fresh collar, he attached it to the button at the back, and again we struggled jointly over fastening the front. Having begun, I did not like to drop my hands as though acknowledging my error.

Now came a more disturbing problem. Going to the chair, he took up my pants and came toward me. As he approached, I eyed him as an unarmed man might eye a hungry tiger. Was I to sit down and be pushed into the pants? Was I to jump and alight in them as he held them open to receive me?

He handed me the garments by the top, and stooping, held the legs just off the floor. Ah, so that was it! I slipped in handily and as my feet came through he dropped the ends. This accomplished, he passed the suspenders over my shoulders and made them fast. I was congratulating myself on this success when: "Which scarf, sir?" he inquired.

I selected one. He passed it through the loop upon my shirt. I waited, but he did not make a move to tie it. The valet in the play of which Janet had reminded me tied his master's scarf. I remembered it distinctly. That shows how much faith you can put in plays and stories. They aren't like real life at all. Going to the mirror, I made the knot. Meanwhile the man stood by in frozen silence, holding my vest ready. This gave me a disagreeable sense of being hurried; I tied the scarf abominably and wished to do it over, but I could not bring myself to keep him waiting longer. Limply I let him put me into my vest and coat.

I was now dressed, so far as I could see. Why was he going to the closet? He reappeared with my Tuxedo suit across his arm.

"I don't find your dress coat or your pumps, sir. I wish to prepare them for this evening, sir."

I have no dress coat. In Canal Dover a Tuxedo answers every purpose. As for pumps I haven't owned a pair since the days of dancing school. But I knew it wouldn't do to say so now. Trying to look surprised, I exclaimed: "Not there?"

"No, sir."

"Strange—very strange," I murmured in a thoughtful tone, wondering if Bluebeard's closet made him as much trouble as mine made me. "I must have forgotten them. I guess I'll wear my Tuxedo and patent leather shoes."

"I don't think there's a pair of patent shoes either, sir."

I had said "guess," he said "think"; I had said "patent," he said "paytent," and added "eyther" for good measure. While I was brooding over this he returned to the closet ("clothes-press") and presently emerged with the shoes I had referred to.

"Here's a pair of paytent *boots*, sir." He held them up.

"They're the ones I meant," I explained. "You call them boots, in England, don't you? In America we call them shoes."

"But these are boots, sir." He held them up in proof, and spoke in his usual respectful tone, but something in his manner seemed to add: "Call them anything you like in America—what they really *are* is boots—*boots!*"

This gave me a curious sense of having been shouted down. The American eagle in me gave a cluck of protest.

"I understand perfectly," I began, with dignity, "that over here you call them boots—it had merely slipped my memory. But in America we call the things that come way up here—to the knees, you know, or higher—boots." I felt that my voice was growing shrill and tremulous.

"Yes, sir. Thank you, sir. *Top*-boots. But I don't think your top-boots are here either, sir."

"No, no!" I cried. "I didn't bring top-boots! I didn't mean that! I was only explaining that *we* just say plain *boots!*"

For a brief moment he was silent, thinking his own thoughts. Then: "Very good, sir. Thank you, sir. You'll dress at seven, sir?"

"Yes, at seven," I repeated, as one consenting to a tryst.

"Thank you, sir." With the air of a triumphant collector of curiosities, he left the room, bearing my Tuxedo suit, my *boots*, and the major portion of my self-respect.

"Boots are boots!" said Janet, later. "There's England in a nutshell."

Together, Janet and I descended the magnificent hall stair and were guided by a footman down a long corridor, at the end of which was situated the blue drawing-room. It was with little pleasure that I now anticipated meeting our friends the Denbeighs. Having been obliged to readjust entirely my impression of their "class," I found myself questioning my first judgment of them generally. Had they really been warm and genial? I was not sure. I felt that I should appear strained before them. But Janet would not. No, thank heaven! Janet is always at her ease. The one bright spot within my vision was her graceful figure, there beside me, in a pretty dress of flowered silk. Janet is tall and lithe—a trifle taller and more lithe, perhaps, than I am. I can't describe her better than by saying that she is the acknowledged belle of Canal Dover and looks like a girl on a magazine cover. Glamorous, that's the word. At least I had no fears for *her* as we entered the blue drawing-room.

My speculations on our host and hostess were ended when I saw them. It was as though they had not changed their clothes since we last met, but had, rather, worn them hard. Denbeigh was delightfully baggy, and Mrs. Denbeigh was a cordial, black-clad ironing-board. They seemed to leave the trimness to the servants, I thought, as I watched a footman serving tea. During the light repast we revived memories of the funny people of the Tyrolese inn; later we strolled about the gardens near the house, and by the time we parted to dress for dinner I was beginning to feel quite at home in Eastherst Hall, castle though it was. But my happiness was short-lived. The valet was already in my room. He had my dress shirt in his hands, and presently had me.

Why rehearse again the miseries of being dressed? It is enough to say that they were many, and that when Janet knocked, to ask if I was ready to go down to dinner, I informed her that I was. This was true so far as mere clothing was concerned; for the rest, I was hot, enraged, and helpless.

Once more we descended into the mysterious inferno of downstairs. My boots, as I now admitted them to be, clumped and creaked at every step. Through the drawing-room doorway came the terrifying sound of many voices. It was a party, and we didn't know a soul! They would stare at me, at my Tuxedo, at my boots! My sensation was like that of one possessed by the familiar evil dream in which one finds oneself walking down a street half-clad. Just outside the door, the feeling came so strong upon me that I stopped in my tracks.

"Oh, gosh!" I moaned. "What *are* we going to do? I don't want to go in there!"

Janet looked at me reprovingly.

"Come on!" she ordered.

383

Like a soldier who hears the word of command and obeys though it means death, I advanced.

Near the door, Denbeigh was talking with a plump old lady in a white lace cap and a black silk evening gown which set off, rather startlingly, a mass of handsome jewels, a pair of short, thick arms, and in lieu of neck, a bust.

"As I said to the dear Duchess, only yesterday," I heard her say, with jerky British emphasis, "one simply can't receive the Prince. He's all well enough for the beer and biscuit barons, but the older families—"

Can't receive the Prince! What in heaven's name, then, would she do about me? My hands clutched at the bottom of my abbreviated coat. The room swam about me. I gulped, and shuffled onward, vaguely conscious of being led about in Janet's train (and once upon it) amid a silence unbroken save for the squeaking of my boots and a battery of names—large alarming names. The names bowed and smiled and said things, and I bowed and smiled but didn't speak. Even the slight comfort of repeating the names was forbidden by the names themselves. "My cousin, General the Honorable Sir Penge Cricklewood"—it struck my senses like a sand-bag. I should have liked to call him something, but didn't know which part of it to choose. One after another the names were hurled at me—Lady Swaffield (the one who drew the line at the Prince)—Lady Cricklewood (a pearl-draped Juno)—Lord Beaufoy (called "Bowfee"; pear-shaped head, blond mustache, and high pink cheekbones)—Mr. and *the Honorable Mrs.* Gerald Poole-

384

Saville (invidious distinction, somewhat counterbalanced by a monocle).

Almost at once, General the Honorable Sir Penge Cricklewood presented his arm to Janet, saying that he believed he was to have the honor of going to dinner with her. At the same moment Denbeigh came over to me and said: "Will you take Lady Cricklewood?"

A desperate bravery came over me. Here I was. I must face the matter out. Searching out the blonde Juno, I offered my arm, saying, as I had heard her husband say to Janet: "I believe I am to have the honor," etc.

Momentarily she seemed doubtful then took my arm without a word. It was not until we had fallen into line that I discovered the reason for her hesitation. I had presented her my left arm. It was a natural error, for I am ambidextrous, but none the less embarrassing for that. As the ranks began to move toward the dining room I had a happy inspiration. Allowing the lady's hand to drop, and giving a humorous little leap over her trailing gown, I made the old railroad joke about "changing to the other side of the train."

She looked surprised and somewhat blank.

"Don't you see?" I explained. "In the *joke* it's a train of *cars*, but *I* mean the train of your dress."

"Train?" she repeated in a puzzled way. "It must be a kind of pun, isn't it?"

I hastened to assure her that it was.

"Do you Americans enjoy puns?" she asked. "I've heard you are so clever and original."

"Why—yes; that is—"

"My husband makes them," she declared. "You must ask him to make you some. He's tremendously clever and original."

Dinner went fairly well at first. Lady Cricklewood told me some humorous Scotch stories, the points of which I did not catch, partially because of the difficulties of the dialect and partially because of inattention, for I felt it necessary to listen to the general table talk in the hope of finding out the proper methods of addressing titles.

In this I was disappointed. They seemed to call the Honorable Mrs. Gerald Poole-Saville "Belle"; Lady Swaffield was "Aunt" to the Denbeighs, while General the Honorable Sir Penge Cricklewood was "Cricky." The four footmen, who served, said "Your Lordship" to Lord Beaufoy and "Your Ladyship" to Lady Cricklewood and Lady

Swaffield. In a story that was told it developed that Lady Swaffield was otherwise the Countess of Swaffield, and that her husband was the Earl of same.

This assorted information was all that I could glean, and I was principally concerned with avoiding the necessity of addressing anyone directly. The ices had been served, when my attention was attracted by a burst of laughter from General the Honorable Sir Penge Cricklewood.

"There!" said the lady at my right. "There, Mr. Wooley, you must ask my husband to tell you that one—you really must, you know."

Trying to assume an expression at once pleasant and compelling, I turned an eager face in his direction. He continued to chuckle at his sally, looking about the table for approval, but I could not catch his eye.

"He's so clever and original," his wife declared, admiringly.

I was becoming quite uneasy, when:

"Penge," the lady said, "Mr. Wooley is very fond of jokes. *Do* tell him yours about the potato clock."

"Certainly!" he cried. "Delighted, I'm sure. Mr. Wooley, did you ever see a potato clock? What?"

I said I hadn't.

"No? Well, I got *up at eight o'clock* this morning!"

He burst into volcanic laughter. I joined, politely.

"And now, Mr. Wooley," said this hero of a thousand verbal slaughters, "You must give us some of your American jokes."

"Yes—yes," said the Countess of Swaffield, fastening a fishy eye upon me. "I have heard that you Americans are very droll. Do tell us some of your amusing tales."

A hideous silence fell about the table. The whole world seemed to stop, look and listen. My heart pumped savagely against the bosom of my shirt. My ears sang. Groping in desperate haste among dusty pigeon-holes of memory, I seized something—anything—and drew it out.

"Well, I don't set myself up as a story teller, you know, but—well, there was once a Frenchman, an Englishman and an American and they were having an argument as to what—"

At this point it struck me that Janet was staring at me strangely.

"—They were having an argument as to what really constitutes a joke," I continued bravely.

386

Janet's face took on a look of horror.

"The Frenchman said that he thought a joke was—"

My wife shook her head violently. There was no mistaking her meaning. I stopped short. She was right—the story wouldn't do. It depended on an exaggerated English dialect—on making the Englishman a fool.

"Yes—?" put in General the Honorable Sir Penge Cricklewood, when the pause had reached a ghastly length. "What did the Frenchman say, Mr. Wooley, eh?"

"To tell the truth," I declared, blushing up into my hair, "I was trying to remember what he *did* say. You see I don't set up as much of a story teller. I haven't told this one in a long time. Somehow it doesn't quite come to me."

There was an aching silence.

"We must have it later, Mr. Wooley, when you recall it," said Mrs. Denbeigh, with kindly tact.

The male Cricklewood stared for a moment, cast a sidelong glance at Janet, and burst into a roar of laughter.

"Ah ha!" he said. "I see! I see! Not precisely a dinner-table story, eh? Well, we shall have it with the port, Mr. Wooley—what?"

He had intercepted Janet's signal and mistaken its significance. Little as I liked his interpretation, I preferred it to the alternative of rank stupidity.

When, shortly after this, the ladies withdrew and the port came on, I devoted all my energies to drawing out the military punster. Tiresome as this occupation was, I vastly preferred it to the paradoxical alternative of trying to finish an improper story which had never existed.

After he had smoked one good cigar and made four bad puns, we withdrew to the music room, where the Honorable Mrs. Gerald Poole-Saville and Lady Cricklewood sang French and German songs, which everybody seemed to understand. I was glad of the chance to sit down quietly and merely applaud and smile at intervals; gladder still when the butler announced Lady Swaffield's motor at the door and the company broke up.

Janet was charmed with it all. I wanted to discuss the situation with her, but her maid was waiting and I felt obliged to leave her at her bedroom door. I was shocked to find the maid up at so late an hour.

387

The servants ought to be in bed. I hoped my valet was. The thought of being put to bed by him was horrible. Opening the door I was delighted to discover that he was not in my room. But I had barely started to remove my collar when I heard the familiar, dreaded, "Rap, rap, rap!"

I waited in silence, hoping he would go away, but he knocked again, this time a little louder. It was a compelling knock that could not be ignored.

"Who is it?"

"Herne, sir."

"You needn't trouble about me tonight," I said, unlocking the door and looking at him as kindly as I could. "I'm sorry you sat up. I can manage very nicely."

"Thank you, sir. Very good, sir. But I have some water for you, sir." He made as if to come in.

I placed my foot against the door. Once inside, he would not leave until he had undressed me, heard my prayers, and tucked me in.

"Just give me the water," I said, reaching through the narrow opening.

He placed the carafe in my hand reluctantly, I thought, and with a "Good night, sir," closed the door.

Donning the bathgown of my shame I made the pilgrimage to Janet's room, intent on talking matters over, but she was in the clutches of the maid. Knowing the futility of waiting, I returned to my kingly suite and after some silent moments devoted to moody contemplation of the appalling bed I was to occupy, shut off the electric light and clambered in. The bed proved comfortable—more so than my own reflections.

Nor were my dreams agreeable. I ran, climbed, jumped, pursued by

countless servants who wished to put me through an exaggerated toilet. Like a terrified figure in a moving picture, I fled through the woods, across rivers, up hills and down, through great houses where I rushed from room to room slamming the doors behind me. It was in my own vast chamber that they cornered me at last. I piled the furniture against the door. Outside they yelped and pounded. The door began to give—give. As I rushed for the closet, they burst in, seized me and— I awoke.

My shriek of terror, as they caught me, was ringing in my ears. I did not open my eyes, but lay there shivering and thankful. After all, it had been only a nightmare.

This comforting reflection was broken, suddenly, by the sound of stealthy footsteps. A flash of the dream-horror shot through me. I opened my eyes.

By the dresser, motionless, his back turned toward me, stood the living figure of the tyrant of my dreams. If he had heard the cry I gave at the termination of the nightmare, he believed that I still slept. He was gazing at something, something soft, which he held aloft derisively in his two hands. I recognized the something instantly. It was underwear—the nether part of a single suit which I had bought in Paris—pink, with red stripes running round and round. Alas, where it had once seemed merely giddy, it achieved now, in the valet's hands, an appearance ribald and indecent.

Putting the garment down, the man fumbled the contents of the open drawer. Then, with a cynical shake of the head, he drew forth a plain balbriggan undershirt and, placing it beside the vicious drawers, surveyed the ghastly combination.

The horrid truth now burst upon me. The pink and red suit would have been bad enough, but, worse, I had brought but a half-portion of it. The man was gloating over the uncanny combination I should have to wear. He would stand by in grim, insulting silence and make me put it on.

Contemplation of this new catastrophe plunged me into panic as acute as I had suffered in my dreams. Closing my eyes in pretense of sleep, I struggled with my scattered thoughts. My breath came heavily; I wished to gasp, but feared to draw my servitor's attention. Peeping through my lashes, I saw him bear the depraved garments to the dressing room and drape them gracefully across a chair. Emerging, he moved toward the hall door. This roused a sudden hope. If he went out I would spring up and turn the key. Why, oh why, had I failed to take that precaution ere retiring? The door had been unlocked all night. No doubt he had come in from time to time and, leaning vampire-like, had listened to the frightened babblings of my dreams.

My back was toward the door; I was eager to see if he had left the room, but did not dare turn over. A rumbling metallic sound came from behind me. When my tormentor reentered my narrow range of vision he was trundling a large tin bathtub. After placing it in the dressing room, he went again to the hall; again I waited, praying that the door might close; again he reappeared, this time with two great metal pitchers. As the water splashed into the tub, a new vista of dismay was opened for me. Would he bathe me? Thoughts of resistance galloped through my mind. I would refuse, point-blank, to rise. I would defy him! But even as I planned, I knew I had not courage to oppose his orders; orders which a formal drapery of servile language seemed to make only more imperative.

Emerging from the dressing room, he gazed at me for a long moment during which I ceased to peep between my lashes. I do not think he penetrated my 'possum-like defense, for he now ceased to tread quietly and, walking to the door, rapped briskly. My time had come! I turned over, rubbed my eyes, and looked at him.

"Good morning," I let fall in an apathetic voice. "What sort of a day is it?"

"Good morning, sir. Bright and fine. Your bath is ready, sir."

I must trick him into leaving.

"Is my shaving water here?"

"It is, sir." That hope took flight.

"Please give me a glass of water."

Going to the table, he poured a glass from a fresh carafe.

I drank it very slowly, striving to think of something he had not already brought. Then, looking at the ceiling as I handed him the empty glass: "Herne," I said, "I'm very fond of flowers. Could you get me a few roses for that bowl?"

In the brief pause which followed I knew I had defeated him.

"Very good, sir." He moved toward the door, and it had hardly closed when I turned the key. Slipping out of my pyjamas as I went, I made for the dressing room. My plan was settled. By clothing myself hurriedly and foregoing my bath I would cheat my persecutor of the chance to see me in the shameful underwear. I snatched the revolting garments from the chair. But no! The clear bath water caught my eye. It would betray me. Time was short, but I must soil the water. I tested the temperature with my foot and was shocked at the glacial touch. Catching up soap and wash-cloth I rinsed them violently in the tub. The result was a gratifying gray. Ceasing only long enough to slip into my undergarments I repeated the operation. The water now took on a hue so murky that I began to fear that by discoloring it too much I had opened a new field for the valet's speculations on my habits. As a final touch of realism I spattered water on the mat and towels. This accomplished, I resumed my dressing, conducting it with such dispatch that the detested "Rap, rap, rap!" found me safe in shirt and trousers.

I fancied I detected a fleeting look of disappointment in the equine eyes as they observed the progress I had made. Having placed the roses on the table, Herne assisted me silently with the remainder of my toilet; nor did I forget to make occasional excursions to the bowl of flowers, gazing and smelling at them like an impassioned horticulturist. When at last there was absolutely nothing more for Herne to do, he left the room—reluctantly, I thought.

Sinking into a chair to review the situation, I was struck by a new thunderbolt of apprehension. I rose quickly and, after taking the usual precaution, hastened to the dresser. My worst fears were confirmed by a brief investigation of its contents. There was not another undergarment there.

Bad as was the last dilemma, this one was infinitely worse. The thought of wearing a suit of underwear a second time while staying in a castle, was incongruous, but that of being valeted into this ill-assorted underwear again upon the morrow, when it would lack even the pitiful excuse of freshness, was insupportable. What was to be done? Time would go on in its inexorable flight. To-morrow's sun must rise, and so must I. One course alone was open.

When Janet entered, ready to go down to breakfast, I was laying plans.

"Good morning, dear," she cried. "You ought to have been out long ago. It's a gorgeous day. I've been in the rose garden with Mrs. Denbeigh, and I've such a surprise for you—"

"Janet," I broke in peevishly, "you ought to knock before coming in. You startled me. I thought it was the valet."

"Indigestion again?" she suggested, it seemed to me irrelevantly.

391

"Nothing of the kind!" I had meant to tell her all, but the conversation had opened unpropitiously.

"Oh, yes. I know your symptoms."

"I need a sea voyage, or something."

"You'll have one next week."

"I need it now. This place doesn't agree with me."

"Take this instead," she said, handing me a digestive tablet. "And wait until you hear my news!"

I took the tablet gloomily.

"What news? Are we going?"

"Going! Just the opposite! We're to stay over for the County Ball, to-morrow night. It's the great event of the season. We'll see *every* one. There'll be a duke and duchess there—I mean to dance with the duke, too! Why, we'll—"

"Janet," I began, solemnly, but she cut me short.

"Oh, come on down to breakfast. You'll feel better afterwards."

My mind was made up. Janet liked Eastherst Hall, and fitted it. She could go to the County Ball. For my part I should act, and act alone. The valet should harass me no more. No county families, no duke and duchess, should gaze upon my Tuxedo and my boots unless they pursued me all the way to Canal Dover.

Sad, but determined, I rose and followed Janet down to breakfast. It proved to be one of those fine old English meals, comprising eggs and bacon, scones, marmalade, and tea with rich cream. Just the breakfast that I like. But Janet's statement that I had an attack of indigestion wanted bearing out, so I took only tea and toast. I don't like tea and toast.

"I know all about this Sunday morning indigestion," said Mrs. Denbeigh, smiling. "You may stay home from church, Mr. Wooley. That will cure it."

"Oh, no, indeed," I said. "I *want* to go to church. I don't wish to miss Mr. Denbeigh's sermon."

"What is the sermon to be about?" asked Janet.

"Your husband's namesake, Joseph, and his coat of many colors," he returned.

I felt the warm blood mounting to my hair. Of course mine wasn't a *coat*, but it might be fairly called the next thing to it.

"Why, Joseph!" cried Janet. "You have a *face* of many colors now. What is it?"

392

"I'm a little feverish, I think."

At this Mrs. Denbeigh said it was settled that I should not go to church.

"Herne will stay and see to you," she added. "He's excellent in a sick room."

"No, no!" I cried. "I wouldn't think of breaking in on the poor fellow's Sunday—not for worlds! I'm not really ill; only indisposed. Perhaps I *had* better stay here, but *he* mustn't—no indeed!" I feared for the moment that I had been too vehement. Would they suspect me, later? I said no more. The question was allowed to drop, on the understanding, I took it, that I should stay and Herne should not.

My scant meal over, I retired hungry to my room, cast myself into a chair, and there remained until I heard the motor drive away.

They were gone. The time for action had arrived. Hastily I collected my belongings and flung them into my bag, consulted a time-table, and scrawled a note to Janet.

"Going to London. Tell them I was sick. Don't worry. Am all right. Will explain later. Expect you on train arriving Victoria Station about noon Tuesday.

"With love,

"Joseph.

"P.S.—Be sure to tip all servants well."

Sealing the envelope, I placed it on Janet's dresser. Then I opened the hall door and listened. The house was silent. Taking up my bag I tiptoed to the stairs and peered into the hall below. Deserted. I descended stealthily and was making for the outer door when another door opened and I found myself face to face with Herne.

As I look back on this occasion I am astonished at the coolness I displayed.

"I thought you were at church, Herne."

"No, sir, I——"

"Herne," I interrupted, "I've been taken ill and am going up to London to consult a specialist."

Herne looked politely alarmed. "Very sorry, sir. Might I ask the nature of the ailment, sir?"

"Appendicitis," I fired at random, suiting the word with a twisting of the body and a grimace intended to suggest sharp pain.

393

"In that case, sir," said Herne, "you will be glad to know that the estate of Sir Frederick Bownes, one of our great surgeons, adjoins Eastherst Park. Appendicitis is Sir Frederick's speciality."

"But I'm not certain it's appendicitis," I explained. "That's just the trouble. It may be lungs. I was just thinking that the pain comes rather high for appendicitis, and"—I coughed violently—"you see I cough."

"Yes, sir, but Sir Frederick—"

"It would be most unfortunate," I interrupted, edging toward the door, "if Sir Frederick took out my appendix and then discovered it was lungs after all."

"Indeed it would, sir."

"So that's why I've decided to go to London and see my regular specialist. I must hurry to catch the train."

"I'll have a car around at once, sir, and I'll be ready in a moment." So saying, he dispossessed me of my bag.

"No, don't send for a car. I'll walk."

"But the car—"

"I need the walk. It will do me good."

"Very well, sir. As you wish. I'll come along with the bag after procuring my hat and coat."

"But why? I can take the bag. It's light."

"Of course, sir, I shall accompany you to London."

"No, no! You mustn't think of it! It won't do at all! I must go alone. I'm perfectly well except for occasional slight pain, but I'm very nervous—it makes me nervous to have people near! Besides, it may be something infectious. You'd catch it. I've heard that bubonic plague begins with pains like I have. No indeed, you mustn't come!"

"It would be as much as my place is worth to let you leave alone and ill, sir," he said firmly. "Mrs. Denbeigh's express orders were that I should watch after you, sir."

Open resistance was useless. I must resort to cunning.

"I'm sure it's very good in you," I said, submissively. "The fact is, I'm feeling much better now. Perhaps I won't have to go after all. I'll just walk about the rose garden and see how I feel. Then, if I decide to go, perhaps you *had* better come along."

"Thank you, sir. Very good, sir. In the meantime I'll fetch my hat and coat so I shall be ready, sir, at all events."

He started for the door, but with his hand upon the knob, hesitated.

Then he turned back and took my bag from the corner where he had set it down, saying:

"I had best keep your bag by me, sir. Most of the other servants are at church, and strangers have a way of prowling about the park, or even entering the hall itself, sir."

The instant he left I broke for the open air. No one was in sight. The drive stretched out before me like an invitation. Along that line lay freedom. If only I had my bag! Yet have not hundreds of men made long and perilous journeys without bags? And after all, what did mine contain? Merely a few toilet articles, a little clothing, and—sickening thought—some crumpled underwear.

I looked at my watch. A scant half hour lay between me and the train. Herne was by this time in the servants' quarters, at a remote corner of the castle. It was now or never! I started down the drive at a brisk gait and when I reached the cover of the woods, quickened my pace to a trot.

On emerging at the other side of the little forest I slowed to a rapid walk, fearing that I might be noticed, but another glance at my watch sufficed to make me oblivious of appearances. Eighteen minutes! Again I trotted on, slowing to a walk only as I passed the lodge. The gate-keeper surveyed me critically, but saluted as I hurried by.

In the village street I could not run without becoming too conspicuous. I walked rapidly—very rapidly. Presently I recognized the thatched cottages I had seen as we arrived. How long ago it seemed! What sweet little homes they were! What deliciously untrammeled lives their tenants led—the mothers without maids, the children without nurses, the fathers without valets.

I was in sight of the station when the shrill whistle of a locomotive spurred me on. That train must be caught. If not, I should be! I fancied Herne making me captive, dragging me back to Eastherst Hall, stripping me at once of freedom and fantastic undergarments, putting me to bed, summoning the famous British surgeon and robbing me of my appendix—all before the family returned from church. The vision of death was hardly less repulsive than that of a long convalescence with Herne forever playing nurse. I ran frantically.

The train and I approached the station simultaneously. It had stopped ere I bounded down the steps. As I attained the platform, the carriage doors were slamming shut; the cars began to move.

I heard a shout behind me. A man was making wild gestures with an umbrella and telling me to stop. I rushed on. The train gathered speed. A red-faced guard on the platform caught me by the sleeve, but I shook him off. The last car was passing. There was an open window and I jumped for it. My hands gripped the sash; my feet found the footboard. I was on if not in the train!

Looking through the window, I met the astonished gaze of an old gentleman. He had white side whiskers, and a pleasant face.

"Hello, hello, hello!" he remarked. "You'd best come in out of that!"

He extended his hand, and with its aid I scrambled through head first.

He gazed at the receding station, then:

"Hello, hello, hello!" he said. "Friend of yours?"

I looked back. There, upon the platform, stood Herne. My bag lay at his feet. Even at that distance it was plain that he was a very different Herne from the one I had left at Eastherst Hall. His face had lost its stolid, equine expression. It was red and full of wrath. His collar was undone; it stood out jauntily at one side, like a wing. He was pointing after the receding train and saying something—something vehement, I judged, from the faint bellowings that reached me above the rumble of the cars. He seemed to be addressing the world in general, and the guard who had not stopped me in particular. Was he perhaps stating his opinion of my underwear?

Janet telegraphed that she would come to London on the four o'clock train. She did so, bringing my bag and her own opinions.

As we drove across the city, I tried to explain, but it was difficult, as I had feared it would be.

"But what on earth possessed you to run away like that?" she scolded.

She did not know that certain invisible red stripes were helping her to grill me.

"I simply *had* to have a change," I said.

396

FOWL PLAY

IAN HAY

TOOT, TOOT, TOO-O-O-T!

The punctilious motorist, bowling along a Scottish highway at twenty
miles an hour, had espied a small farmstead by the roadside—a group
of insignificant whitewashed buildings. He disengaged his clutch, applied
gentle pressure to the footbrake, and blew three long and considerate
blasts upon his horn.

Instantly there came a rush, a scramble, and a scurry; and a perfect
avalanche of hens dashed out of a gateway into the path of the car,
intent apparently upon indulgence in the risky but fascinating pastime
of "Last across the road." They were followed by a waddling cohort of
ducks. Both brakes went on hard, but it was too late to do anything.
Before the slithering motor-car could be brought to a standstill, it had
ploughed its way right through the squawking, fluttering mob of fowls
—the ducks had prudently halted and turned tail—and taken full toll.

"Fairly asked for it that time, they did," observed Charles the chauffeur reposing in the back seat.

But the conscience-stricken owner of the car drew up at the side of
the road and alighted. Simultaneously a patriarchal and wrathful old

397

gentleman in tweed knickerbockers and a Balmoral bonnet emerged at the double from the farm gate. He was followed by a silly-looking youth of fourteen.

The old gentleman surveyed the havoc—two hens lying dead upon the road, while another scuttered in the dust with a broken wing—and raised clenched hands to heaven.

"Is that the way," he roared, "for a body tae gang raging past a man's farm gate?"

He crossed the road, and, picking up the hen with the broken wing, wrung its neck methodically. Then he turned again to the assassins, as if seeking further necks. The chauffeur, affecting extreme terror, took refuge behind the car. But the farmer addressed himself to the arch-culprit.

"What for," he demanded, "could ye no give a bit toot on your horn?"

"I did," said the owner meekly; "three times."

The old gentleman turned to his simple-looking companion.

"Heard ye ever the like of that?" he inquired in outraged tones.

The boy shook his head, obviously pained that a man should be so depraved as to add falsehood to murder.

"I'll need tae be asking you gentlemen for your names and addresses," pursued the owner of the fowls grimly; "for tae give tae the polis. We canna allow—"

"Not *quite* so much of it, if you please," requested the chauffeur,

lighting a cigarette. "You know you ain't no legal rights over us at all. If you choose to allow your chickings to wander all over the bloomin' road, they must put up with the consequences—see? Ain't that right, sir?"—to his employer.

The employer, who was quite as hazy upon Scots law as the chauffeur himself, nodded timidly.

"Of course I am quite willing to pay for the fowls killed," he said.

At this the owner of the slaughtered animals made a distinct and obvious effort to mitigate the severity of his expression—no light feat when you possess a long, lean face encompassed by whiskers, together with a clean-shaven upper lip.

"I canna tak' less than ten shillings a heid for them," he announced.

"Reg'lation price for a hen is four-and-six," interposed the chauffeur, glib from long practice in such computations.

The farmer turned a pitying eye upon him.

"Man," he inquired witheringly, "have ye ever rin over a hen before?" The chauffeur tactfully ignored this query. He turned to his employer.

"Six 'alf-crowns will do him proud, sir," he announced confidently.

The bereaved owner fought for breath.

"Can you no see for yoursels what sort these hens are?" he roared. "There's nane like them for twenty miles. It's lucky for you the guidwife is no in, or ye'd get a sorting frae her, I'm telling you! She had a name for every birrd on the place."

"What's the name of that one in your 'and?" inquired the chauffeur. "George Washington?"

But his contrite employer begged him by a gesture to refrain from complicating the negotiations by badinage, and was about to speak, when the venerable orator broke forth afresh.

"They're no the thrawn hauf-starved beasts ye would be getting in the south. Did ever ye rin over sic hens as those in the streets of London?"

The owner of the motor-car, with the old gentleman's basilisk eye piercing his very soul, was constrained to admit he never had.

"Then gie us seven-and-six a heid for them," was the prompt reply.

"Tirpitz, old feller," observed the chauffeur with conviction, "you are absolutely It. Six 'alf-crowns is what you'll get—and easy money too!"

The old man turned with a dramatic gesture to his companion.

"Away and bring the polis!" he cried.

"Can I drive you?" inquired the chauffeur politely. "I noticed a copper about fifteen miles back. Diggin' potatoes in a field, 'e was."

"Say six-and-six," said the owner of the motor-car, looking at his watch.

The final compromise was six-and-nine. The chauffeur was anxious to retain the corpses, as was his undoubted right; but the owner of the car was five hundred miles from home and declined to burden himself with decomposing poultry. Five minutes later, after a constrained farewell, the car and its occupants disappeared from sight over the hill.

The old gentleman slipped the money into his pocket and handed the bodies of the slain to the silly-faced boy.

"Take you these tae the mustress, Jock," he said, "and tell her I'm roarin' for my dinner. And feed the hens before you get your ain!" His eyes snapped.

The silly-faced boy nodded and disappeared within. Presently he returned. In one hand he carried a bowl of Indian corn, in the other an aged motor-horn.

He walked out of the gate, and, having emptied the contents of the bowl into the very middle of the highway, sounded his horn long and loudly.

The hens rushed out.

HOW BEAUTIFUL WITH MUD

HILDEGARDE DOLSON

PERHAPS the surest way to tell when a female goes over the boundary from childhood into meaningful adolescence is to watch how long it takes her to get to bed at night. My own cross-over, which could be summed up in our family as "What on earth is Hildegarde *doing* in the bathroom?" must have occurred when I was a freshman in high school. Until then, I fell into bed dog-tired each night, after the briefest possible bout with toothbrush and washcloth. But once I'd become aware of the Body Beautiful, as portrayed in advertisements in women's magazines, my absorption was complete and my attitude highly optimistic. I too would be beautiful. I would also be Flower-Fresh, Fastidious and Dainty—a triple-threat virtue obviously prized above pearls by the entire male sex, as depicted in the *Ladies' Home Journal*.

Somehow, out of my dollar-a-week allowance, I managed to buy Mum, Odorono, Listerine and something called Nipso, the latter guaranteed to remove excess hair from arms and legs, and make a man think, "Oooo, what a flawless surface." It's true that I had no men, nor was I a particularly hairy child, having only a light yellow down on my angular appendages. Nevertheless, I applied the Nipso painstakingly in the bathroom one night, with Sally as my interested audience. I had noticed the stuff had a rather overpowering, sickish sweet scent, but this was a very minor drawback, considering the goal I had in mind. After Sally had been watching me for a few minutes, she began holding her nose. Finally she asked me to unlock the door and let her out. "Don't you want to see me wash it off?" I asked, rather hurt.

"No," Sally said. "It smells funny."

In the next hour, as my father, mother and brothers followed their noses to the upstairs hall, there were far more detailed descriptions of just how Nipso affected the olfactory senses. Jimmy, being a simple child, merely said "Pugh" and went away. My father thought it was

401

most like the odor of rotten eggs, but Bobby said No, it was more like a mouse that's been dead quite a while. Mother was more tactful, only remarking that Nipso obviously wasn't meant to be applied in a house people lived in. Since it certainly wasn't meant to be applied in a wooded dell, either, I was prevailed upon to throw the rest of the tube away.

I didn't mind too much, because I already had my eye on something that sounded far more fascinating than Nipso. This was a miraculous substance called Beauty Clay, and every time I read about it in a magazine advertisement, the words enveloped me in rapture. Even the story of its discovery was a masterpiece in lyrical prose. Seems this girl was traveling in an obscure European country (name on request) and ran out of those things ladies always run out of at the wrong time, such as powder and make-up lotion. The worst part was that the girl really *needed* such artifices to cover up bumps. Through some intuitive process which escapes me at the moment, she had the presence of mind to go to a near-by hamlet, pick up a handful of mud, and plaster it on her face. Then she lay dozing in the sun, by a brook. When she came to, washed the claylike mud off her face, and looked at her reflection in the brook, she knew she had hit the jackpot. Boy, was she beautiful. Looking at the Before-and-After pictures, I could see that *this* beauty was more than skin-deep, having benefited even her nose, eyes and hair.

After pondering all this, I could well understand why a jar of the imported Beauty Clay cost $4.98. In fact, it was dirt cheap at the price, and my only problem was how to lay my hands on $4.98. Certainly I had no intention of enlisting financial support from my parents. For one thing, it was too much money, and for another thing, parents ask too many questions. Far better, I thought, to let the transformation of their oldest daughter come as a dazzling surprise.

Due to the fact that I had such important things as Beauty Clay on my mind, it was understandable that my monthly marks in algebra should cause even more distress than usual in the bosom of my family. Each month, the high-school honor roll, consisting of the names of the ten highest students in each class, was published in the *Franklin News-Herald*. (The *Herald*, as I'd known it on Armistice Day, had been taken over by the *News*.) And each month, my own name was prominently absent. Appeals to my better nature, my pride, and the honor of the Dolsons did no good. I honestly meant well, and I even went so far

402

as to carry books home from school and carry them back again the next morning. But freshman algebra, implying as it did that X equals Y, was simply beyond me. Finally my father said that if I got on the Honor Roll he'd give me five dollars. Wobbly as I was in mathematics, it took me only a flash to realize this sum was approximately equal to $4.98, or the piddling price of the Beauty Clay. From there on in, I was straining every muscle. When I say that I got 89 in algebra and climbed to the bottom rung of the Honor Roll, I am stating a miracle simply. What is more important, I got the five bucks.

My father said that if I liked, he'd put most of it in my savings account. Bobby said, with even more enthusiasm, that he knew where I could get a bargain in a second-hand pistol. I declined both offers, marveling at the things men could think of to do with money, and made my way, on foot, to Riesenman's drugstore. When Mr. Riesenman said he had no Beauty Clay, I was grieved. When he said he'd never even heard of the stuff, I was appalled. It took three trips to convince him that he must order it immediately, money on the line.

Then I went home and waited. With admirable restraint, I waited five days. After that, I made daily inquiries on my way home from school. If I was with friends, I'd say I had to do an errand for Mother and would catch up to them later. They must often have wondered, in the next thirty days, at the number of unobtainable items my mother demanded of a drugstore. Finally came the wonderful afternoon when Mr. Riesenman said, "Here you are, Hildegarde." His jovial air may have been due to the fact that he was rid of me at last. My own joy was primitive and unconfined. At last I'd got hold of a rainbow.

It took a week more before I could achieve the needed privacy for my quick-change act. Mother was taking Jimmy and Sally down town to get new shoes, Bobby was going skiing, and my father, as usual, would be at the office. I got home to the empty house at twenty minutes of four, and made a bee-line for the Beauty Clay. According to the directions, I then washed off all make-up, which in my own case was a faint dash of powder on my nose, and wrapped myself in a sheet "To protect that pretty frock," or, more accurately, my blue-serge middy blouse. Then I took a small wooden spatula the manufacturer had thoughtfully provided, and dug into the jar.

The Beauty Clay was a rather peculiar shade of grayish-green, and I spread this all over my face and neck—"even to the hairline where tell-tale wrinkles hide." The directions also urged me not to talk or

403

smile during the twenty minutes it would take the clay to dry. The last thing in the world I wanted to do was talk or smile. That could come later. For now, a reverent silence would suffice. In fact, as the thick green clay dried firmly in place, it had to suffice. Even though my face and neck felt as if they'd been cast in cement, the very sensation reassured me. Obviously, something was happening. I sat bolt upright in a chair and let it happen.

After fifteen minutes of this, the doorbell rang. I decided to ignore it. The doorbell rang again and again, jangling at my conscience. Nobody at our house ever ignored doorbells, and I was relieved when it stopped. In my eagerness to see who had been calling on us, I ran to my window, opened it, and leaned out. The departing guest was only the man who brought us country butter each week, I was glad to note. Hearing the sound of the window opening above him, he looked up. When he saw me leaning out, his mouth dropped open and he let out a hoarse, awful sound. Then he turned and ran down the steep hill at incredible speed. I couldn't imagine what had struck him, to act so foolish.

It wasn't until I'd remembered the clay and went to look in a mirror that I understood. Swathed in a sheet, and with every visible millimeter of skin a sickly gray-green, I scared even myself.

According to the clock, the Beauty Clay had been on the required twenty minutes, and was now ready to be washed off. It occurred to me that if twenty minutes was enough to make me beautiful, thirty minutes or even forty minutes would make me twice as beautiful. Besides, it would give me more lovely moments of anticipation, and Mother wouldn't be home till after five.

By the time my face was so rigid that even my eyeballs felt yanked from their sockets, I knew I must be done, on both sides. As I started back to the bathroom, I heard Bobby's voice downstairs yelling "Mom!" With the haste born of horror I ran back and just managed to bolt myself inside the bathroom as Bobby leaped up the stairs and came down the hall toward his room. Then I turned on the faucet and set to work. The directions had particularly warned "Use only gentle splashes to remove the mask—No rubbing or washcloth." It took several minutes of gentle splashing to make me realize this was getting me nowhere fast. Indeed, it was like splashing playfully at the Rock of Gibraltar. I decided that maybe it wouldn't hurt if I rubbed the beauty mask just a little, with a nailbrush. This hurt only the nailbrush. I myself remained embedded in Beauty Clay.

By this time, I was getting worried. Mother would be home very soon and I needed a face—even any old face. Suddenly it occurred to me that a silver knife would be a big help, although I wasn't sure just how. When I heard Bobby moving around in his room, I yelled at him to bring me a knife from the dining-room sideboard. Rather, that's what I intended to yell, but my facial muscles were still cast in stone, and the most I could do was grunt. In desperation, I ran down to the sideboard, tripping over my sheet as I went, and got the knife. Unfortunately, just as I was coming back through the dusky upstairs hall, Bobby walked out of his room and met me, face to face. The mental impact, on Bobby, was terrific. To do him justice, he realized almost instantly that this was his own sister, and not, as he had at first imagined, a sea monster. But even this realization was not too reassuring.

I had often imagined how my family would look at me after the Beauty Clay had taken effect. Now it had taken effect—or even permanent possession of me—and Bobby was certainly reacting, but not quite as I'd pictured it.

"Wh-what?" he finally managed to croak, pointing at my face.

His concern was so obvious and even comforting that I tried to explain what had happened. The sound that came out alarmed him even more.

Not having the time or the necessary freedom of speech to explain any further, I dashed into the bathroom and began hitting the handle of the knife against my rocky visage. To my heavenly relief, it began to crack. After repeated blows, which made me a little groggy, the stuff had broken up enough to allow me to wriggle my jaw. Meanwhile, Bobby stood at the door watching, completely bemused.

Taking advantage of the cracks in my surface, I dug the blade of the knife in, and by scraping, gouging, digging and prying, I got part of my face clear. As soon as I could talk, I turned on Bobby. "If you tell anybody about this, I'll kill you," I said fiercely.

Whether it was the intensity of my threat or a latent chivalry aroused by seeing a lady tortured before his very eyes, I still don't know, but Bobby said, "Cross my heart and hope to die."

He then pointed out that spots of the gray-green stuff were still very much with me. As I grabbed up the nailbrush again, to tackle these remnants, he asked in a hushed voice, "But what *is* it?"

"Beauty Clay," I said. "I sent away for it."

405

Bobby looked as though he couldn't understand why anyone would deliberately send away for such punishment, when there was already enough trouble in the world. However, for the first time in a long, hideous half hour, I remembered why I'd gone through this ordeal, and I now looked into the mirror expecting to see results that would wipe out all memory of suffering. The reflection that met my eye was certainly changed all right, varying as it did between an angry scarlet where the skin had been rubbed off, to the greenish splotches still clinging.

Maybe if I got it all off, I thought. When it was all off, except those portions wedded to my hair, I gazed at myself wearily, all hope abandoned. My face was my own—but raw. Instead of the Body Beautiful I looked like the Body Boiled. Even worse, my illusions had been cracked wide open, and not by a silver knife.

"You look awfully red," Bobby said. I did indeed. To add to my troubles, we could now hear the family assembling downstairs, and Mother's voice came up, "Hildegarde, will you come set the table right away, dear?"

I moved numbly.

"You'd better take off the sheet," Bobby said.

I took off the sheet.

Just as I reached the stairs, he whispered, "Why don't you say you were frostbitten and rubbed yourself with snow?"

I looked at him with limp gratitude.

When Mother saw my scarlet, splotched face, she exclaimed in concern. "Why, Hildegarde, are you feverish?" She made a move as if to feel my forehead, but I backed away. I was burning up, but not with fever.

"I'm all right," I said, applying myself to setting the table. With my face half in the china cupboard, I mumbled that I'd been frostbitten and had rubbed myself with snow.

"Oh, Cliff," Mother called. "Little Hildegarde was frostbitten."

My Father immediately came out to the kitchen. "How could she be frostbitten?" he asked reasonably. "It's thirty-four above zero."

"But her ears still look white," Mother said.

They probably did, too, compared to the rest of my face. By some oversight, I had neglected to put Beauty Clay on my ears. "I'm all right," I insisted again. "I rubbed hard to get the circulation going."

This at least was true. Anyone could tell at a glance that my circulation was going full blast, from the neck up.

Bobby had followed me out to the kitchen to see how the frostbite story went over. As Mother kept exclaiming over my condition he now said staunchly, "Sure she's all right. Let her alone."

My father and mother both stared at him, in this new role of Big Brother Galahad. In fact, my father reacted rather cynically. "Bobby, did you and your friends knock Hildegarde down and rub her face with snow?" he asked.

"Me?" Bobby squeaked. He gave me a dirty look, as if to say, "You'd better talk fast."

I denied hotly that Bobby had done any such thing. In fact, I proceeded to build him up as my sole rescuer, a great big St. Bernard of a brother who had come bounding through the snowdrifts to bring me life and hope.

Bobby looked so gratified at what he'd been through in my story that I knew my secret was safe.

Sally, always an affectionate child, began to sob. "She might have died. Bobby saved her from freezing."

My father and mother remained dry-eyed. Against this new set-up of Brother Loves Sister they were suspicious, but inclined to do nothing.

And in a way I *had* been frostbitten, to the quick. Lying in bed that night, still smarting, I tried to think up ways to get even. It wasn't clear to me exactly whom or what I had to get even with. All I knew was that I was sore and unbeautiful, and mulcted of five dollars. With the hot and cold fury of a woman stung, I suddenly conceived my plan for revenge. It was so simple and logical and yet brilliant that my mind relaxed at last. Some day I, too, would write advertisements.

407

THE RANSOM OF RED CHIEF

O. HENRY

It looked like a good thing: but wait till I tell you. We were down South, in Alabama—Bill Driscoll and myself—when this kidnapping idea struck us. It was, as Bill afterward expressed it, "during a moment of temporary mental apparition"; but we didn't find that out till later.

There was a town down there, as flat as a flannel-cake, and called Summit, of course. It contained inhabitants of as undeleterious and self-satisfied a class of peasantry as ever clustered around a Maypole.

Bill and me had a joint capital of about six hundred dollars, and we needed just two thousand dollars more to pull off a fraudulent town-lot scheme in Western Illinois with. We talked it over on the front steps of the hotel. Philoprogenitiveness, says we, is strong in semi-rural communities; therefore, and for other reasons, a kidnapping project ought to do better there than in the radius of newspapers that send reporters out in plain clothes to stir up talk about such things. We knew that Summit couldn't get after us with anything stronger than constables and, maybe, some lackadaisical bloodhounds and a diatribe or two in the *Weekly Farmers' Budget.* So, it looked good.

We selected for our victim the only child of a prominent citizen named Ebenezer Dorset. The father was respectable and tight, a mortgage fancier and a stern, upright collection-plate passer and forecloser. The kid was a boy of ten, with bas-relief freckles, and hair the color of the cover of the magazine you buy at the newsstand when you want to catch a train. Bill and me figured that Ebenezer would melt down for a ransom of two thousand dollars to a cent. But wait till I tell you.

About two miles from Summit was a little mountain, covered with a dense cedar brake. On the rear elevation of this mountain was a cave. There we stored provisions.

One evening after sundown, we drove in a buggy past old Dorset's house. The kid was in the street, throwing rocks at a kitten on the opposite fence.

"Hey, little boy!" says Bill, "would you like to have a bag of candy and a nice ride?"

The boy catches Bill neatly in the eye with a piece of brick.

"That will cost the old man an extra five hundred dollars," says Bill, climbing over the wheel.

That boy put up a fight like a welter-weight cinnamon bear; but, at last, we got him down in the bottom of the buggy and drove away. We took him up to the cave, and I hitched the horse in the cedar brake. After dark I drove the buggy to the little village, three miles away, where we had hired it, and walked back to the mountain.

Bill was pasting court-plaster over the scratches and bruises on his features. There was a fire burning behind the big rock at the entrance of the cave, and the boy was watching a pot of boiling coffee, with two buzzard tail-feathers stuck in his red hair. He points a stick at me when I come up, and says:

"Ha! cursed paleface, do you dare to enter the camp of Red Chief, the terror of the plains?"

"He's all right now," says Bill, rolling up his trousers and examining some bruises on his shins. "We're playing Indian. We're making Buffalo Bill's show look like magic-lantern views of Palestine in the town hall. I'm Old Hank, the Trapper, Red Chief's captive, and I'm to be scalped at daybreak. By Geronimo! that kid can kick hard."

Yes, sir, that boy seemed to be having the time of his life. The fun of camping out in a cave had made him forget that he was a captive himself. He immediately christened me Snake-eye, the Spy, and announced that, when his braves returned from the warpath, I was to be broiled at the stake at the rising of the sun.

Then we had supper; and he filled his mouth full of bacon and bread and gravy, and began to talk. He made a during-dinner speech something like this:

"I like this fine. I never camped out before; but I had a pet 'possum
409

once, and I was nine last birthday. I hate to go to school. Rats ate up sixteen of Jimmy Talbot's aunt's speckled hen's eggs. Are there any real Indians in these woods? I want some more gravy. Does the trees moving make the wind blow? We had five puppies. What makes your nose so red, Hank? My father has lots of money. Are the stars hot? I whipped Ed Walker twice, Saturday. I don't like girls. You dassant catch toads unless with a string. Do oxen make any noise? Why are oranges round? Have you got beds to sleep on in this cave? Amos Murray has got six toes. A parrot can talk, but a monkey or fish can't. How many does it take to make twelve?"

Every few minutes he would remember that he was a pesky redskin, and pick up his stick rifle and tiptoe to the mouth of the cave to rubber for the scouts of the hated paleface. Now and then he would let out a warwhoop that made Old Hank the Trapper shiver. That boy had Bill terrorized from the start.

"Red Chief," says I to the kid, "would you like to go home?"

"Aw, what for?" says he. "I don't have any fun at home. I hate to go to school. I like to camp out. You won't take me back home again, Snake-eye, will you?"

"Not right away," says I. "We'll stay here in the cave awhile."

"All right!" says he. "That'll be fine. I never had such fun in all my life."

We went to bed about eleven o'clock. We spread down some wide blankets and quilts and put Red Chief between us. We weren't afraid he'd run away. He kept us awake for three hours, jumping up and reaching for his rifle and screeching: "Hist! pard," in mine and Bill's ears, as the fancied crackle of a twig or the rustle of a leaf revealed to his young imagination the stealthy approach of the outlaw band. At last, I fell into a troubled sleep, and dreamed that I had been kidnapped and chained to a tree by a ferocious pirate with red hair.

Just at daybreak, I was awakened by a series of awful screams from Bill. They weren't yells, or howls, or shouts, or whoops, or yawps, such as you'd expect from a manly set of vocal organs—they were simply indecent, terrifying, humiliating screams, such as women emit when they see ghosts or caterpillars. It's an awful thing to hear a strong, desperate, fat man scream incontinently in a cave at daybreak.

I jumped up to see what the matter was. Red Chief was sitting on Bill's chest, with one hand twined in Bill's hair. In the other he had the sharp case-knife we used for slicing bacon; and he was industriously and

410

realistically trying to take Bill's scalp, according to the sentence that had been pronounced upon him the evening before.

I got the knife away from the kid and made him lie down again. But, from that moment, Bill's spirit was broken. He laid down on his side of the bed, but he never closed an eye again in sleep as long as that boy was with us. I dozed off for a while, but along toward sun-up I remembered that Red Chief had said I was to be burned at the stake at the rising of the sun. I wasn't nervous or afraid; but I sat up and lit my pipe and leaned against a rock.

"What you getting up so soon for, Sam?" asked Bill.

"Me?" says I. "Oh, I got a kind of pain in my shoulder. I thought sitting up would rest it."

"You're a liar!" says Bill. "You're afraid. You was to be burned at sunrise, and you was afraid he'd do it. And he would, too, if he could find a match. Ain't it awful, Sam? Do you think anybody will pay out money to get a little imp like that back home?"

"Sure," said I. "A rowdy kid like that is just the kind that parents dote on. Now, you and the Chief get up and cook breakfast, while I go up on the top of this mountain and reconnoitre."

I went up on the peak of the little mountain and ran my eye over the contiguous vicinity. Over towards Summit I expected to see the sturdy yeomanry of the village armed with scythes and pitchforks beating the countryside for the dastardly kidnappers. But what I saw was a peaceful landscape dotted with one man plowing with a dun mule. Nobody was dragging the creek; no couriers dashed hither and yon, bringing tidings of no news to the distracted parents. There was a sylvan atti-

411

tude of somnolent sleepiness pervading that section of the external outward surface of Alabama that lay exposed to my view. "Perhaps," says I to myself, "it has not yet been discovered that the wolves have borne away the tender lambkin from the fold. Heaven help the wolves!" says I, and I went down the mountain to breakfast.

When I got to the cave I found Bill backed up against the side of it, breathing hard, and the boy threatening to smash him with a rock half as big as a cocoanut.

"He put a red-hot boiled potato down my back," explained Bill, "and then mashed it with his foot; and I boxed his ears. Have you got a gun about you, Sam?"

I took the rock away from the boy and kind of patched up the argument. "I'll fix you," says the kid to Bill. "No man ever yet struck the Red Chief but he got paid for it. You better beware!"

After breakfast the kid takes a piece of leather with strings wrapped around it out of his pocket and goes outside the cave unwinding it.

"What's he up to now?" says Bill, anxiously. "You don't think he'll run away, do you, Sam?"

"No fear of it," says I. "He don't seem to be much of a home body. But we've got to fix up some plan about the ransom. There don't seem to be much excitement around Summit on account of his disappearance; but maybe they haven't realized yet that he's gone. His folks may think he's spending the night with Aunt Jane or one of the neighbors. Anyhow, he'll be missed today. Tonight we must get a message to his father demanding the two thousand dollars for his return."

Just then we heard a kind of warwhoop, such as David might have emitted when he knocked out the champion Goliath. It was a sling that

Red Chief had pulled out of his pocket, and he was whirling it around his head.

I dodged, and heard a heavy thud and a kind of a sigh from Bill, like a horse gives out when you take his saddle off. A nigger-head rock the size of an egg had caught Bill just behind his left ear. He loosened himself all over and fell in the fire across the frying pan of hot water for washing the dishes. I dragged him out and poured cold water on his head for half an hour.

By and by, Bill sits up and feels behind his ear and says: "Sam, do you know who my favorite Biblical character is?"

"Take it easy," says I. "You'll come to your senses presently."

"King Herod," says he. "You won't go away and leave me here alone, will you, Sam?"

I went out and caught that boy and shook him until his freckles rattled.

"If you don't behave," says I, "I'll take you straight home. Now, are you going to be good, or not?"

"I was only funning," says he, sullenly. "I didn't mean to hurt Old Hank. But what did he hit me for? I'll behave, Snake-eye, if you won't send me home, and if you'll let me play the Black Scout today."

"I don't know the game," says I. "That's for you and Mr. Bill to decide. He's your playmate for the day. I'm going away for a while, on business. Now, you come in and make friends with him and say you are sorry for hurting him, or home you go, at once."

I made him and Bill shake hands, and then I took Bill aside and told him I was going to Poplar Grove, a little village three miles from the cave, and find out what I could about how the kidnapping had been regarded in Summit. Also, I thought it best to send a peremptory letter to old man Dorset that day, demanding the ransom and dictating how it should be paid.

"You know, Sam," says Bill, "I've stood by you without batting an eye in earthquakes, fire and flood—in poker games, dynamite outrages, police raids, train robberies, and cyclones. I never lost my nerve yet till we kidnapped that two-legged skyrocket of a kid. He's got me going. You won't leave me long with him, will you, Sam?"

"I'll be back some time this afternoon," says I. "You must keep the boy amused and quiet till I return. And now we'll write the letter to old Dorset."

Bill and I got paper and pencil and worked on the letter while Red

413

Chief, with a blanket wrapped around him, strutted up and down, guarding the mouth of the cave. Bill begged me tearfully to make the ransom fifteen hundred dollars instead of two thousand. "I ain't attempting," says he, "to decry the celebrated moral aspect of parental affection, but we're dealing with humans, and it ain't human for anybody to give up two thousand dollars for that forty-pound chunk of freckled wildcat. I'm willing to take a chance at fifteen hundred dollars. You can charge the difference up to me."

So, to relieve Bill, I acceded, and we collaborated a letter that ran this way:

Ebenezer Dorset, Esq.:

We have your boy concealed in a place far from Summit. It is useless for you or the most skilful detectives to attempt to find him. Absolutely, the only terms on which you can have him restored to you are these: We demand fifteen hundred dollars in large bills for his return; the money to be left at midnight tonight at the same spot and in the same box as your reply—as hereinafter described. If you agree to these terms, send your answer in writing by a solitary messenger tonight at half-past eight o'clock. After crossing Owl Creek on the road to Poplar Grove, there are three large trees about a hundred yards apart, close to the fence of the wheat field on the right-hand side. At the bottom of the fence-post, opposite the third tree, will be found a small pasteboard box.

The messenger will place the answer in this box and return immediately to Summit.

If you attempt any treachery or fail to comply with our demand as stated, you will never see your boy again.

If you pay the money as demanded, he will be returned to you safe and well within three hours. These terms are final, and if you do not accede to them no further communication will be attempted.

Two Desperate Men.

I addressed this letter to Dorset, and put it in my pocket. As I was about to start, the kid comes up to me and says:

"Aw, Snake-eye, you said I could play the Black Scout while you was gone."

"Play it, of course," says I. "Mr. Bill will play with you. What kind of a game is it?"

"I'm the Black Scout," says Red Chief, "and I have to ride to the stockade to warn the settlers that the Indians are coming. I'm tired of playing Indian myself. I want to be the Black Scout."

"All right," says I. "It sounds harmless to me. I guess Mr. Bill will help you foil the pesky savages."

"What am I to do?" asks Bill, looking at the kid suspiciously.

"You are the hoss," says Black Scout. "Get down on your hands and knees. How can I ride to the stockade without a hoss?"

"You'd better keep him interested," said I, "till we get the scheme going. Loosen up."

Bill gets down on his all fours, and a look comes in his eye like a rabbit's when you catch it in a trap.

"How far is it to the stockade, kid?" he asks, in a husky manner of voice.

"Ninety miles," says the Black Scout. "And you have to hump yourself to get there on time. Whoa, now!"

The Black Scout jumps on Bill's back and digs his heels in his side.

"For Heaven's sake," says Bill, "hurry back, Sam, as soon as you can. I wish we hadn't made the ransom more than a thousand. Say, you quit kicking me or I'll get up and warm you good."

I walked over to Poplar Grove and sat around the post-office and store, talking with the chaw-bacons that came in to trade. One whiskerando says that he hears Summit is all upset on account of Elder Dorset's boy having been lost or stolen. That was all I wanted to know. I bought some smoking tobacco, referred casually to the price of black-eyed peas, posted my letter surreptitiously, and came away. The postmaster said the mail-carrier would come by in an hour to take the mail to Summit.

415

When I got back to the cave Bill and the boy were not to be found. I explored the vicinity of the cave, and risked a yodel or two, but there was no response.

So I lighted my pipe and sat down on a mossy bank to await developments.

In about half an hour I heard the bushes rustle, and Bill wabbled out into the little glade in front of the cave. Behind him was the kid, stepping softly like a scout, with a broad grin on his face. Bill stopped, took off his hat, and wiped his face with a red handkerchief. The kid stopped about eight feet behind him.

"Sam," says Bill, "I suppose you'll think I'm a renegade, but I couldn't help it. I'm a grown person with masculine proclivities and habits of self-defense, but there is a time when all systems of egotism and predominance fail. The boy is gone. I sent him home. All is off. There was martyrs in old times," goes on Bill, "that suffered death rather than give up the particular graft they enjoyed. None of 'em were ever subjugated to such supernatural tortures as I have been. I tried to be faithful to our articles of depredation; but there came a limit."

"What's the trouble, Bill?" I asks him.

"I was rode," says Bill, "the ninety miles to the stockade, not barring an inch. Then, when the settlers was rescued, I was given oats. Sand ain't a palatable substitute. And then, for an hour I had to try to explain to him why there was nothin' in holes, how a road can run both ways, and what makes the grass green. I tell you, Sam, a human can only stand so much. I takes him by the neck of his clothes and drags him down the mountain. On the way he kicks my legs black and blue from the knees down; and I've got to have two or three bites on my thumb and hand cauterized.

"But he's gone"—continues Bill—"gone home. I showed him the road to Summit and kicked him about eight feet nearer there at one kick. I'm sorry we lose the ransom; but it was either that or Bill Driscoll to the madhouse."

Bill is puffing and blowing, but there is a look of ineffable peace and growing content on his rose-pink features.

"Bill," says I, "there isn't any heart disease in your family, is there?"

"No," says Bill, "nothing chronic except malaria and accidents. Why?"

"Then you might turn around," says I, "and have a look behind you."

Bill turns and sees the boy, and loses his complexion and sits down

416

plump on the ground and begins to pluck aimlessly at grass and little sticks. For an hour I was afraid of his mind. And then I told him that my scheme was to put the whole job through immediately and that we would get the ransom and be off with it by midnight if old Dorset fell in with our proposition. So Bill braced up enough to give the kid a weak sort of a smile and a promise to play the Russian in a Japanese war with him as soon as he felt a little better.

I had a scheme for collecting that ransom without danger of being caught by counterplots that ought to commend itself to professional kidnappers. The tree under which the answer was to be left—and the money later on—was close to the road fence with big, bare fields on all sides. If a gang of constables should be watching for any one to come for the note, they could see him a long way off crossing the fields or in the road. But no, sirree! At half-past eight I was up in that tree as well hidden as a tree toad, waiting for the messenger to arrive.

Exactly on time, a half-grown boy rides up the road on a bicycle, locates the pasteboard box at the foot of the fence-post, slips a folded piece of paper into it, and pedals away again back towards Summit.

I waited an hour and then concluded the thing was square. I slid down the tree, got the note, slipped along the fence till I struck the woods, and was back at the cave in another half an hour. I opened the note, got near the lantern, and read it to Bill. It was written with a pen in a crabbed hand, and the sum and substance of it was this:

Two Desperate Men.

Gentlemen: I received your letter today by post, in regard to the ransom you ask for the return of my son. I think you are a little high in your demands, and I hereby make you a counter-proposition, which I am inclined to believe you will accept. You bring Johnny home and pay me two hundred and fifty dollars in cash, and I agree to take him off your hands. You had better come at night for the neighbors believe he is lost, and I couldn't be responsible for what they would do to anybody they saw bringing him back. Very respectfully,

Ebenezer Dorset.

"Great pirates of Penzance," says I; "of all the impudent—"

But I glanced at Bill, and hesitated. He had the most appealing look in his eyes I ever saw on the face of a dumb or a talking brute.

"Sam," says he, "what's two hundred and fifty dollars, after all?

417

We've got the money. One more night of this kid will send me to a bed in Bedlam. Besides being a thorough gentleman, I think Mr. Dorset is a spendthrift for making us such a liberal offer. You ain't going to let the chance go, are you?"

"To tell you the truth, Bill," says I, "this little he ewe lamb has somewhat got on my nerves too. We'll take him home, pay the ransom, and make our getaway."

We took him home that night. We got him to go by telling him that his father had bought a silver-mounted rifle and a pair of moccasins for him, and we were to hunt bears the next day.

It was just twelve o'clock when we knocked at Ebenezer's front door. Just at the moment when I should have been abstracting the fifteen hundred dollars from the box under the tree, according to the original proposition, Bill was counting out two hundred and fifty dollars into Dorset's hand.

When the kid found out we were going to leave him at home he started up a howl like a calliope and fastened himself as tight as a leech to Bill's leg. His father peeled him away gradually, like a porous plaster.

"How long can you hold him?" asks Bill.

"I'm not as strong as I used to be," says old Dorset, "but I think I can promise you ten minutes."

"Enough," says Bill. "In ten minutes I shall cross the Central, Southern, and Middle Western States, and be legging it trippingly for the Canadian border."

And, as dark as it was, and as fat as Bill was, and as good a runner as I am, he was a good mile and a half out of Summit before I could catch up with him.

ON RIDING

CORNELIA OTIS SKINNER

PERHAPS it's spring and the sap rising in the limbs of trees, as well as in those somewhat passive members of my own, that yearly stirs in me an ambition to become athletic, to find some enjoyable form of sport in which the enjoyment is not purely on the side of those who watch me.

Certain years I decide upon tennis, other seasons swimming; yet one crowded bus trip to the courts on the upper West Side or a single frisk in the chlorine bosom of a New York swimming pool discourages the ambition at burgeoning, until the ensuing year when it again sends forth new shoots. This spring it blossomed in a desire to ride, a desire that might quickly have found satiety in one Sunday's contemplation of the equestrians in the Park had not a Virginia friend informed me that I was the perfect build for a sidesaddle (I, simple soul, took it as a compliment, not a geographical survey). And had not a card arrived from London's most famous bootmakers, to the effect that their Mr. Judkin would be at the Murray Hill Hotel and that unless I permitted him to measure me for a pair of riding boots he would probably have a long crying spell.

I hated to spoil Mr. Judkin's trip; besides, I have always secretly entertained a Winterhalter vision of myself romantically cantering on a horse named "Prince" down wooded avenues with a bright smile for the yokel and a kind word for the poor woodcutter. It seemed a lady's sport and I broached a horsey friend on the possibilities of my learning it.

"Pooh!" he said. "You'll do it as easily as rolling off a log." (His whimsical way of substituting the word log for horse.)

He was, of course, the last person on earth I should have consulted. He lives, talks and breathes horses. He almost eats them (maybe he does, in Paris). His favorite pastime is riding to hounds, and he takes a broken collar bone or a fractured skull as if it were a scene from the Marx Brothers. His ambition is to die on the hunting field. Altogether he is the original "Heigh-ho the fox!"—I suspect slightly pathological.

He so expatiated upon the amenities of the sport with all the charm and lack of accuracy of an old English print that I was all for rushing home to unpack the divided skirt in which at the age of sixteen I rode down the Grand Canyon on a mule named "Carrie Nation." However, my friend, meticulous to the degree that a badly tied stock or an ill-fitting jodhpur causes him to turn a bright Hunter's Pink, failed to respond with any great warmth to the idea of the divided skirt. Accordingly, at the end of ten days I found my bank account emptied and my closet filled with a sidesaddle habit that has as many mysterious parts as a novel by Proust.

The sidesaddle, I'm told, was invented for a crippled woman; and the truth of that statement I am willing to prove, as are the clerks at the corner drug store where I now take most of my standing meals, the sidesaddle being less an effect than a cause. And it looks so pretty, so

420

easy. I, at least, thought so as I waited that first morning in the stable of a riding academy. The walls were gay with French equestrian prints, charming Victorian ladies in flowing skirts and green veils rocking on contented hobby-horses beneath trees of emerald sponge. *"Première Leçon d'Equitation"*—it sounded very elegant and, in that most deceiving of languages, as remote from "First Riding Lesson" as "Oo la-la!" is from "Whoopee!" Jauntily I pulled at my gloves, already completely on. I sniffed the rich scent of the stable and, despite a tendency to be ill, told myself it was delicious.

I was to ride Luke. Luke is the Academy's oldest horse and is credited with all the virtues of his apostolic namesake. He is considered as suitable for children and invalids as Bovril and has never been known to step on anyone—an attribute scarcely extraordinary in other domestic animals, but in a horse nothing short of miraculous. While my courage oozed and I stood wondering if I couldn't have my habit made over into a bicycling costume, there appeared a groom with one tooth and Luke. I buried myself in an old copy of "Town & Country," but the groom, with no respect for my study, accosted me with the question did I prefer to mount from the block or the ground. Pride forbade my telling him my preference lay in not mounting at all, so I croakingly indicated the block. The groom implied that his conversation was a mere formality by announcing that Luke wouldn't go up to the block, which simplified things.

Luke was standing in what looked to be a Buddhistic trance that it seemed a pity to disturb. The groom, however, approached him, at the same time clasping his hands in a manner that led one to assume that he and Luke were about to execute a Japanese tumbling act. He told me to give him my foot and to jump when he counted three. I

gave him my right foot which he informed me wasn't right. I then gave him the left and jumped when he counted two. We managed to laugh that off and the next time I jumped on the "three" but not on the horse. The spring and the straining groom landed me at the same awkward angle one reaches trying to climb over the side of a swimming pool, when progress in either direction seems impossible.

The groom, staggering, but with British doggedness, pushed and I pulled until I found myself lying on Luke gracefully if perpendicularly in an attitude the equestrian clown Poodles Hanneford would have paid fifty pounds sterling to copy.

At that unfortunate moment one of those hateful little girls of five, who ride sixteen-hand hunters in the Park and race Sunday mornings with Grover Whalen, happened in with a shrill, "Oh, look at the funny lady!" Pretending I had been examining the saddle on the far side, I managed to right myself and to wind my leg about the pommel. The groom, whose wind was slightly broken, asked me how the stirrup was. I replied I trusted it was well, and he led Luke with his precious cargo to the ring where Mr. Benedict took us in tow, literally as well as figuratively; for Luke, inclined still to continue his meditations, had to be persuaded about the ring by a leading strap held by Mr. Benedict.

Mr. Benedict is the riding master and the ring is a square. It is covered in a tanbark that encourages violent hay fever and is bordered with a mirror wherein one can see what one's best friend couldn't tell one. We walked about it for a time with dignity, while Mr. Benedict discoursed on the principles of riding as Socrates might have expounded to Crito the meaning of Good. It sounded simple and rather beautiful. Then he announced that we'd go for a bit of a trot. His horse, a creature that might easily be called a steed, broke into an exquisite prance. Luke, who borders on the nag, followed in an animated Morris Dance. Mr. Benedict placed a steadying hand under my arm.

"Rise!" he shouted. "Rise and breathe! Sit up! Keep your left toe in and your heel down! Put your right shoulder back! Hold your hands down! Lean away from the pommel! Relax! Relax and breathe!"

"Shall I say 'Ah' too?" I gasped.

"No, just breathe!" he replied.

I had never before known such emphasis to be placed on that seemingly ordinary physical process. Mr. Benedict has succeeded in making me horribly self-conscious about it. There are times now when I pause in the midst of the most simple pursuits to wonder if I'm breathing; and

422

my nights are hideous with lying awake, terrified lest in my sleep I forget to continue that essential function.

"Lean to the right! To the right!" Mr. Benedict continued, in the tone of a captain of a sinking vessel.

"I don't dare. I suffer from height phobia!" I screamed. "It makes me want to jump!"

"If you don't lean to the right your saddle will slip around under your horse."

"It has already," I stated.

It had. My weight on the stirrup had pulled the saddle until I was rising at an angle of forty-five degrees from Luke's patient belly. I have seen cowboys in rodeos ride this way as a particularly hazardous stunt, but Mr. Benedict, who lacks a sense of the dramatic, failed to appreciate my act.

Luke, meantime, was continuing his Morris Dance to an accompaniment of sounds such as the Sicilians inform us issue from Etna before an eruption. His ears were twitching and his lips (I presume he has lips), were curled back in a grin of intense pain. Once, twice, thrice, four times round the ring we rode. I kept assuring myself that all things have an end, even a horse, and that, in the words of Voltaire, *"Tout lasse, tout casse, tout passe"*; and wondered if it would be the girth that would *casse*. Mr. Benedict kept ordering me to do everything but pat my head and rub my stomach, and my eyes filled with tears of self-pity at the thought of my limp body being carried home on a shutter.

The half hour finally ended, but not my troubles. Three weeks have passed and I as yet show no signs of becoming the Diana Vernon of the Reservoir. True, I no longer mount as if I were climbing the Righi. In fact, I now require two grooms for the purpose, one to help me spring and the other to keep me from o'erleaping myself, like vaulting ambition, and falling completely clear of the animal. Nor have I yet fallen off. But that is because Luke, who has an instinct of pity, senses the way I'm going and jumps beneath to catch me. I still list to port until I am parallel with the ground, my right foot still does a wild tattoo on the horse's shoulder, and Mr. Benedict tells me I still don't breathe.

All I have learned about horses is that they are beautiful over-rated creatures and are all born quite insane, Luke and Black Beauty notwithstanding. There is no comprehending their psychology because they possess none. They will pass a phalanx of onrushing traffic on the way to the Park with cool unconcern; but, let them espy a discarded Cracker Jack box in the shrubbery, they will go mad with fright and dance about it like an intoxicated coryphee. They will pass their own reflection in the Academy mirror a hundred times, then suddenly notice it and bolt; whether with fright or pleasure is an open question. In the case of Luke and myself this last idiosyncrasy is understandable. Mr. Benedict says I don't co-ordinate.

"But," he adds, "you're getting on, my dear, you're getting on."

And in my brooding heart I wonder if he refers to my riding, or my years.

HORSES

RICHARD ARMOUR

They head the list
  Of bad to bet on,
But I insist
  They're worse to get on.

"Hello, remember me?"

PART TWO
TOASTMASTER'S HANDBOOK

FOREWORD
FOR TOASTMASTER'S HANDBOOK

I HAVE ALWAYS had a hitherto useless knack for remembering hundreds of unrelated anecdotes about unrelated people. In the minds of some this has constituted me a "raconteur"; in the mind of my wife, who has had to listen to the same yarns a hundred times, it has inspired justifiable thoughts of mayhem. It is not always possible to avoid her eyes and put boyish zest into a "That reminds me of a funny thing that happened just yesterday" at the same time. If it does nothing else, this book may persuade Mrs. Cerf that remembering stories isn't a complete waste after all.

To supplement my own memory, I have pored through countless issues of *The New Yorker*, *Time*, *Life*, *Newsweek*, *Variety*, *Reader's Digest*, and *Coronet* in quest of additional anecdotes. I have devoured reams of columns by Winchell, Lyons, Sobol, Wilson, Skolsky, Hoffman, and their fellows. I have listened to radio programs until I thought that one more singing commercial would destroy my sanity entirely. Some of the choicest material comes from new books and old ones. I have tried to give credit wherever possible, but anecdotes are bandied about so generally and new stories sweep the country so quickly that it is often impossible even to discover who put a story into the public prints first, let alone find out who actually originated it.

Column conductors and radio comics are engaged in a highly competitive business, and their anxiety to establish the originality of their material is thoroughly understandable. It has always struck me as faintly ridiculous, however, for them to cry "Thief! Thief!" at rivals who very possibly overheard the gem in dispute at the

429

same night-club table or in the same gentlemen's room. They seem to forget that they actually create very few of the bright quips and amusing anecdotes they chronicle, and that the people who tell *them* their stories probably repeat them to a dozen others that very evening.

One of the most amusing features of my research for this volume was the frequency with which certain classic yarns bobbed up with entirely different casts of characters. In one instance, Bernard Shaw had said something to H. G. Wells; in another, Ilka Chase had delivered the same bon mot to Hedda Hopper. An identical witticism was credited to Oliver Wendell Holmes, Winston Churchill, and Charles Boyer. A Dorothy Parker sally of 1936 found its way into a feature story about Gypsy Rose Lee in 1944. Columnists and "raconteurs" (odious word) discovered long ago that the public laughs harder and is more impressed when a line is delivered by somebody whose keen sense of humor is already established. Any honest celebrity who subscribes to a clipping service will admit that he learns about some of his cleverest punch-lines for the first time when he reads that he has delivered them. This is a harmless and amiable practice and generally flattering to the beneficiaries, but it makes the business of tracking anecdotes to their actual source complicated indeed.

Many of the paragraphs in this volume appeared originally under my name in my weekly "Trade Winds" column in the *Saturday Review of Literature,* and in *Esquire, Coronet, Liberty, American Mercury, Reader's Scope,* and *Town and Country.* You will recognize dozens of them. For every new anecdote, I have included two that are hoary with age. I did not make them up; I *collected* them. If they remind you of some good ones you had forgotten; if they add a few more to your repertoire; above all, if they provide a few honest thrills and belly-laughs, *this* (collection) will have achieved the purpose for which it was compiled.

BENNETT CERF
New York

1. What this country needs is a new show for the Marx Brothers. It's all very well to recall their patter of years gone by, and chuckle reminiscently over it, but something fresh along the lines of *The Coconuts* or *Animal Crackers* would give Broadway an unbelievable fillip. The funniest lines usually fell to Groucho. He revived on the radio the other night his "I never forget a face—but I'm willing to make an exception in your case."

One of his funniest routines concerned his African hunting trip which began with "Did I ever tell you how I shot a wild elephant in my pajamas? How he got into my pajamas I'll never know. Getting his tusks off was quite a problem. In Alabama the Tuscaloosa." He came home in a rickshaw. The meter registered $11.40. "Confound it," he roared to the driver. "Didn't I *tell* you not to go through India?"

Then there was the skit where Groucho and Chico served as opposing lawyers. Chico became tongue-tied when it was his turn to question the witness. The judge thundered, "Well, ask your witness some questions." "All-a-right," said Chico. "What's a big-a da animal wid four legs an' a trunk in da front?" "That's irrelevant," screamed Groucho. "Dat's a right," agreed Chico. Groucho crossed the stage, planted his portfolio on the judge's bench, and declared, "I rest my case."

And the time when Groucho proposed to that wonderful foil, Mrs.

431

Rittenhouse. "Your eyes shine," he told her, "like the seat of my blue serge pants." "But you'll have to get out of that house you're living in," he added. "I don't like Junior crossing the tracks. In fact, come to think of it, I don't like Junior."

The weak sister of the Four Marx Brothers on the stage was Zeppo, but when he quit the greasepaint and became an agent, he ended with more pelf than the other three put together. Harpo, who never says a word on the stage, is the wittiest conversationalist in private life, and was one of Alexander Woollcott's favorite companions. Harpo once flew all the way from Hollywood to Bomoseen, Vermont, for a week-end to surprise Woollcott. He painted himself from head to foot with hideous hues, paddled to the Island, and howled like a banshee. Nobody was frightened, however. In fact, nobody was on the Island. Another time, Harpo appeared in a broken-down Model-T Ford. "What on earth do you call that?" scoffed Woollcott. "This is my town car," said Harpo grandly. "Yes," answered Woollcott, "and the town is Pompeii."

Chico's wife invited an elderly relative to spend a few weeks at his house one time. The visitor was very charming, but her English was on the sketchy side. When Irving Thalberg and his wife, Norma Shearer, were coming for dinner, Chico took the old lady aside. "When Mr. Thalberg says 'pleased to meet you,' " he instructed her, "all you have to do is answer with one word: 'likewise.' " The old lady repeated the word several times, and swore that she would uphold her end without mishap. The Thalbergs arrived. "Pleased to meet you," said Thalberg as expected. The old lady beamed at him. "Wise guy," she said.

The Marx Brothers once became the managers of a prize fighter. He was a lumbering giant named Cohen, and richly earned the nickname of "Canvasback" by an invariable custom of getting himself knocked cold in Round One of every fight. The boys had a great time with Canvasback Cohen until one day, according to legend, Groucho knocked him out in a gymnasium workout. That was too much. Harpo claims that Canvasback started as a lightweight, but was hit so many times that he swelled out into a heavy.

As long as I have rambled on this far about the Marx Brothers, I'd better quote a few other of their more famous lines, if only to avoid the wrath of thousands of enthusiasts who remember their dialogues almost word for word and are ready to fight at the drop of a wisecrack. In *Horse Feathers*, Groucho informed his son, "I'd horsewhip you—if I had a horse."

His secretary interrupted him to announce, "Jennings has been waiting to see you for hours, and he is waxing wroth." Groucho's reply to this was, "Tell Roth to wax Jennings for a change."

When Chico entered the scene, Groucho commented, "Hey, you look a lot like a guy I know by the name of Ravelli." "I am Ravelli," declared Chico. "Aha," said Groucho, "that accounts for the resemblance."

In *Monkey Business*, Groucho discovered a large automatic pistol and near it a few small pearl-handled revolvers. "This gat," announced Groucho, "had gittens." Almost immediately after that deduction, the ship's captain hove into view. "I've got a complaint," roared Groucho. "What is it?" said the captain testily. "Last night when I was in bed in my cabin, who do you think came tiptoeing along the corridor and tapped on my door?" The captain said he didn't know. "Nobody did," declared Groucho, "and that's my complaint."

Marx Brothers addicts will never forget their burlesque of Madame Du Barry. Groucho, essaying the role of high minister, was feverishly embracing Du Barry when Chico came charging into the scene. "Who are you?" snarled Groucho. "King of France," averred Chico. "What?" said Groucho. "You the king? And I the prime minister? France is certainly in one hell of a fix!"

* * *

2. O'Neill never could stand the ordeal of his own first nights. On the memorable occasion of the premiere of *Strange Interlude*, he wandered unrecognized down Broadway. Unrecognized, that is, by all but a single passerby, who clapped him on the back and boomed, "Eugene O'Neill, by all that's holy! Haven't seen you since we shipped together on the *Southern Cross!* What on earth ya been doin' with yourself since?"

"I can't stand this place—it has cockroaches!"

433

3. Drama critics have to see so many horrible "turkeys" in the course of a season that they may be excused if they occasionally forget their manners in print.

Brooks Atkinson wrote the shortest review on record. It read: "Such-and-such opened last night. Why?" Another critic declared that a musical "arrived in town after an insufficient number of postponements." "The picture version of *Panama Hattie* needs a certain something," wrote David Lardner, and added pensively, "Possibly burial." Burton Rascoe announced that a certain actress' performance "sickened him." The next day she sent him a bottle of castor oil.

Percy Hammond closed a review with "I have knocked everything except the knees of the chorus girls, and nature anticipated me there." David Lardner is credited with "The plot was designed in a light vein that somehow became varicose." A Detroit music reviewer contributed: "The Blank Quartet played Brahms last night. Brahms lost."

Somebody met George Kaufman after a particularly gruesome opening. "What did you think of it?" ventured the stranger. "It's not quite fair for me to say," Kaufman assured him. "I saw it under peculiarly unfortunate circumstances. The curtain was up."

* * *

4. William Collier one time was toastmaster at a big banquet where first an admiral, and then a general, talked on and on while the audience writhed. Collier finally rose and restored everybody to good humor by his comment: "Now at last I know what they mean by the Army and Navy Forever."

* * *

5. Miss Helen Hayes, the actress, met her husband, Charles MacArthur, at a cocktail party at the home of Neysa McMein. According to legend, MacArthur had a bag of peanuts in his hand. He took one look at Helen and handed her the peanuts. "I wish they were emeralds," he said. (In January 1944, MacArthur, now a major in the U. S. Army, flew with a mission to India. He came upon a couple of small but perfect emeralds and sent them to his wife. The accompanying card read, "I wish they were peanuts.")

434

6. During the run of *Mary of Scotland*, Miss Helen Hayes noticed that after five or six consecutive matinees, a little boy stood at the stage door waiting for her to come out. He never spoke to her, and when one afternoon she smiled and said "Hello there," he turned brick red, and ran. After the next matinee he was waiting for her again. He thrust a little box into her hand and was gone. Inside the box she found a silver medal. The inscription read, "For scholarship. Public School 42. 1933."

* * *

7. The Hayes-MacArthur home is situated in Nyack, New York—about fifty miles from Broadway.

Gilbert Miller was playing host to an elaborate party at the Waldorf one evening a few years ago, when Miss Hayes took him to one side.

"Charlie is a bit high," she said, "and is having too much fun to leave now. I've got an early rehearsal tomorrow, and want to slip away. Won't you see that Charlie gets to bed O.K.?"

Miller promised. When the party broke up, he dutifully bundled MacArthur, now sound asleep, into his car and drove the full fifty miles to Nyack. When he got there, he was surprised to find that the house was boarded up and padlocked. There was nothing left to do but drive back to town and deposit MacArthur on a spare couch in the Miller apartment.

The next morning Miss Hayes called in a panic. "What have you done with Charlie?" she demanded. Miller explained that he had taken him all the way to Nyack and back.

"Good heaven," said Helen Hayes. "I forgot to tell you. We're living at the Waldorf for the winter."

* * *

8. Ilka Chase's first husband was the actor, Louis Calhern. Miss Chase describes their brief romance very frankly in her autobiography, *Past Imperfect*. After their divorce Calhern married Miss Julia Hoyt. A month or so later Ilka found in her trunk a box of beautiful calling cards engraved, "Mrs. Louis Calhern." "It seemed a pity to waste them," relates Miss Chase, "so I mailed the box to my successor. But, aware of Louis' mercurial marital habits, I wrote on the top of one, 'Dear Julia: I hope these reach you in time.' I received no acknowledgment."

* * *

9. One of the sharpest and most devastating wits in the theatre is the property of Beatrice Lillie, in private life Lady Peel. She was virtually unknown in America in 1924 when an unpretentious musical called *Charlot's Revue* opened, and made stars overnight not only of Miss Lillie, but of her co-players Gertrude Lawrence and Jack Buchanan.

Years later Bea Lillie was being fitted for a number of dresses by a leading Chicago modiste. A lady who had married into the Swift hierarchy was next on the appointment calendar, and fussed and fumed because she was being kept waiting. "Tell that actress in there," she said very loudly, "that she is delaying Mrs. Swift!" This tactic, of course, resulted only in Miss Lillie's taking a half hour longer in the fitting room. Finally she tripped blithely out and, as she passed the fuming Mrs. Swift, said airily to the modiste, "Tell that butcher's wife that Lady Peel has finished now."

436

10. Howard Dietz and Arthur Schwartz once accepted a radio job that kept them turning out a new song every day for thirty-nine weeks. "Doesn't that take a lot out of you?" asked an interviewer. "Yes," said Dietz, "but it also takes a lot out of Bach, Beethoven, and Brahms."

* * *

11. Of all the movie producers in Hollywood, the most famous is undoubtedly Samuel Goldwyn. Part of this fame he has achieved by a series of outstanding and notable productions, part by a collection of weird statements and a misuse of the English language. Some of the sayings are undoubtedly authentic; more of them are pure inventions by Hollywood wits.

There follows a handful of the choice Goldwynisms. It is impossible to say how many of them actually sprang from the lips of Sam Goldwyn. For a time he was suspected of actually encouraging their manufacture and circulation. In those days, any kind of publicity was considered good publicity. Shrewd and intuitive character that he is, however, Goldwyn sensed that a new mantle of dignity and artistic consciousness was about to descend upon the cinema, and he began to disavow these tales in increasingly testy tones. Recently, upon reading a prediction on the future of Hollywood, signed by himself, in a Sunday supplement, he is said to have remarked indignantly, "This fellow has no idea of my literary style. Tell him to read the piece my last man wrote for me."

Mr. Goldwyn's most famous dicta undoubtedly are his "Gentlemen, kindly include me out," and the matchless "In two words I tell you my opinion of that picture: im-possible." In an argument over possession of a big star's services, a Paramount man suggested that the decision be left to arbitration. "O.K.," said Goldwyn reluctantly, "if it's understood that I get him."

Another time he called up L. B. Mayer, of MGM. "Louis," he said sadly, "both of us are in trouble." "How come?" asked Mayer. "It's this Clark Gable," said Goldwyn. "You got him; I want him." When he was introduced to Aldous Huxley he beamed, "I understand you are practically a genius." He counseled a friend, "Keep what I'm telling you under your belt." A cousin told him he had named his new baby William. "What did you do that for?" disapproved Goldwyn. "Every Tom, Dick, and Harry is named William." The first time he saw a sundial, and learned what it was, he murmured, "Tsk! Tsk! What won't they think of next!"

When Goldwyn's lovely wife, Frances, persuaded him to forsake movie-making long enough to sail to Hawaii for a vacation, a farewell party was whipped up in his honor at the studio. Every one of his employees was there. His press agent whispered in his ear, "They expect you to say a few words." Goldwyn cleared his throat, and the crowd fell silent. "Well, fellows," said Sam, "bon voyage!"

His secretary complained that the files had grown so cluttered that it was growing impossible to find anything. "At least," she begged, "let me destroy the letters that are ten years old or more." "O.K.," said Sam reluctantly, "but don't forget to make copies." He asked a newly signed actor where he hailed from. "Idaho," said the youngster. "Out here, young man," Goldwyn advised him, "we pronounce it Ohio."

In a bridge game, Goldwyn drew Connie Bennett as a partner against two experts. The men wanted to play for fifty cents a point, but Connie sagely declared that her limit was a penny. Goldwyn volunteered to carry her. That meant that he was playing for ninety-nine cents a point. Everything went reasonably well until one hand when, with both sides vulnerable, the man at Goldwyn's right bid "one heart." Goldwyn, in a voice that spoke volumes, said "I pass." The third man also passed. Connie said "one spade." "Two hearts," declared the first bidder. "I pass," said Goldwyn a little more loudly. Connie went to two spades; the man next to her bid three hearts. "I pass," Goldwyn virtually shouted. Eventually Miss Bennett bid four spades, was doubled, and went down four tricks—eleven hundred points. Goldwyn was apoplectic. As the last card was played, he leaped to his feet, pounded on the table, and screamed at his partner: "Damn it, couldn't you HEAR me keeping quiet?"

One time he stubbed his toe with a foreign beauty named Anna Sten. Goldwyn starred her in a version of Zola's *Nana* and lost a fortune on the venture. Some time previously he had signed a new director and assured him, "I don't want 'yes men' around me. I want you to 'no' me once in a while—even if it costs you your job." This intrepid soul took him at his word, told him the script of *Nana* was terrible and Miss Sten was miscast, and refused to have anything to do with the project. Goldwyn fired him. For years thereafter, if anybody suggested that this director be used on another picture, Goldwyn would shake his head vigorously, and declare, "No, *sir!* That man was connected with my greatest failure."

Goldwyn wants top-flight men working for him and will pay any price to get them. He is responsible for the presence of some of the world's greatest authors in Hollywood. He hired Louis Bromfield at a huge salary, greeted him upon his arrival with, "It's good to have you with us, Mr. Bloomberg." One of his earliest importations was Maurice Maeterlinck. "I know you don't understand picture technique," Goldwyn assured him. "You don't have to. Just go home and write your greatest book over in the form of a scenario. I don't care how long it takes you." Some weeks later Maeterlinck came back with a finished script. "Now we'll see something," beamed Goldwyn, and took it into his sanctum sanctorum. Two minutes later he rushed out tearing his hair. "My God," he screamed. "The hero is a bee!"

12. Hollywood lifted eyebrows over the marriage of Victor Moore, the 67-year-old comedian, to a girl of 22. "What's wrong with that?" queried Buddy de Sylva. "When she is 100, he will only be 145."

* * *

13. Van Cartmell tells the story of a housewife who asked a little grocery boy his name. "Humphrey," answered the boy, and added that the last name was Bogart. "Humphrey Bogart, eh?" said the housewife. "That's a pretty well-known name." "It darn well ought to be," the boy agreed. "I've been delivering groceries in this neighborhood for four years."

439

14. W. C. Fields was certainly the greatest juggler in the world, and some folks will swear he was the greatest comedian too. His real name was Claude William Dukenfeld, which he signed to an original scenario every now and then just for the hell of it. He was born in Philadelphia, but ran away from home when he was eleven. Some very tough years followed. "I was a big city Huck Finn," he said. Constant colds and hacking coughs gave him his husky and rasping voice, repeated punches in the nose from older and heavier aggressors swelled and reddened his proboscis to an extraordinary degree. These two characteristics became a sort of trademark; he kept them up to snuff with frequent libations of Irish whiskey, a liquid to which he was not allergic. A lad came to see him once who declared he was a long-lost son. Fields was skeptical, but asked him in. "Drink?" he inquired. "Coca-Cola," said the lad. Fields ejected him with a roar of rage. "An obvious impostor," he explained. Another time he returned from four weeks of location work in a town that was bone-dry. "Can you imagine me subsisting all those days," he marveled, "on nothing but food and water?"

Fields' first professional job was a combination of juggler and drowner at an Atlantic City beer joint. When business slackened, he would dive into the briny, and be saved just as he was going down for the third time. The crowd was expected to order beer and wienies while the waiting emergency squad restored him to consciousness. One July Fourth he "drowned" seven times.

His first great hit on Broadway was scored in the Ziegfeld Follies. He did a combination juggling-and-hokum act with a trick billiard table that simply defies description, and that would bring just as many howls of laughter today as it did then. One night Fields got a laugh where he didn't expect it. Upon investigation, he found Ed Wynn hiding under the table, mugging at the audience. Fields, whose temper was not improved by his years of hobo camps and slow freights, hauled off and conked Wynn with a billiard cue. The crowd roared appreciatively, and laughed again every time Wynn clasped his sore head and moaned in agony. Fields calmly continued with his act, and later suggested that they include the routine every night. Wynn never butted into his number again.

"When I was a tot," confessed Fields, "I swore that if I ever got in the chips, I'd help kids who were homeless waifs like I had been. For years I couldn't afford it. Then came Hollywood and riches." "Did you start a foundation as you had planned?" asked a girl interviewer eagerly. "No," said Fields, "I'm afraid I didn't. I said to myself, 'To hell with them.'"

Every time Fields went to the theatre he wrote a note to the house manager. It read, "My wife and I will be in your theatre tomorrow evening. We will occupy seats number G-108 and 110, where my wife will lose a pair of white silk gloves."

* * *

15. Cecil B. De Mille once produced a motion picture allegedly based on E. Arnot Robertson's story of the Indo-Chinese jungle, *Four Frightened People*. The star was Claudette Colbert. De Mille took the author to a preview. "How did you like it?" he asked when the lights went on again. Miss Robertson reflected a moment. "Mr. De Mille," she said slowly, "do you remember the roar of an off-stage lion that came in somewhere about reel three? Well, I do believe that you took that straight from my story."

* * *

16. Two agents sat together watching a preview of an important picture. One happened to be the agent for the male star of the piece, the other for the female lead. They sat silently while several reels were unwound and then one nudged the other in the ribs. "Look at those two hams up there," he said with some disgust, "getting eighty percent of our dough."

* * *

17. A few years ago a new edition of Thackeray's *Henry Esmond* was published in the Modern Library series. To the amazement of the editors, there arrived a letter some days later from a prominent Hollywood agency addressed to William Makepeace Thackeray, Esq. It read as follows:

"We have read your recent book *The History of Henry Esmond, Esq.* and believe it possesses material adaptable for motion pictures.

"We are recognized agents for writers at all studios and as such would like to represent you in the sale of both your own personal services and your literary products.

"In the event you have already made a commitment to some agent for the above book, we nevertheless are impressed with your potential possibilities as a screen writer and would be interested in both your services and future stories.

441

"We would appreciate your advising us by return mail whether or not you are represented here in Hollywood; and in the event that you are not and desire us to represent you, we would be happy to forward to you a copy of our agency agreement with writers for your information and guidance."

A busy publisher always has time to enter into the spirit of an affair of this sort, so the following note was promptly sent back:

"Thank you for your letter telling me that you believe that my recent book, *The History of Henry Esmond*, possesses material adaptable for motion pictures. This effort is a rather crude attempt, I fear, but I am now working on a new novel which I think will be a natural for pictures. I am thinking of calling the new book *Vanity Fair*.

"I will be interested in hearing what you think of this title.

Sincerely yours,
William Makepeace Thackeray"

Three days later another letter arrived from the agency:

"Acknowledging receipt of your letter of December 28, in reply to our previous communication, we feel that the title which you are thinking of giving your new book, namely *Vanity Fair*, is a good one. We would greatly appreciate receiving a manuscript on this story. Perhaps you could also send us a manuscript at this time, or if not, a copy of the book, *The History of Henry Esmond*.

"We would like to submit this, if we are authorized to do so by you, to the studios for their consideration."

There the matter rests.

* * *

18. There was a time when the most famous beard in the literary world adorned the countenance of a reasonably distinguished Irish critic who could be heard pontificating practically any afternoon near the bar of whatever publisher's cocktail party chanced to be in progress. He would stroke his beard with a gentle and tentative gesture comparable to a movie star milking a cow for a publicity photograph, and emote at length on any subject from Abyssinia to Zoroaster. . . .

At any rate, the fame of this critic's beard was long ago eclipsed by that of Monty Woolley, Yale professor, bon vivant, wit, and motion-picture star, whose whiskers are his trademark and have been impressed in the pavement of Grauman's Chinese Theatre alongside Charles Chaplin's shoes and Betty Grable's legs. Woolley was one of the guests at a Cole Porter party some years ago where the composer introduced a new number he had written called "Miss Otis Regrets She's Unable to Lunch Today, Madam." The burden of this lugubrious chant concerned an urgent appointment that Miss Otis had with the public hangman, necessitating a complete curtailment of her social activities. Woolley fell passionately in love with the song and sang it constantly at every party he attended for the next year. He sang it so well, in fact, that people began to suspect he was wasting his time at Yale. He was talked into a substantial part in a musical comedy called *On Your Toes* where he held his own against such accomplished show-stealers as Ray Bolger and Louella Gear, and then really reached the heights when Kaufman and Hart had the happy inspiration to cast him as Alexander Woollcott in *The Man Who Came to Dinner*.

Woolley is reported to have summoned his butler one morning (this
443

story is also credited sometimes to J. S. Bache) and said, "I'd like to know what my household expenses really amount to. If you will be good enough to leave out of the bills your rake-off on food, liquor, laundry, gasoline, and God knows what else, I will be happy to add it to your salary at the end of the month." "Mr. Woolley," said the butler gravely, "you couldn't afford it."

On one of his visits to New York between pictures, Woolley gave a party for his old friends. It was a very formal affair, and Woolley didn't consider it amusing at all when Cole Porter showed up with a bearded lady from the circus as his escort. Porter listened to Woolley's remonstrances for a moment, then turned to the bearded lady and remarked, "Madam, your son has atrocious manners."

At a bond rally in Hartford, Woolley sat toying with his famous beard, next to a prominent lady author, waiting for his turn to address the assemblage. Suddenly he belched. The lady author gave him a horrified look. Woolley bridled. "And what did you expect, my good woman?" he inquired. "Chimes?"

Woolley was so pleased with this line that he insisted it be written into his next role in Hollywood.

* * *

19. Some years ago, the Hotel Ambassador played host to the first International Crossword Puzzle Tournament. This was a purely spontaneous affair and the fact that the entire executive board of Simon and Schuster and the publishers of Webster's Dictionary happened to be buzzing around was purely coincidental. The winnah and undisputed champeen turned out to be a legal gentleman named William Stern, who was not quite prepared for the prize that rewarded his great effort. It was one of those walloping big dictionaries that should come equipped with their own electric hoisting machines. The chairman managed to deposit it in Mr. Stern's outstretched hands. Mr. Stern thereupon fell flat on his face, closely followed by the chairman. The defeated contestants cheered mightily.

* * *

20. Harold Ross, the late editor of *The New Yorker*, once tried to stop private telephone calls in his office and went so far as to install a public coin booth in the reception room. The next morning he found the booth torn loose from its roots, on its back in his own private office. Stretched out inside it, a calla lily clutched in his hand and a wreath on his head, lay James Thurber. When Ross once complained, "Thurber's women don't have any sex appeal," Marc Connelly reminded him, "They do for Thurber's men."

"Herman,—please!"

21. The technical term for the transposition of letters or sounds in a word, or series of words, is metathesis, but the more familiar designation is "Spoonerism." The Rev. W. A. Spooner, Warden of New College, Oxford, achieved this dubious claim to fame when he announced to his congregation: "Let us now sing the hymn 'Kinquering congs their titles take.'" Another time he caused a mild commotion in church by demanding "Is this pie occupewed?" A radio announcer created two classics of his own when he referred to New Juinea gungles instead of New Guinea jungles, and topped it with slote flulo for flute solo. Emily Wedge of Baltimore's famous Enoch Pratt Library quotes a gentleman who declared, "My wife says I have had tee many martoonis, but I am not so much under the alfluence of incohol as some pinkle theep. I mean *thinkle peep.*"

445

22. Alexander Woollcott settled down for an indefinite run as the country's most respected drama critic, most relentless and feared gossip, and infinitely most accomplished raconteur. All three qualities made a radio career inevitable, and as "The Town Crier" Woollcott became famous, wealthy, and more ruthless and domineering than ever. His social life was unbelievably complicated. He summoned whomever he willed to his home on East 52nd Street (named "Wits' End" by Dorothy Parker); surprisingly few refused. He spent weeks at the White House, and told the Roosevelts whom to have in to dine with him. He spoke at department-store book fairs, autographing copies of his own anthologies, and insulting his audience and other authors who appeared with him. He bought an island in Vermont, charged his guests hotel rates, and banished them when they wouldn't play croquet, cribbage, or hearts according to his own special rules. . . . His opinions became more and more didactic, his prose style more lush and untrammeled.

The Man Who Came to Dinner was the direct result of a typical Woollcottian sojourn at Moss Hart's new Bucks County estate. He bullied the servants, condemned the food, invited friends of his own from Philadelphia to Sunday dinner, and wrote in Hart's guest book, "This is to certify that on my first visit to Moss Hart's house I had one of the most unpleasant times I ever spent." He also suggested that Moss write a play in which he could star. The next day Hart was describing Woollcott's behavior to George Kaufman. "Wouldn't it have been horrible if he had broken a leg or something and been on my hands the rest of the summer!" The collaborators looked at each other with dawning delight in their faces and took the cover off the typewriter.

Once Woollcott filled a lecture date in Newark, and wheedled Hart into driving him over and back. "I'll do it on one condition," proposed Hart. "I once clerked in a bookstore in Newark and I'd like to show them that I'm a big shot now. I want you to let me sit on the platform with you, and be introduced to the audience." When they entered the hall there was a single folding chair, sure enough, to the left of the speaker's table. Hart sat down, and began crossing and uncrossing his legs, while Woollcott delivered his lecture without making the slightest reference to him. At its conclusion, he said, "I usually have a question period at this time but tonight we'll dispense with it. I'm sure you'd all want to know the same thing: who is this foolish-looking young man seated here on the platform with me?" With this he retired, leaving Hart to get out of the hall as best he might.

446

23. Thomas Craven, author of *Men of Art*, has a young son who was asked by his history teacher to name the principal contribution of the Phoenicians. The youngster's answer, given without hesitation, was "Blinds."

* * *

24. The accountant of a publishing house whose name you would recognize is reported to have burst into the office of the head of the firm in a state of wild jubilation one day last week. "After five long years," he chortled, "I am pleased to report to you that we now are no longer in the red!" "Glory be," cried his chief. "Make up five copies of the annual report at once so that I can wave them in the face of that so-and-so bank." "But I have no black ink," said the accountant. "We haven't needed any for so long." "Go out and buy a bottle," the chief said. "I should say not," was the reply. "In that case, we'd be back in the red."

* * *

25. Elizabeth Chevalier, author of the best-selling novel, *Drivin' Woman*, wrote in a letter to Macmillan, "Have you heard the one about the novelist who met an old friend? After they had talked for two hours, the novelist said, 'Now we've talked about me long enough—let's talk about you! What did you think of my last novel?'"

* * *

26. The inmate of a St. Louis asylum borrowed three long books from the library each morning, returned them the same afternoon. The librarian tested him with the city telephone directory. Sure enough, he was back with it a few hours later. "Don't tell me you've finished that big book already," said the librarian. "I certainly have," answered the touched one. "The plot was rotten, but oh boy, *what a cast!*"

* * *

27. Fanny Hurst is the kind of lady who never does things by halves; when she decided to reduce, she made such a thorough job of it that some of her best friends found it difficult to recognize her. One such was the late Irvin Cobb who strolled down Fifth Avenue directly behind her for a half-dozen blocks without doffing his chapeau to her. "Well," she declared finally, "are you going to say hello to me or aren't you?" "Don't

447

tell me you're Fanny Hurst," said the astonished Cobb. "The same Fanny Hurst," she assented coldly. "No, no," decided Cobb. "The same Hurst I will concede—but definitely *not* the same Fanny."

* * *

28. When Danny Kaye made a great hit in James Thurber's *Walter Mitty*, Producer Sam Goldwyn thought he'd like to have Thurber as a permanent addition to his writing stable. The catch lay in the fact that Thurber was working very happily for the late *New Yorker* Editor Harold Ross and had no desire whatever to dally further with picture-making. "I'll pay you five hundred dollars a week," wrote Goldwyn. "Sorry," answered Thurber after some delay, "but Mr. Ross has met the increase." Goldwyn thereupon raised the ante to a thousand, then fifteen hundred, and finally twenty-five hundred a week, but each time got nothing for his pains but the courteous response, "Mr. Ross has met the increase." There followed a long interim of silence. Then one day Mr. Goldwyn wrote again. This time, for some unknown reason, his offer went down to fifteen hundred. Thurber wrote back, "I'm sorry, but Mr. Ross has met the decrease."

* * *

29. The day that my publishing house decided to add the *Complete Works of Tacitus*, the Roman historian, to the Modern Library series, we chose as editor Professor Moses Hadas of Columbia University and persuaded that academic luminary to attend a conference in the Random House sanctum. We had a fine talk on the subject of Tacitus and agreed as to exactly what things were to go into the anthology. Just as he was leaving, the professor turned to me and asked with a most innocent expression: "Tell me, Mr. Cerf, exactly when did you read that encyclopedia article on Tacitus?" Caught red-handed, I admitted that I had read it exactly ten minutes before his arrival. "Neat recitation," commented Hadas. "You see, I happened to write that article."

* * *

30. Channing Pollock, in his autobiography, *Harvest of My Years*, told the story of a train acquaintanceship made on his first journey, when he was fourteen. His fellow passenger, a stockily built man, took an interest in his youthful views on Byron and Dickens. Finally he inquired, "Have you ever read *Sherlock Holmes?*" "Don't you think," said Pollock pontifically, "that detective stories are a waste of time?" "No, I don't," said the stranger. "You see, I write them. My name is A. Conan Doyle."

* * *

31. When Quentin Reynolds completed the manuscript of one of his many best-sellers, *Only the Stars Are Neutral*, he dispatched it to his publisher from London by clipper plane. The postage bill was for $16. "What on earth was your hurry?" his publisher cabled him. "You know we are not going to publish the book for three months. Stop throwing your dough around that way." The cable office called up a few minutes later. "We sent Mr. Reynolds your message," they said. "The charge is $20.81."

Reynolds reports he has given up the practice of drinking two cups of coffee at breakfast. "I found," he says, "that they kept me tossing around all morning."

* * *

32. Don Marquis' favorite story had to do with revenge of a subtle kind back in the Blue Ridge range in the rootin', tootin', feudin' country. An ornery sprout of the McGregor family plugged a member of the Larrabee family in the back one day. The victim never knew what had hit him. One old Larrabee buck pointed out that a simple killing was too merciful for the varmint. His ingenious suggestion, promptly passed unanimously, was that once every day a shot be fired at McGregor that would *just miss him*. For twenty years, this amiable pastime was put into effect. When Marquis saw the victim, his hair was snow-white, his face and hands twitched continuously, his glance darted madly from one side to another. He was reaching for a bottle of soda pop when a shot rang out. The bottle was shattered into a thousand fragments. McGregor howled like a coyote. "They'll do it every day to him," commented a villager dispassionately, "till he hangs hisself."

* * *

33. A ladies' club in New Jersey invited a femme book reviewer to speak at its May meeting. She told the plot of a triple-A tear jerker, and the entire assemblage broke into tears. All but one, that is—a lady who sat dry-eyed and unmoved through the entire recital. After the lecture, the

449

reviewer asked her why she hadn't cried. The lady's answer stopped her cold. "Oh, I'm not a member," she explained.

* * *

34. Before the war, Elliot Paul maintained an apartment in Paris. One day his friends learned that he had rented desk space in the restaurant on the first landing stage of the Eiffel Tower. An incredulous reporter from the *Paris Herald* found him there, typing away contentedly on a story. "Well," said the reporter, "you certainly must be attached to the Eiffel Tower!" "Attached to it!" snorted Paul. "This is the only place in Paris where I can avoid seeing the damn thing!"

* * *

35. Harry Kurnitz, author of most of *The Thin Man* scenarios, relates

that when he was a struggling young reporter in Philadelphia, the gay blades with whom he associated acquired, one by one, raccoon coats. They were a badge of distinction in those happy days of John Held flappers and bathtub gin; Kurnitz was extremely mortified that he could not afford one. Then one day he spied a coat made of wolf skin in a second-hand shop. It was barely within his means, but he bought it without a second's hesitation. "Did this end your inferiority complex?" I asked. "Could you once more dally with your fellow creatures on an even footing?" "It was superb," answered Kurnitz. "I wore it all winter, rain or shine. I had only one bit of trouble with it. It seems that every time there was a severe snowstorm, I found myself running madly after sleighs."

*   *   *

36. Bernard Shaw finally consented to a screen version of *Pygmalion*, but a Hungarian named Gabriel Pascal was the producer, not Goldwyn. The story goes that Pascal won Shaw by an approach that certainly was novel. "Not only do I want your permission to make a picture of *Pygmalion*," was his proposition, "but I want you to help me to raise twenty-five thousand pounds to finance it. The fact is, I'm broke at the moment."

Mr. Shaw attended the preview of *Pygmalion*, and signed autographs that one night as happily as the veriest Hollywood ham. He even consented to appear on the stage at the conclusion of the picture. Somebody in the gallery cried "boo." Shaw waved merrily, and said, "My friend, I quite agree with you, but what are we two against so many?" The picture was very successful both in England and America, largely due to a sensitive and characteristic performance by the late Leslie Howard. Shaw claimed that the picture netted him twenty-nine thousand pounds, but that it cost him fifty thousand in war taxes. "Another success like that," he grumbled, "and I am ruined."

When Cornelia Otis Skinner opened in a revival of Shaw's *Candida*, he cabled, "Excellent. Greatest." Miss Skinner, overwhelmed, cabled back: "Undeserving such praise." Shaw answered, "I meant the play." Miss Skinner bristled, and replied, "*So did I.*"

Shaw did most of his reading standing up, often dressing or undressing at the same time. "I never shut a book," he told Mr. Pearson, "but put the next book on top of it long before it's finished. After some months

there is a mountain of buried books, all wide open, so that my library is distinguished by the stain of dust or soot on it."

In an unusual burst of modesty, Shaw once confessed: "In moments of crisis my nerves act in the most extraordinary way. I size up the situation in a flash, set my teeth, contract my muscles, take a firm grip on myself, and without a tremor, always do the wrong thing." "When I die," he says, "I want to be thoroughly used up. The harder I work, the more I live. Life is no brief candle for me. It is a sort of splendid torch, which I have got hold of for the moment. I want to make it burn as brightly as possible before handing it on to future generations."

* * *

37. Arthur Kober sent his mother to a hotel in the Catskills for a vacation, but she didn't like it much. "The food here is plain poison," she wrote, "and such small portions!"

38. A worried merchant sought the aid of a psychiatrist, explaining, "All day long I eat grapes." "So what?" scoffed the analyst. "Everybody eats grapes." The merchant gasped, "What? Off the *wallpaper?*"

* * *

39. Robert Benchley was caught in a thunderstorm one afternoon, and came home soaked to the skin. "George," he called to his servant, "get me out of this wet suit and into a dry martini."

* * *

40. The Book Committee arranged a noonday rally at the New York Public Library one day and announced that Gypsy Rose Lee and Clifton Fadiman would be the guests of honor. Two thousand people turned up. A script had been prepared for Fadiman, but Miss Lee declared that she preferred to stick to a few impromptu remarks of her own. Panicked at the last moment, however, by the seething throng before her, Miss Lee reached for a script at hand. It was Mr. Fadiman's, of course, and an enraptured audience heard her open her address with the sweeping statement, "All my life has been spent in the world of books." Two sponsors swooned.

* * *

41. The Junior Literary Guild recently distributed a book about penguins. "This book," reported a conscientious young subscriber, "told me a good deal more about penguins than I like to know."

* * *

42. Sir Harry Lauder was so tight that he himself made a joke of it, and was the first to relate that when he opened his purse one day to take out a dollar, four moths flew out. He attended a dinner of twenty, one evening. It was of the caviar-champagne variety, and when the check came, it was a whopper. Several guests reached for the check, but Sir Harry's voice rang out, "No, no, gentlemen! This dinner is on me!" The

next morning's headline, avers Sir Harry, read, "Scottish ventriloquist murdered!"

A.W.H.

43. One of the elder DuPonts of Wilmington had a collection of Ming china second to none in the world. He kept it in a little museum on his estate, and allowed occasional visitors to inspect his treasures.

A young couple were there by invitation. While waiting for their host, the girl picked up a delicate vase. To her horror, it slipped from her fingers and smashed into a hundred fragments on the stone floor. Just then little Mr. DuPont came pattering up.

"Oh, Mr. DuPont," wailed the girl, "I have broken the little vase that stood in this niche. I do hope it wasn't one of the valuable pieces."

Mr. DuPont took a quick look at the broken fragments. "Fortunately,

454

my dear," he said, with a reassuring pat, "it wasn't valuable at all. Don't trouble your pretty head about it."

Then he fainted dead away.

* * *

44. Heywood Broun, the writer, blithely ignored small-time hecklers who poked fun at his theories on education and politics. When friends asked him why he didn't hit back at his self-appointed critics, Broun said, "Why use dynamite when insect powder will do?"

* * *

45. Lucius Beebe awoke in his bed one morning with a bad hangover and rang for his man. "Send out the suit I had on last night for a cleaning," he ordered. "As I recall, an accident befell it." The valet hesitated. "Make it snappy," said Beebe. "All right," said the valet, "but do you want me to send it out as it is now—or would you like to take it off first?"

* * *

46. Stanton Griffis, head of Paramount Pictures, Madison Square Garden, the Brentano book chain, and Lord knows what else, was the man who signed Bob Hope for Paramount. That was like a publisher getting six Book-of-the-Month Club selections in a row. At a dinner, Mr. Griffis introduced Mr. Hope with these lines: "I want to present the funniest comedian in pictures, one of the screen's handsomest leading men, and the fellow who wrote this introduction for me—Bob Hope."

* * *

47. There are a host of stories based on the penny-pinching habits of John D. Rockefeller. He got used to the sensation of signing away millions, but actual cash out of his pocket was something else again. His famous ten-cent tips were cause for hilarity the country over. His clothes concerned him little, if at all. One suit had a big patch on the coat, and a bright shine on the pants. "What's wrong with this suit?" he asked crankily when a friend urged him to discard it. "Everything," said the friend. "Your father would be ashamed of you. You know how neatly he used to dress." "But," protested Rockefeller triumphantly, "I'm wearing a suit of my father's right now."

Mr. Rockefeller spent his last winters in Florida. Down there they tell a story that one day he went to the dentist to have a tooth pulled. "How much?" he asked in advance. "Three dollars," said the dentist, who didn't even know who his client was. "Hmph! Three dollars to pull a tooth!" grumbled John D. "Here's a dollar. Loosen it a little bit!"

* * *

48. Bob Lovett, the banker, when in the War Department, was entertaining Bob Benchley and Donald Ogden Stewart, among others, at his Locust Valley home one evening, when he was called to the telephone. "Why, yes!" his awestricken guests heard him say. "*Let* Austria have eight million dollars." Next day Stewart wired him, "You have made me the happiest little country in the world." The signature was "Austria."

* * *

49. Mrs. Harrison Williams, frequently voted by modistes "the best-dressed woman in the United States," once bought a hat from a Paris milliner for a rather staggering sum, but with the assurance that the model would not be duplicated. The very night she returned to America, she was dancing at the Stork Club when another woman appeared with the identical hat on her head.

Mrs. Williams was indignant for a moment, but then realized that the other woman must have been bilked the same way that she was. When they passed close to one another on the floor, she pointed first to her hat, then to the other's, and smiled. The other lady looked straight through her. "Maybe she didn't understand," Mrs. Williams said to her partner. "Dance me over next to her again." This time her gestures were so broad that no misunderstanding was possible. She pointed to both hats, shook her head, and then smiled again. The woman cut her dead.

Mrs. Williams was pretty miffed until she went to the powder room and took a look into the mirror. She was wearing a different hat altogether that evening.

* * *

50. A visitor from the sticks, whom Abel Green of *Variety* was entertaining at "21," asked if they have a regular $2 dinner there. "Sure," said Abel. "Do you want it on white or rye?"

456

51. John M. Weyer, reported Leonard Lyons, gave a dinner for gourmets, and told a new maid, "Please remember to serve the fish whole, with tail and head, and a slice of lemon in the mouth." The maid appeared surprised, but said nothing. That evening she bore the fish triumphantly to the table, complete with tail and head. And in her mouth she carried a slice of lemon.

* * *

52. A maharajah who entertained Neysa McMein when she was in India queried a servant on the progress she was making in hunting. "The beautiful lady shoots divinely," reported the impeccable Hindu, "but Providence is merciful to the birds!"

* * *

53. Perhaps you have heard of the twelve-year-old girl who fell into the habit of dropping in on Dr. Einstein every day on her way home from school. Her parents were gratified, but somewhat mystified too. One evening the mother found an opportunity to ask the professor, "What do you two talk about every day?" "Oh," laughed the professor, "she brings me cookies and I do her arithmetic for her."

* * *

54. An employer told his secretary, "There are two words I must ask you never to use in my presence. One of them is 'lousy,' the other is 'swell.' " "That's all right by me," said the secretary. "What are the two words?"

* * *

55. Those two eminent scientists, the Doctors Piccard, were exact twins, as identical, to coin a phrase, as peas in a pod. This fact enabled them to play a harmless prank on a barber in their native Switzerland.

The stratosphere flier assured the barber that he had the toughest, most stubborn beard in captivity, and offered to bet that the best shave in the world would only last him a few hours. The barber angrily offered him another shave free if he should need it within twenty-four hours. He spent an hour giving him the closest shave possible without skinning him alive.

An hour later, the other brother arrived with a formidable beard and collected a free shave—after the bewildered barber had been given a strong restorative.

* * *

56. Another story always credited to Cardinal Hinsley features a lecturer who told his audience that the world would probably end in seven billion years. "How long did you say?" came a terrified voice from the rear. "Seven billion years," the lecturer repeated firmly. "Thank God," said the voice. "I thought for a moment you had said seven *million*."

* * *

57. Irwin Edman, brilliant author and famous philosopher of Columbia University, was that stock comedy character, the absent-minded pedagogue, in actuality. Beloved by his students for his wit, erudition, and uncanny ability to make the most abstruse subject sound easy, he was also the source of a whole saga of campus humor. One day he stopped a student on Riverside Drive and asked, "Pardon me, but am I walking north or south?" "North, Professor," was the answer. "Ah," said Edman, "then I've had my lunch."

* * *

58. Elihu Root liked to have aggressive and independent people working for him, but one promising young office boy sometimes went too far. There was the day, for instance, when he sauntered into the office, propped his elbows on Mr. Root's desk, and said, "Say, boss, there's a ball game at the Polo Grounds today I'm dying to see. Will you give me the afternoon off?"

"James," said the courtly Mr. Root, "that is not the way to ask a favor. Now you sit down in my chair and I'll show you how to do it properly."

The boy thought this was a delightful idea. He settled himself in his employer's chair. Mr. Root went outside. Then he entered softly, cap in hand, and said meekly, "If you don't mind, sir, there is a ball game today that I would like to see. Do you think you could spare me for the afternoon?"

In a flash the boy answered, "Certainly I can, Jimmie—and here's fifty cents to pay your way in."

"Yoo-hoo!"

459

59. A distinguished scientist, said Louis Sobol, who probably saw him, was observing the heavens through the huge telescope at the Mt. Wilson Observatory. Suddenly he announced, "It's going to rain." "What makes you think so?" asked his guide. "Because," said the astronomer, still peering through the telescope, "my corns hurt."

* * *

60. A tale that may take a few of our high-powered traveling salesmen down a peg concerns the visit of a man in quest of a bottle of catsup to Finkelstein's Grocery Store. The shelves of the entire store were solidly lined with bags of salt—hundreds upon hundreds of them. Mr. Finkelstein allowed as how he had a stock of catsup, but had to go down to the cellar to fetch a bottle. The customer went with him, and there, to his surprise, found another huge stock of salt stacked on all sides. "Say," commented the customer, "you certainly must sell a lot of salt in this store!" "Nah," said Mr. Finkelstein with resignation. "I can't sell no salt at all. But the feller who sells *me* salt! Can *he* sell salt!"

* * *

61. Lewis Miller was the sales manager of a sizable enterprise. In his salad days he covered New York State in a Model-T Ford and made his daily collections from customers en route. He was heading for home one evening with seven hundred dollars in his jeans when, just outside of Ossining, a man in shabby, ill-fitting clothes beckoned for a hitch. Miller stopped for him, and soon learned that his companion had just completed a ten-year stretch at Sing Sing for robbery. Suddenly he remembered the seven hundred dollars in cash in his pocket.

With what he considered a master-stroke of ingenuity, he pushed the accelerator all the way to the floor. The old Ford could still do sixty. A motorcycle cop could not be far behind; Miller would have police escort to the nearest station house.

The motorcycle cop arrived on schedule, bawled the daylights out of him, and wrote a ticket calling for his appearance in court the following Monday! In vain, Miller pleaded to be arrested on the spot. His passenger pulled his cap over his eyes and said nothing. Reluctantly, Miller started his car again. As they approached the darkest Bronx, he had already written off the seven hundred dollars in his mind.

Suddenly the passenger announced, "This is it, brother." Miller stopped the car. His moment had come. The man in shabby clothes stuck out his hand. There was no gun in it!

"Thanks for the lift," he said. "You've been very good to me. This is the least I could do for you."

He handed Miller the motorcycle cop's black leather summons book.

62. In front of an East Side delicatessen, a well-known art connoisseur noticed a mangy little kitten, lapping up milk from a saucer. The saucer, he realized with a start, was a rare and precious piece of pottery.

He sauntered into the store and offered two dollars for the cat. "It's not for sale," said the proprietor. "Look," said the collector, "that cat is dirty and undesirable, but I'm eccentric. I like cats that way. I'll raise my offer to five dollars." "It's a deal," said the proprietor, and pocketed the five-spot. "For that sum I'm sure you won't mind throwing in the saucer," said the connoisseur. "The kitten seems so happy drinking from it." "Nothing doing," said the proprietor firmly. "That's my lucky saucer. From that saucer, so far this week, I've sold thirty-four cats."

63. A traveler for a big publishing house couldn't wait to get to St. Louis, where his oldest friend owned a prosperous bookstore. "Sam," he said to the owner the moment they were alone, "I want you to lend me $2000." "The answer, Joe," said Sam, "is positively no." "But, Sam," protested the salesman, "in 1929, when Bond and Share broke from 189 to 50, who gave you ten thousand dollars to keep you from being wiped out?" "You did," admitted Sam. "And in 1931, when your daughter Shirley had that tropical disease, who took her down to Florida because you couldn't get away from business? Who did, Sam?" "You, my friend, you did." "And in 1933, when we were fishing together, who dove into the rapids and saved you from drowning at the risk of his own life?" "You did, Joe. It was wonderful!" "Well, then, Sam, in Heaven's name, why won't you lend me $2000 now when I need it?" "All the things you say are true," said Sam, nodding his head slowly. "But what have you done for me lately?"

* * *

64. Willie Howard once appeared in a sketch which showed him and a few companions freezing and starving on an Antarctic ice floe. He turned on the radio just in time to hear an announcer describing a Thanksgiving dinner back home. "We'll start with a plate of hot, luscious soup," said the announcer.

"With noodles?" groaned Howard.

"Yes," said the voice on the radio—"with noodles."

* * *

65. Screwball journalism of the type portrayed so hilariously in the Hecht-MacArthur play *The Front Page*, and in Robert J. Casey's *Such Interesting People*, is a thing of the past. Rip-snorting reporters whose motors ran strictly on alcohol, who were as likely to wind up in the local hoosegow as the city desk, but who brought in the scoops that sent circulations soaring, went out with Prohibition and Babe Ruth. They have been replaced by "boiler plates" and syndicates, and less colorful but infinitely more efficient wire services that supply hundreds of newspapers and magazines at a time with last-minute news, impersonal, impartial, and prosaic.

Journalism was a rollicking profession in the twenties, however, if you happened to be on the right papers. Casey happened. Most of the time he

462

operated out of Chicago, where feature reporters, influential lawyers, and gun-toting hijackers seemed to be somewhat interchangeable. The title of his colorful collection of yarns stems from the time-honored observation of the yokels who meet gentlemen of the press: "Gee, it must be wonderful to be a journalist. You meet such interesting people!" Winchell once answered, "You certainly do, and every one of them is in the newspaper business."

Casey went to bat with lots of outsiders, however, not all of whom were rank. There was a queer customer in Cairo, for instance, named Captain Eddy, who talked in telephone numbers, and was listed as a phony. One day he remarked in passing that he had three of the world's greatest pearls in his possession, and was looking for more. Eager to show up the Captain at last, Casey's companion summoned the greatest pearl expert in Egypt. Captain Eddy nonchalantly tossed his three pearls on the table. The expert studied them a moment, looked at the rumpled and unshaven Captain in amazement, and said in slow, careful English:

"If you would sell them, I shall give you fifty thousand pounds for them. . . . They are worth more but that is all I can afford."

"No, siree," said the Captain. "I'm saving those pearls for my daughter."

He stuffed them back in his pocket, and shuffled off into the night.

Newsmen, swears Casey, are simple boys at heart. They treasure clippings with typographical errors for months. . . . They play infantile tricks on one another. They wake up outraged strangers by 4 A.M. phone calls. In Chicago they found an unfortunate innocent named "Upjohn" in the directory, and called him in relays all night long to inquire sweetly, "Are you Upjohn?" A Boston group found a Paul Revere in the book, and yanked him from bed with a phone call to demand, "Why aren't you on a horse? The British are coming!" I myself know of a sophisticated group spearheaded by no less a personage than Harold Ross, late editor of *The New Yorker*, who spent a deliriously happy afternoon calling Long Island society matrons, and saying that they spoke for a nationally-known yeast manufacturer. They offered five thousand dollars for a signed testimonial, and further played on their victim's vanity by adding: "Of course, you won't keep this vulgar money yourself. We will leave it to you to pass it on to your favorite charity." The matron would coo with pleasure and then the tormentor plunged in the harpoon. "We simply want you to say," he would murmur into the mouthpiece, " 'A year ago, before I discovered Blank's yeast, my face was an unholy

463

mess of pimples and unseemly blotches.' " . . . There usually was a violent click at the other end of the wire at this point.

"Who's doing this—you or me?"

66. In Fort Smith, Arkansas, the mayor's wife died and the old icehouse burned on the same day. The local gazette printed a two-column portrait of the deceased lady on page one with a caption that made the issue a rare collector's item: "Old Eyesore Gone at Last!"

*   *   *

67. A novice on the *American* once asked Casey, "How do you spell pinochle?" Casey told him. The next day his story appeared in print. "Adolph Klepperman," it began, "has reached the pinochle of success."

*   *   *

68. Casey's prize story of transposed headlines concerns the *New York Herald Tribune*, which ran big stories one day on an address by Mr. Hamilton Fish and a new formula for feeding tropical fish, issued by the

Aquarium. It was George Dixon, on the night shift of the rival *Mirror*, who discovered that the headlines for the two stories had been mixed in the shuffle. He called the *Tribune* and announced himself as Mr. Fish. The managing editor himself came to the phone. "We know why you are calling, Mr. Fish," he said hurriedly. "It was a dreadful mistake." Then he launched into an elaborate explanation of how things like that sometimes could happen in the best-regulated newspaper offices. Dixon was extremely gracious, and accepted the apology.

At midnight Dixon was relieved by another bright young man named Dolan who also called up the *Tribune*. A brand-new voice, equally suave and apologetic, had gotten halfway through the same involved explanation, when the managing editor got back on the wire. "Mr. Fish," he asked, "didn't you call us about this mistake barely an hour ago?" "Oh, no," said Dolan haughtily. "That must have been Mr. Hamilton Fish. This is Mr. *Tropical* Fish."

* * *

69. Bill Shirer, Elliot Paul, Jay Allen, and Ed Taylor were fellow reporters on the same fabulous sheet, the *Paris Tribune*. One day Elliot Paul announced that he was ready to begin work on the Great American Novel, and his confrères volunteered to give up their day off for a period of weeks so that Paul could devote his best efforts to the new book. For months thereafter Elliot only came to the office one day a week. "If this sheet was properly staffed," he grumbled one morning, "I wouldn't have to show up at all." After a long stretch of this routine, Paul, a consummate actor, staggered into the *Tribune* office one morning clutching at his heart and stammering that he had left the finished manuscript on a bus on the Boulevard Raspail. To this day nobody knows whether there ever was a manuscript at all; certainly the French police could find no trace of one.

* * *

70. The story goes that Mrs. Vanderbilt once demanded to know what Fritz Kreisler would charge to play at a private musicale, and was taken aback when he named a price of five thousand dollars. She agreed reluctantly, but added, "Please remember that I do not expect you to mingle with the guests." "In that case, Madam," Kreisler assured her, "my fee will be only two thousand."

465

71. Toscanini had a painful experience one evening with a soloist who began his cadenza bravely enough but soon got into difficulty. Obviously flustered, he wandered farther and farther off key. The maestro and the entire orchestra held their breaths. Just before their cue to resume playing, the soloist managed to recover the original key. Toscanini bowed and said, "Welcome home, Mr. Ginsberg."

* * *

72. In New York, a five-year-old girl was taken to a concert, warned that she must remain quiet in her seat. She listened respectfully to two intricate pieces, then turned to her mother and asked gravely, "Is it all right if I scream now?"

* * *

73. And of course everybody must have heard about the night that Leopold Stokowski was conducting the Philadelphia Symphony Orchestra in the rendition of Beethoven's *Leonore* Overture No. 3, and the offstage trumpet call twice failed to sound on cue. Directly the last note

466

of the overture had been played, the apoplectic Stokowski rushed into the wings with murder in his heart. He found the trumpeter struggling in the clutches of an infuriated and burly watchman. "I tell you you can't blow that damn thing here," the watchman kept insisting. "There's a concert going on inside!"

* * *

74. Oliver Herford and a famous military man were joint guests of honor at a banquet. The hostess suddenly announced, "Mr. Oliver Herford will now improvise a poem in honor of the occasion."

Herford, a modest and retiring man, shriveled in his chair. "Oh, no," he protested. "Have the general fire a cannon."

* * *

75. James Thurber has had a few frightening motoring experiences. Once he was driving with a cherished aunt on Christmas eve in Columbus, Ohio, and died a thousand anticipatory deaths while she tooted merrily through green and red traffic lights at forty miles an hour. "Why, honey," she explained later, "I thought the city had put up those lights for the Christmas festivities!" Another time he was driving himself, quite at peace with the world, when he suddenly noticed a gauge on his dashboard that registered "1650." Expecting the car to blow up any instant, he nosed it gingerly into a wayside garage, where the attendant reassured him: "That's your own radio dial, Mac. You got her set at WQXR."

* * *

76. Edward R. Hewitt, in *Those Were the Days*, tells the story of the first time Mrs. Hamilton Fish took the controls of her shiny new electric runabout. She was hurtling down Third Avenue at a ten-mile-an-hour clip when a burly pedestrian stepped directly into her path. She tried to stop, but pushed the lever too far forward, thus increasing her speed. Her victim was just beginning to figure what had hit him when the flustered Mrs. Fish jammed her car into reverse, and got him again on the way back. Once more she jammed her lever forward too far. "Hit 'im again, lady!" cried an entranced onlooker. The pedestrian rolled out of her way. "Twice, madam, is sufficient," he informed her.

77. James Whitcomb Riley became a poet via the unlikely route of purveyor of a cure-all patent medicine. In his early twenties he traveled all over the country with a quack doctor, and wrote poems on the backs of envelopes while the doctor was hornswoggling ruralites into buying bottles of his worthless elixir.

It was Riley who taught the doctor a routine that later became famous on the vaudeville circuits. The doctor would begin his spiel in a voice so hoarse and feeble that even the hicks in the front row couldn't hear him. Then, with a shaking hand he would pour himself a tablespoonful of his patent remedy. He would swallow it with evident relish, smack his lips, and then roar in a voice that could be heard three blocks away, "AND NOW, FOLKS . . ."

* * *

78. Mark Twain made a fortune out of his books, went bankrupt when he turned publisher himself, and then paid every cent of his debts and became rich again by virtue of new writings and fabulously successful lecture tours. His financial troubles did not increase his affection for the banking fraternity. He defined a banker as a man who "loaned you an umbrella when the sun was shining and demanded its return the moment it started to rain." He invented the story of a bank president who was proud of a glass eye that had been made for him by the greatest artist in Paris. "Twain, you need $5000," he quoted this gentleman. "I'll give it to you if you can guess which of my eyes is the glass one." "It's the left one, of course," snapped Twain. "It's the only one with a glint of human kindness in it." On another occasion, Twain sought to borrow a book from a banker who lived next door to him. "You'll have to read it here," said the neighbor. "I make it a rule never to let any book go out of my library." The next night the banker asked for the use of Twain's lawnmower. "Sure thing," agreed Twain. "But you'll have to use it on my lawn. I make the same rules you do."

Mark Twain is credited with the classic remark, "Everybody complains about the weather, but nobody does anything about it," but Robert L. Cooke claims he can prove that Charles Dudley Warner actually coined the phrase. Twain *did* say, "If you don't like the weather in New England, just wait a few minutes." "Cauliflower," he said, "is nothing but cabbage with a college education." He told a lecture audience, "If you pick up a starving dog and make him prosperous, he will not bite you. This is the principal difference between a dog and a man."

Mark Twain's wife, whom he adored, was a genteel and highly moral product of Eastern society. She disapproved highly of his picturesque Western vocabulary, and often persuaded him to censor some of the more outspoken passages in his manuscripts. Her intentions were the best, but her unceasing efforts to remold Twain's character probably were largely responsible for the inner tumults and confusions that assailed him in his declining years. Twain cut himself while shaving one morning, and cussed vociferously for five minutes straight. His wife heard him and, intent upon shaming him, repeated every blasphemy he had spoken. Twain listened calmly, and told her, "You have the words, my dear, but I'm afraid you'll never get the tune." She had an appointment to meet him at the Waldorf for luncheon one day, but was very late. He left a note for her with the head waiter: "Never the Twains shall meet!" He wanted to take her to see Sarah Bernhardt, but when she heard that balcony tickets were three dollars apiece, she raised the roof. "And you're the man," she reproached him, "who told me you couldn't afford to raise our poor maids three dollars a month! You take that six dollars right out to the kitchen and give it to them!" Twain sheepishly did her bidding. The maids added four dollars of their own to the six he had given them, and went to see Sarah Bernhardt—in the orchestra.

"This is my last vacation trip by water!"

469

79. Charles Lee is showing friends a cartoon he clipped from an English weekly. It depicts a couple of fellows playing darts in a London saloon. One of the darts has gone out of line and clipped a table sitter in the back of the noggin. The table sitter's girl friend is impatiently grumbling, "Oh, you and your stabbing pains in the head."

* * *

80. A publisher's wife told Irving Hoffman, "It's not true that I married a millionaire. I made him one." "What was he before you married him?" asked Irving. The wife answered, "A multi-millionaire."

81. John Barrymore once confounded an audience in New York, at the height of the run of *Redemption*. There was an epidemic of coughing throughout the first act. When it broke out again in the second, Barrymore was all set. He suddenly yanked a five-pound sea-bass from under his coat and flung it over the footlights. "Busy yourselves with *this*, you

470

damned walruses," he bellowed, "while the rest of us proceed with the libretto!"

* * *

82. There was a time when Charles MacArthur fancied himself as a chess expert. He had run roughshod over the feeble opposition offered by fellow members of the West Side Tennis Club in Hollywood, and was growing pretty insufferable about it. He took to speaking in what he fondly believed was a Spanish accent, and telling newcomers that he was the champion, José Capablanca.

Eventually Capablanca himself visited Los Angeles and MacArthur's lacerated companions sensed the opportunity for a beautiful revenge. They brought him to the West Side Tennis Club, and introduced him to MacArthur as Mr. Spelvin. "Spelvin plays a pretty good game of chess," they said. "Indeed," beamed MacArthur. "I, señor, am Capablanca. We play a game or two, eh?" And so, while the entire membership watched in unalloyed delight, the real Capablanca and the bogus one sat down to play.

Of course, MacArthur was in the soup by the sixth move. To make matters more embarrassing, the champion, by prearrangement, would make his move in one second flat, and then dart off to the swimming pool, leaving MacArthur to sweat over *his* next move for twenty minutes or so. Then he'd saunter back, make another lightning move, and disappear again. MacArthur, perspiring freely, demanded a second game. There is no telling where the gruesome scene would have ended, had not Helen Hayes, MacArthur's wife, arrived, and learned what was afoot. She dashed to an outside telephone and called her husband. "That's the *real* Capablanca you're playing against, you loon!" she cried. "The whole club is laughing at you."

MacArthur claimed feebly that he had known all the time whom he was playing against. "Anything to give you fatheads a laugh," was his attitude. But he never impersonated Capablanca again.

* * *

83. Edgar Saltus, author of that lush chronicle of Roman times, *The Imperial Purple*, told another tale about Nero's simple efforts to keep his Romans amused. There came a time when there were no more early Christians left in captivity to feed to the lions, and other prisoners were pressed into the service. These poor wights were given a fifty-fifty

471

chance. They were allowed to pull a slip from a helmet. If the one they selected read "no" they were sitting pretty; if it read "yes" it was a break for the lions.

One culprit was in the jug because he had an annoying habit of stealing friends' and countrymen's wives. Indignant cuckolded husbands were determined that he be erased from the picture once and for all; they marked both of *his* slips "yes." A female gladiatrix managed to tip him off in the nick of time. "Think nothing of it," warbled the irresponsible lady-killer. "I'll meet you at the Zeusevelt Bar in twenty minutes." He reached into the helmet, picked up a slip, read it, tore it into shreds, laughed merrily, and started to walk off. "Just a minute," cried the infuriated captors. "What did your slip say?" "Never mind that," said the prisoner. "Just read the one you have left!"

* * *

84. One of the most famous and most respected of the colleges that make up the great university of Oxford is Balliol. For some reason the venerable institution attracts African potentates and Indian nabobs in addition to eminent white students; its alumni include more black-skinned men, probably, than all the rest of the colleges combined. This gave rise to a story that has a very high rating in British circles.

An explorer was going about his business in darkest Africa when a hungry cannibal tribe bagged him in full flight and considered its Sunday-dinner problem solved. He weighed about two hundred on the hoof, and there were murmurs of genuine satisfaction when they had seasoned him with salt and lowered him into the pot. He was just beginning to simmer when the cannibal chief suddenly remembered his manners.

"Jove," he ejaculated, "you sound like an Oxford graduate. What college?"

"Balliol," gasped the half-baked explorer.

"Release this man," cried the chief. "Balliol men never eat one another!"

* * *

85. One day President Lincoln journeyed to the front to inspect the Union defenses; the task of piloting him fell to young Oliver Wendell Holmes. Holmes pointed out their enemy; the President stood up to look.

Wearing his high plug hat, he made a magnificent target. A snarl of musketry fire came from the enemy trenches. The young officer dragged him under cover.

Later Holmes remembered to his horror that he had muttered "Get down, you fool!" He was relieved, however, when Lincoln came to him before returning to the capital. "Good-bye, Captain Holmes," he said. "I'm glad to see you know how to talk to a civilian."

* * *

86. Some years after he had been President, William Howard Taft had to make a sudden trip to Chicago. Only an upper was left. Taft noticed that the lower of his section was assigned to an insignificant Casper Milquetoast, and resorted to a bit of psychology. "Last time I occupied an upper," he announced cheerfully, "it collapsed. I certainly hope this one will hold me." Then he went off to the club car. When he returned the little man was neatly buttoned up in the upper berth.

"How about you sleeping in an upper and me sleeping in a lower for a change?"

87. Most of the amusing anecdotes concerning President Coolidge relate to his taciturnity and respect for his bankroll. In Northampton one day his wife fell for the blandishments of a traveling book salesman and bought one of those 1800-page "home medical advisers" for something like fifteen dollars. Misgivings assailed her the moment the salesman's hypnotic presence was removed. "What will Calvin say?" was the thought that plagued her. "How am I going to tell him?" Finally, she decided to put the book down on the centre of the library table, and await the explosion when her husband discovered it. To her amazement he said nothing about it at all—either the first evening or for several days thereafter. Mrs. Coolidge couldn't understand it—until one morning she opened the book and found that he had written a note on the fly-leaf. "I have looked carefully through all 1800 pages of this work," it read, "and find no cure whatever for a sucker."

88. Jane Addams, the famous social worker and founder of Hull-House, told this story on herself. She met an old friend on a train one afternoon, and greeted her cordially, but simply couldn't remember her name. "The conversation is bound to give me a clue," she thought, but for a half-hour she got nowhere. Then the friend said, "My poor brother is working himself to death these days." Miss Addams felt that her moment had come. "Ah yes, your dear brother," she exclaimed. "And what is he doing now?" Her companion glared. "He is still President of the United States," she remarked coldly.

* * *

89. The Baseball Writers presented the great catcher, Bill Dickey, with a plaque as the Player of the Year. Dickey responded with his longest speech on record: "It shore is purty. Much obliged." The night the last World Series ended, the victorious Yankees, including Bill Dickey, went off the wagon with a bang. At the height of the festivities a man he hadn't seen in twenty years, now a beribboned officer, slapped Dickey on the back and chortled, "Remember me, Bill?" "I don't recall the name," mused Dickey. "But you shore were a sucker for a high curve inside!"

* * *

90. The Dizzy Dean Dictionary should never have omitted the classic repartee that featured a tense spot in the first Series game at Detroit. The fans were riding him hard that day, and didn't like it at all when he struck out the entire side in one inning, and came swaggering to the bench. "If I was your wife," hollered one lady enthusiast, "I'd give you poison." "If I wuz your husband," snapped back Mr. Dean, "I'd take it!"

* * *

91. The old Carlisle Indians were a tricky and colorful outfit, especially when they had Jim Thorpe in the backfield. They invaded Cambridge one fall to tussle with a fine Harvard team, and had leather patches sewed on their jerseys that looked exactly like footballs. In the first few scrimmages, the Harvard team thought all eleven opponents had pigskins tucked under their arms, and didn't know whom to tackle. One Carlisle back added to the confusion by slipping the real football under the back of his jersey and galloping unmolested over the goal line. Officials had to change the rules the following season.

475

CLARENCE BIERS

92. Knute Rockne had a brief whirl at professional football in its early days. In one of his first games, he faced Jim Thorpe and his Canton Bull-dogs at the Polo Grounds. The great Indian athlete was long past his prime, growing fat and sluggish, but he was still a great drawing card. Rockne was desperately anxious to make good. On one of the opening plays, Thorpe came lumbering around his end. Rockne spilled him. As he rose, Thorpe whispered, "Listen, Rock. Don't do that no more. People paid to see Old Jim run. Next time, let him go." On the next play, Rockne spilled him again. Thorpe said nothing this time, but on the very next play, he summoned some reserve force, and for a moment was the flailing, irresistible runner of old. Rockne was knocked cold, and Thorpe gal-loped for a touchdown while the crowd cheered. Then the Indian re-turned to where Rockne was coming to, helped to pick him up, and grinned. "That's a good boy, Rock. You let old Jim run!"

* * *

93. Dick Hanley once coached a Northwestern team that gave him many a gray hair. On a certain Saturday the boys surpassed themselves, and fumbled so often that Hanley literally fell off the bench with rage.

476

He signaled his last substitute backfield man to warm up, then promptly forgot about him. A substitute centre kept passing the ball faithfully to the lad on the sidelines, but Hanley never signaled him to enter the game. Finally the boy missed a practice pass. From the silence of the dejected Northwestern rooting section came a raucous voice: "Put him in now, Hanley; he's ready!"

* * *

94. The most lopsided football game in the record books took place in 1916. Georgia Tech defeated Cumberland College, 220-0. There lives a man who admits he quarterbacked that Cumberland team: George Allen, former commissioner of the District of Columbia. Allen treasures a yellowed clipping which reads, "Allen spearheaded the Cumberland offensive with a brilliant run around left end that resulted in only an eight-yard loss." He tackled one Tech man on the thirty-yard line and hung around his neck all the way to the goal line. "Once I fumbled," he remembers, "and as three Tech ogres bore down, another Cumberland stalwart shied away from the loose ball. 'Pick it up,' I yelled to the guy, but what do you think he answered? 'Pick it up, hell,' he said. '*I* didn't drop it!' "

* * *

95. Harvard and Princeton once broke off football relations for years because their games were getting too rough and bad feeling was rife. The last game before the split wasn't made any gentler by a joke that appeared in the Harvard *Lampoon*, published the morning of the match. "Are you a Princeton man?" queried a sweet young thing. "No," was the answer, "a horse stepped on my face." The Princeton team didn't forget *that* when the whistle blew.

* * *

96. Bob Considine told the story of a Notre Dame star who went to a sterling but absent-minded priest every week for confession. The priest had the habit of marking the number of sins on his sleeve with a piece of chalk in order to mete out the proper penance.

"Father," said the player one day, "I ran clear across the field to clip a player in our last game."

"That was very wrong, my son," said the priest, making a chalk mark.

"When he fell, I kicked him in the teeth."

477

"How terrible, my son! Will you never learn true Christianity?" (Four more chalk marks.)

"And then when the referee wasn't looking, I chewed off a piece of his ear."

"Saints preserve us! You're a disgrace to your fine teachers and the college!" By this time the chalk marks were clear up to the priest's elbow. "What was the team you were playing, my son?"

"Southern Methodist," said the player.

"Oh," beamed the priest, rubbing off every mark on his sleeve. "I guess boys will be boys."

A few years ago a forlorn little football squad from a jerkwater college came down to open the season against one of Notre Dame's most powerful elevens. The coach was trying to instill some spirit into his justifiably terrified protégés. "Sure you'll get trimmed," he assured them. "Nobody expects you to do more than your best. At least, show that mob in the stadium that you've got the old moxie—that you can fight to the end for your alma mater. Let's run out on that field as though we expected to win the game!"

He threw open the door of the locker room. The inspired squad dashed out with a whoop—and, as one man, fell smack into the Notre Dame swimming pool.

478

97. Thornton Wilder is credited with the tale of an inebriated Yale student who saw a signpost in Providence that read, "New Haven 126, Cambridge 54." "Yippee," cried the scholar, "I always knew we could trim those guys!"

* * *

98. When Dempsey was training for his first fight with Tunney, he sent a scout named Mike Trent over to his rival's training camp, to pick up some pointers on Tunney's style of hitting power.

Trent returned in high glee. "It's a set-up," he reported. "I seen the lug reading a book!"

* * *

99. When Quentin Reynolds was an undergraduate at Brown, he became the unexpected hero of an intercollegiate championship swimming meet.

Brown had a renowned plunger on the squad that year who was counted on to bring the first-place trophy home to Providence, but he came down with flu the morning of the meet. The coach was tearing his hair when he spied the two-hundred-pound Quent lumbering across the campus. "Hey, you," he cried, "you look like a guy who can plunge! You gotta plunge your damn head off for Brown tonight."

Reynolds protested weakly that he had never plunged in his life, and then proceeded into town to get most royally plastered. At nine-thirty, sharp, a pistol barked, and five young giants, including Reynolds, took off from the side of the tank. Reynolds went to the bottom like a plummet, and passed out cold. By the time they fished him out of the tank, however—check the records if you don't believe me—he had negotiated the entire length of the pool and broken the intercollegiate record. He had also turned blue. When he came to, they gave him a gold medal and put him on probation for thirty days. He has never plunged since.

* * *

100. A yarn of Saratoga concerns a young honeymoon couple who shared a passionate love of gambling. For five hectic days they were dogged by persistent bad luck; on the morning of the final day of the meet, they had only two dollars left between them.

"Let me go out to the track alone today, honey," pleaded the boy. "Wait for me at the hotel. I've got a hunch."

A friend drove him out to the track. He picked a 40-to-1 shot on the

479

first race, and won. Every succeeding race was captured by a rank outsider. He was backing it every time. At the end of the afternoon he had over ten thousand dollars.

On the way back to the hotel, he decided to cash in further on his lucky streak, and stopped at one of the clubs that ran gaming rooms in rather open defiance of the state laws. His luck held. He ran his stake up to forty thousand. He was on the point of leaving when the wheel began spinning once more. Suddenly he put the entire forty thousand on "black."

The ball bounced, and settled. "Number fourteen," called the croupier. "*Red*."

The boy walked back to the hotel. The girl was waiting for him on the verandah.

"How did you make out?" she called eagerly.

The boy lit a cigarette. "I lost the two dollars," he said.

* * *

101. When Francis Meynell, the great typographer and founder of the Nonesuch Press, visited America, he was tendered a dinner by the American Institute of Graphic Arts. Aware that students of printing as far away as Kansas City were going to journey to New York to hear his talk, Meynell spent days in feverish preparation, and marched off to the dinner with a sixteen-page typewritten manuscript in his pocket.

Unfortunately, a preliminary "cocktail party," hosted by the genial Rockwell Kent, lasted a full two hours longer than had been anticipated, owing in part to Mr. Kent's discovery of a half-dozen bottles of prime Irish whiskey, in part to the fact that most of the guests began falling on their faces. When Meynell faced the Institute audience, he swayed a bit, forgot all about the prepared speech in his pocket, and told the following story:

In the time of Nero, when sport-loving Romans crowded the Colosseum every Saturday to see a Christian tossed to the lions (on some Sundays there were double-headers), there was one special victim who had given the authorities untold trouble before he was rounded up. Nero had eleven of his most ferocious lions starved for a full week to assure a neat performance when they were turned on this Christian the following Saturday. Eighty thousand spectators turned out, not including the press. The Christian stood alone in the centre of the arena, calm and unafraid.

The first lion was released. He made a bee-line for the Christian. The crowd wetted its lips. But then an amazing thing happened. The Christian bent down and whispered something in the lion's ear. The lion's tail went between his legs, he lowered his head, and slinked out of the arena. When the same performance was followed by six more half-starved kings of the forest, and the gallant crowd was beginning to holler for its money back, Nero, sore as a pup, summoned the Christian and curtly said, "If you will tell me what you say to those lions to make them act that way, I will grant you a full pardon." "It's very simple, Nero," explained the Christian. "I just whisper in their ears: 'Remember, you'll be expected to say a few words after dinner!'"

* * *

102. Shaggy-dog stories, as almost everybody must know by this time, are the kind of tales in which animals talk, humans do inexplicable things, and the punch lines make no sense at all. They are generally anathema to literal-minded females. There is nothing like a string of shaggy-dog stories to make your wife's Aunt Minnie cut short a visit and go back where she came from. They receive their name from the following legend.

A Kansas City barfly picked up a year-old copy of the London *Times* one day—don't ask me how it got there—and found therein a personal ad offering a ten-pound reward for the return of a very shaggy dog to its bereft owner in Bishop's Bowes, Essex. Ten minutes later he stumbled over the shaggiest darn pup you ever saw. Being a man of decision, he promptly bundled the canine under his arm, took the Twentieth Century to New York, the *Queen Mary* to Southampton, and a limousine to Bishop's Bowes. In keen anticipation, he sought out the lady who had advertised, and rang her bell. She answered herself.

"You lost a shaggy dog, madam," he reminded her, holding up the pooch. "Would this be it?"

"Good heavens, no," she snapped. "It wasn't *that* shaggy"—and slammed the door in his face.

Well, now that we've settled that, we propose to give you some examples of the species.

103. Two race horses fretted impatiently in adjoining stalls the night before a Kentucky Derby. "You might as well save yourself the effort of competing tomorrow," spoke one, "I've got the Derby sewed up." "Says you," scoffed the other. "What makes you so sure of yourself?" "Didn't you see my owner whispering in my ear just now?" said the first horse. "He was telling me that if I won tomorrow, he'd give me two extra bales of hay. And, brother, that ain't money!"

* * *

104. A customer entered a saloon and ordered a dozen martinis. He poured the liquor onto the floor, and began munching contentedly on the glasses themselves. The stems, however, he would have no traffic with. A barfly watched the performance with absorbed interest, but pointed to the twelve stems. "You darn fool," he said. "You're leaving the best part."

"Shall we? Just for the hell of it?"

483

105. Sitting opposite Miss Haas on a northbound subway train one evening sat a man calmly reading his paper with three pigeons resting on top of him—one on his head, the others on his shoulders. Miss Haas contemplated the situation until she could stand it no longer. She tapped his paper, and said, "Pardon me, but what on earth are you doing with those pigeons in the subway?" "Them?" said the man. "I really don't know, lady. They musta got on at 59th Street."

A.W.H.

106. A crotchety old bachelor saw a gaily plumed parrot go under the hammer at a country auction, and suddenly decided that the bird might be good company for him on lonely evenings. The bidding grew unexpectedly stiff, but the bachelor was carried away by the spirit of the occasion and before he quite realized what he had done, he bought the Poll for forty-nine dollars. He carried it home, and stood it on the table before him. "Now," he commanded, "talk to me!" The parrot simply drew in its head and glared at him. "I said talk to me," repeated the man. "After all, I bought you to keep me company." Again the parrot glared

484

but said nothing. "Good heavens," cried the exasperated gentleman. "Do you mean to say that after what I paid for you, you can't even *talk?*" "Can't even talk?" echoed the parrot. "Who in hell do you think it was that bid you up to forty-nine dollars?"

* * *

107. A worm met another worm coming up from the ground and declared, "You're very beautiful and I'd like to marry you." "Don't be a dope," was the reply. "I'm your other end."

* * *

108. A doctor saved a baby elephant's life in the jungle, then returned to America. Years later he was down on his luck, and had to borrow a quarter to see the circus when it came to town. Out came the elephants. One of them saw the doctor, and trumpeted recognition. He wrapped his trunk around the doctor, lifted him out of the twenty-five-cent seat—and planked him down in a box seat worth three dollars.

* * *

109. A kangaroo yanked her young one out of her pouch and gave it a healthy smack on the backside. "I'll teach you," she declared, "to eat crackers in bed!"

* * *

110. When the manager of the Brooklyn ball club lost his star centre fielder on the eve of a crucial swing through the West, he sent out a frantic call for a replacement. Almost a week went by and there were no applications. The manager sat dejectedly on the bench with his head in his hands. He heard an apologetic whinny behind him, and looking around, saw a horse standing there.

"Go away," he said to the horse. "Can't you see I've got a headache?"

"But I'm applying for that spot in centre field," said the horse.

"That's ridiculous," snapped the manager. "Horses don't play baseball—not even in Brooklyn!"

The horse insisted, however, and finally the manager allowed him to exhibit his wares. It developed that he could field like Tris Speaker and hit like Joe DiMaggio. The delighted manager promptly inserted him into the lineup.

In the ninth inning of that day's game, with the score 0-0, the horse strode to the plate and lashed a wicked liner against the right-field fence.

Then—to everyone's amazement—he stood stock still at the plate, twirling his bat.

"Run, you idiot, run!" beseeched the manager. "This means the game!"

"Don't be silly," said the horse. "Who ever heard of a horse running bases?"

* * *

111. A colony of ostriches—ninety-nine birds in all—had their heads buried neatly in the sand when ostrich number one hundred came ga-lumping onto the scene. He looked about in a puzzled way and inquired, "Where on earth *is* everybody?"

* * *

112. "Do you realize," said a man in a cafeteria to a stranger across the table, "that you are reading your newspaper upside down?"

"Of course I realize it," snapped the stranger. "Do you think it's easy?"

113. A pigeon came home very late for dinner one evening, with his feathers bedraggled, and his eyes bloodshot. "I was out minding my own business," he explained, "when bingo! I get caught in a badminton game!"

* * *

114. At a gala ship concert aboard a liner, a trained parrot did his act, and then teetered excitedly on his perch in the wings while an extraordinary magician performed feats of legerdemain. First he made a goldfish disappear, then a buxom blonde assistant, finally a chest containing three husky sailors. At that moment the liner was struck by a torpedo. The parrot found himself all alone on the Atlantic Ocean, bobbing up and down on a piece of driftwood, with nothing else in sight. "Amazing," marveled the Poll. "What will he think of next?"

* * *

115. Two brothers, identical twins, often went fishing together. One twin was always lucky. The other could never catch a thing. They could stand right next to each other and one brother would haul in fish after fish while the other's line dangled idly in the water. One day the unlucky twin decided on a desperate course. He woke in the middle of the night and put on his brother's clothes. He took his brother's rod and went to the spot where his brother had caught thirty-four trout the day before. For three hours he stood without getting a nibble. Finally his hopes rose when he saw a trout swimming his way. The fish ignored the bait and, leaping out of the water, called, "Hey, bud, where's your brother?"

* * *

116. Clarence Budington Kelland presided the day that Nicholas Murray Butler, then Columbia University prexy, was the guest of the Dutch Treat. "For years," said Kelland, gazing fondly at Dr. Butler, "organizations have been besieging this retiring gentleman to address them—with remarkable success."

* * *

117. Harry Hansen climbed into a taxicab, told the driver where he wanted to go, and added, "Please don't go down Third Avenue. I don't like those El pillars."

"Yessir," said the driver—and went right down Third Avenue.

"Didn't you hear me?" screamed Hansen. "I said not to go weaving in and out around those El pillars. It drives me crazy."

The driver stopped his cab and looked at Hansen reproachfully. "Listen, Buddy," he remarked. "What do you suppose it does to *me?*"

118. A man dropped in to pay a friend an unexpected visit, and was amazed to find him playing chess with his dog. The man watched in silence for a few minutes, then burst out with "That's the most incredible dog I ever saw in my life!" "Oh, he isn't so smart," was the answer. "I've beaten him three games out of four!"

* * *

119. The twelve-year-old daughter of a publisher of the *New York Times* volunteered to help her mother pass cocktails at an informal reception whipped up for a visiting General. Everything progressed beautifully until the horrified mother heard her daughter say to the General's wife, "May I serve you your eighth martini?"

* * *

120. And Leonard Lyons' young hopeful watched his mother try on a new dress. "You sure are beautiful," he assured her. "You look just like Abraham Lincoln!"

* * *

121. Olin Clark reported the story of a mother who lost her young daughter in the week-end confusion at Penn Station. After a frantic search, she finally located her in the midst of a group of nuns. Both the little girl and the nuns seemed to be having a very good time. "I hope my daughter hasn't been giving you too much trouble," exclaimed the relieved parent. "On the contrary," chuckled the Mother Superior. "Your little girl seems to have the notion that we are penguins."

* * *

122. Dialogue overheard on a cannibal island: "Who is that lady I seen you with last night?" "That wasn't no lady. That was my dinner."

* * *

123. When one famous explorer went on his Antarctic expeditions, report had it that the personnel invariably included the ugliest old crone he could sign up. "She's my yardstick," he explained. "When she starts looking good to me—I know it's time to start for home."

* * *

124. A gent boarded a cab on 42nd Street, and pointing to the revolving electrical news sign on the Times Building, commanded, "Just follow that sign."

* * *

125. There is a bone-dry town in Oklahoma where an honest-to-goodness rattlesnake bite is the only way to get a shot of whiskey. One native came home angry and thirsty and told his wife, "It's about time this burg had more'n one rattler. I stood in line for three hours today and by the time it was my turn the rattler was so tired he wouldn't bite nobody any more."

126. You have read a lot about the knights of King Arthur who fared forth on coal-black chargers to rescue beautiful maidens from dragons' clutches, but did you ever know that one of them was mounted on a St. Bernard dog? His name was Sir Marmaduke, and he and the St. Bernard performed many a deed of derring-do. One evening, however, they were caught in a torrential thunder-storm, and sought shelter at a nearby tavern. "Reservation?" asked the room clerk. "No," admitted Sir Marmaduke. "Sorry," said the clerk, "no room without a reservation." It was at this moment that he discovered that Marmaduke was sitting astride his faithful St. Bernard. "Hold on," said the clerk. "We'll have to find *something* for you. I wouldn't put out a knight on a dog like this."

* * *

127. Earl Wilson told about a well-known Broadway comedian, in his cups as usual, who careened into the 46th Street Automat, changed two dollar bills into nickels, and began inserting them in the pie slots. He had made a neat pile of four slices of apple pie, three of lemon, and five of peach, and was slipping a nickel into his first coconut pie slot when the manager collared him. "What the hell are you doing with our pies?" he cried. "Cut it out!" "Whaaat?" exclaimed the Broadwayite. "Quit now when my luck's running so good?"

Maybe that's how George Price got the notion for his cartoon of the flabbergasted Automat customer who had deposited a single nickel, and found an assortment of sandwiches, cakes, hard-boiled eggs, and crullers flying into his face. "Congratulations, sir," beamed an attendant. "You've hit the jackpot."

* * *

128. An unprecedented rush of business has made it practically impossible to get a table in a New York restaurant during the dinner hour, and Mr. Garfinkle became increasingly aware of this fact while he tried vainly to fight his way past the lobby of a half-dozen high-class eateries. Finally he staggered into a tiny delicatessen, and planted himself at the solitary marble-topped table in the rear.

To his surprise, a waiter appeared instantly, and said, "What'll you have?"

"A couple of soft-boiled eggs," begged Mr. Garfinkle, "and a few kind words."

Five minutes later the eggs were planked down in front of him. "So here are the eggs," he murmured plaintively. "Now how about the few kind words?"

The waiter leaned over and whispered, "Don't eat them eggs!"

* * *

129. From David Niven, when in London, came the story of the RAF pilot who made a forced landing in Belgium and was rescued by a nun. She shepherded him into her convent, handed him a complete set of nun's habiliments, and counseled: "Lie low. Say nothing. Be as inconspicuous as possible. Sooner or later we will find a way to spirit you back to England." For eight weeks the pilot spoke to no one, shaved eight times a day, was a model convent habitant. One evening, however, he spied a beautiful young sister alone in the pantry, and on a sudden but irresistible impulse, swept her into his arms. A moment later he was reeling from a terrific sock on the jaw. " 'Ere, 'ere, you rum bloke," spoke a deep masculine voice. " 'Old yer 'orses, carn't yer? I been 'ere since Dunkerque."

491

130. Two K.P.'s were staggering under the weight of a steaming kettle they were hauling from the kitchen in Fort Dix, New Jersey. A colonel stopped them. "Get me a ladle," he commanded. One of the K.P.'s rushed for a ladle. The colonel dipped it into the kettle, swallowed a mouthful, gulped, and roared, "Do you call that soup?"

"No, sir," came the meek reply. "That's the water we've been washing the dishes in!"

131. The boys in the South Pacific retain their sense of humor. One writes, "I am raising quite a beard on the instalment plan: a little down at a time." Another explained his plight in a note of exactly four words: "Long time no she."

* * *

132. A new cocktail bar on Pennsylvania Avenue is named "Chez When."

133. The rarest tale of poetic justice comes from dusty Texas, where an erstwhile *New Yorker* cartoonist was laboring in a camouflage unit. A loud-mouthed and overbearing officer drove up one day and bawled the daylights out of the entire company. Their efforts, he informed them, wouldn't befuddle a Jap with one eye missing entirely and the other closed by a cataract. "Take down this claptrap," he bellowed, "and start all over again." The officer then climbed into his jeep and drove smack into the camouflaged headquarters hut.

* * *

134. Ed Wynn, "the Perfect Fool," proved to be just what the doctors ordered for wounded soldiers at U. S. Army hospitals. They roared at his pole eleven feet four inches long, to be used for people you wouldn't touch with a ten-foot pole. They loved his cigarette lighter: when he pushed down on a little wheel an arrow jumped up and pointed to the nearest man with matches.

But the biggest laugh of all came when he demanded of a colonel, "Say, have you seen the morning papers?"; the obliging colonel answered, "No, what's in them?" Wynn cracked, "My lunch, and I'm getting mighty hungry."

Old Wynn enthusiasts believe that he reached his greatest height in a show called *Manhattan Mary*. Wynn was a waiter in one scene. "I don't like all the flies in here," complained one patron. "Show me the ones you don't like," suggested Wynn, "and I'll throw 'em out." When the patron said, "I'm so hungry I could eat a horse," Wynn led a live nag on to the stage. Then he sold it to the customer. "This horse has only one peculiarity," he told the befuddled buyer. "He loves to sit on potatoes. Remember that!" The man made off with his horse, but was back a moment later. "You fraud," he screamed. "I no sooner got that horse to the bridge down the road, when he bolted out of my control, and jumped over the bridge into the river." "Oh, I forgot to tell you," said the contrite Wynn. "That horse loves to sit on fish, too!"

In another scene, Wynn was busy painting a ship. An old dowager entered and asserted, "Mr. Wynn, I have decided to commission you to paint my ancestors." "Oh, I couldn't do that," he protested. "I'm just a ship painter." "Nevertheless," insisted the dowager, "you are the man I want for the job." "But I tell you," he wailed, "I only paint ships." "The question is closed," she announced. "You, and you alone, are going to

paint my ancestors." "All right," agreed Wynn finally. "I'll paint your
darn ancestors. But I want to warn you now: they're going to look like
ships!"

135. If the armed forces ever took a vote for their favorite comedian,
Bob Hope would undoubtedly win by something like the 85,000 miles
he figures he has traveled to spread sunshine—and Hope—wherever
American boys are fighting.

In Africa, he reported, "The boys were so happy to see me they
actually got down on their knees. What a crap game!" In Edinburgh he
told his audience, "This blackout isn't all wasted; I just bumped into
eight Scotchmen on Princes Street developing films." In Palermo, the
Nazis bombed his hotel. "We did a show," said Hope, "and then ran for
our lives. But then, I've never done anything else!" In London, he reported, "I just saw Winston Churchill. Best newsreel I've caught in
months!"

At a base hospital he was introduced to a soldier who was suffering
from anemia and sundry other ailments. "I remember giving a pint of
blood last year," cracked Hope. "I've got an idea that I'm shaking hands
with the guy who got it!"

136. Lt. Col. Rogers wrote from the Pacific area that a hand-lettered sign tacked to the officers' bulletin board reads, "Hats altered to fit any promotion."

* * *

137. A biologist was taken into the army as a captain, and then proceeded to go right on doing the things he always had done before. They let him use his own laboratory, and he didn't even wear an officer's uniform. "Has your life changed in any way?" a reporter asked him. "Well," he answered, " I work the same. I live the same, and I even think the same; but now if a guinea pig bites me, I get the Purple Heart."

* * *

138. A veteran of the Korean fighting, later in officer-candidate school, enjoyed telling about the day he was inducted into the Army. His physical over, he was taken in hand by a sergeant and asked, "Did you go to grammar school?"

"Yes, sir," said the draftee. "I also went through high school, graduated cum laude from college, completed three years of graduate studies at Cornell, and then acquired two more degrees at Columbia."

The sergeant nodded, reached for a rubber stamp, and slapped it on the questionnaire. It consisted of a single word: "Literate."

* * *

139. Aunt Emma grew somewhat eccentric in her declining years, but since the whole family hoped to inherit some of her considerable fortune, she was humored in every impulse. One afternoon, at the height of a furious storm, Aunt Emma decided she'd like a ride in the family convertible, with the top down. Uncle Herbert dutifully escorted her to the car, climbed behind the wheel, and without ever budging from the garage, went through the motions of taking her for a drive. At the end of a half hour Aunt Emma pronounced herself satisfied, and the two of them re-entered the living room.

"Herbert is a fair enough driver," admitted Aunt Emma, "but I do think he's just a little bit off his rocker. Here we were driving through a raging downpour, with the top down, and the darn fool never put on his hat!"

140. Two silver-haired old ladies wobbled down the main street of a New England town in their moth-eaten coupé, made an illegal turn, and compounded their felony by ignoring the outraged traffic officer's endeavors to stop them. He finally caught up with them in front of Ye Olde Waffle Shoppe. "Didn't you hear my whistle?" he demanded angrily. The perky octogenarian at the wheel looked at him coyly and admitted, "Yes, I did, officer—but I never flirt when I'm driving." The cop looked astonished, then broke into a broad grin, and said, "You win, lady! Drive on!"

* * *

141. Ohio State University once invited a distinguished old judge to speak at a convocation. They didn't realize that the gentleman, always eccentric, had grown worse with the years, and was somewhat senile into the bargain. He seized his typescript firmly, plodded up to the lectern, and began reading in a high, cracked voice. When he got to the bottom of Page One, he turned the leaf, and continued reading. It soon became apparent to the startled audience that the judge was rereading Page One. And if that wasn't enough, the third page was another duplicate!

By this time, everybody realized that the typist had delivered the judge's speech in triplicate. Seventeen pages were read three times over by the unsuspecting old gentleman. The chairman then rushed out for an aspirin, and the audience rushed out to have hysterics.

* * *

142. Gertrude Lawrence was starring in a London play that was honored by a visit from the late King and his Queen. As the Queen entered the Royal Box, the entire audience arose to acclaim her. Miss Lawrence, watching from the wings, murmured, "What an entrance!" Noel Coward, on tiptoe behind her, added, "What a part!"

* * *

143. Carl Sandburg was persuaded to attend the dress rehearsal of a very serious play by a very serious young dramatist, but unfortunately slept through much of the performance. The outraged dramatist chided him later, "How could you sleep when you knew how much I wanted your opinion?" Sandburg reminded him, "Young man, sleep *is* an opinion."

144. Monty Woolley slipped on the stairs of the Times Square subway station one rainy night when there were no taxis to be had. Halfway down, he bumped into a stout lady, who toppled against him, and landed in his lap at the bottom of the stairs. Woolley tapped her on the shoulder and pointed out, "Madam, I'm sorry, but this is as far as I go."

* * *

145. Do you remember the New England hurricane of 1938?

A commuter who lived in Stamford had always wanted to own a barometer. Two days before the big blow he finally bought one at Abercrombie and Fitch. He tacked it up on his wall, read it, and exploded with anger. There was no phone in his house, so he walked a mile to the nearest drugstore and called up Abercrombie. "Fine barometer you sold me," he snorted. "I put it up in my Stamford house and what do you think it registers? *Hurricane!*"

"Return it," soothed the clerk. "We'll replace it with a perfect one."

He went back to fetch the barometer, but by the time he got there, his house had been blown away.

146. When the rodeo was packing them in at Madison Square Garden, an elderly lady paused after the show for a cup of java in a beanery down the block. The coffee was too hot for her and she put it down with a sigh, exclaiming, "Oh, dear, my bus leaves in three minutes." A polite cowboy promptly handed his cup to her, explaining, "Lady, I'll be obliged if you drink this coffee of mine. It's already saucered and blowed."

* * *

147. An old bishop in the nation's capital was sick to death of the socials and embassy parties he was expected to attend every other afternoon. At one of them he entered wearily, glanced sourly at the over-familiar cast of characters, and sank into the nearest chair. The hostess asked coyly, "A spot of tea, Bishop?" "No tea," he growled. "Coffee, Bishop?" "No coffee." An understanding woman, she whispered in his ear, "Scotch and water, Bishop?" Said the bishop, brightening, "No water."

148. Bernard Shaw's criticism of the marriage ritual: "When two people are under the influence of the most violent, most insane, most delusive and most transient of passions, they are required to solemnly swear they will remain in that excited, abnormal and exhausting condition continuously until death do them part."

* * *

149. On the maid's day out, a prominent publisher volunteered to take the heat off his wife and tackle the Herculean task of putting their four-year-old to bed. The exhausted wife threw herself on the chaise longue and picked up the evening papers. An hour later the four-year-old stole into the room and whispered, "Daddy's asleep at last!"

* * *

150. Columnist Bob Considine boasts that his sons are the best-mannered lads on Ninety-sixth Street. "I've never had to lay hands on one of them," he declares, "—except in self-defense."

* * *

151. A little boy had been pawing over a stationer's stock of greeting cards for some time when a clerk asked, "Just what is it you're looking for, sonny? Birthday greeting? Message to a sick friend? Anniversary congratulations to your ma and dad?"

The boy shook his head "no" and answered wistfully, "Got anything in the line of blank report cards?"

* * *

152. Despite the best efforts of child psychiatrists, there are still a lot of kids of four or five—even in sophisticated New York—who believe in Santa Claus.

One of them was taken by his mother to the toy department in Macy's on a December morning last year and was duly propped up on Santa's lap. "What do you want for Christmas, my lad?" asked Santa Claus dutifully. "Better write it down," said the lad, "or you'll forget." "Trust me," urged Santa. "My memory never fails." The lad was dubious, but catalogued his demands.

The same afternoon, mother and son arrived at Gimbel's and the lad found himself on Santa's lap for a second time. The Gimbel Santa asked the usual question, "What do you want for Christmas?"

The lad slipped off his lap, kicked him lustily in the shin, and yelled, "You numskull, I *knew* you'd forget!"

* * *

153. A buxom lady tripped on the stairs and broke her leg. The doctor put it in a cast and warned her that she wasn't to attempt going up or down stairs until it came off. Four months later he removed the cast and pronounced her well on the way to recovery.

"Goody, goody," gurgled the lady. "Is it all right for me to walk the stairs now?" "Yes," answered the doctor, "if you promise to be very careful."

"I can't tell you what a relief it will be," confessed the lady. "It was such a nuisance crawling outside and shinnying up and down that drainpipe all the time!"

* * *

154. According to Sam Levenson, an irate mother marched her ten-year-old son into a doctor's office and demanded, "Is a boy of this age able to perform an appendix operation?" "Of course not," snapped the doctor. Mama turned angrily on the boy and shouted, "So who was right? Put it back!"

* * *

155. The greatest surgeon in town was performing a difficult operation before a gallery of fascinated internes. At the most crucial moment another doctor tapped the surgeon on the shoulder and asked, "May I cut in?"

* * *

156. In Washington, a government survey was ordered to study the migratory habits of birds. Thousands of all species were released with metal strips attached reading, "Notify Fish and Wild Life Division. Wash. Biol. Surv." Hugh Newton wrote, "The abbreviation was changed abruptly following receipt of this penciled note from a vexed Alberta agriculturist: 'Gents: I shot one of your crows last week and followed instructions attached to it. I washed it, biled it and surved it. It was awful. You should stop trying to fool the public with things like this.'"

500

157. Dr. Pullman, the society dentist, tried desperately to soothe his richest but most difficult patient, a Mrs. Gruber. "Don't shake your arms like a semaphore and make those faces at me," he begged. "I haven't even started drilling yet." "I know you haven't," said Mrs. Gruber, "but you're standing on my corns."

* * *

158. When Juan and Evita Perón were building a luxurious retreat for themselves some miles outside of Buenos Aires they established a rigid guard around the project to prevent the stealth of valuable materials. Every day at noon, the story goes, the same workman began to appear at the exit gate with a wheelbarrow loaded with straw. The guard, convinced that there was dirty work afoot, searched the straw more carefully daily—even had it analyzed to see if it possessed special chemical values—but could find nothing to substantiate his suspicion, and had to let the workman pass.

A year later, the guard met the workman, evidently enjoying great prosperity. "Now that all is said and done," pleaded the guard, "just what were you stealing every day on that Perón project?" The workman whispered, "Wheelbarrows."

* * *

159. Up in Scotland, a golfer stepped to the first tee, and sliced his ball so badly that it crashed through a window of the clubhouse way off to the right. He rushed to retrieve it, and found a half dozen fellow members in a dither of excitement. "Darnedest ricochet in the history of St. Albans," marveled one. "After that ball broke the window, it bounced off Mrs. McIntosh's head, knocked over MacTavish's whiskey and soda, bounced through another window, and broke the rector's windshield." "Never mind all the chatter," said the golfer severely. "Where's my ball now?"

160. En route by automobile to the Riviera in Southern France, movie tycoon Darryl Zanuck stayed overnight at a small inn south of Vichy. "You must fill out registration papers for the local gendarmes," the proprietor reminded him. "It is the law, you know." "I'm tired of these darn forms and regulations," said Zanuck. "Fill it out for me. My full name is on all the baggage." He went upstairs to refresh himself, and upon returning was presented with his filled-out registration form. The first line read, "Monsieur Warranted Genuine Leather."

* * *

161. A tourist in Algiers told his guide, "I'm tired of seeing all the places you show every American. I want to see the real Africa!" The guide said, "I will take you to the wildest, most exotic café this side of the Sahara. You will never forget it!" The two men walked to a dark and forbidding house on the edge of the town and, after a certain amount of hocus-pocus at the gate, were admitted.

Several nondescript characters were draped about the premises in various abandoned attitudes, but what immediately caught the tourist's eye was an English colonel, impeccably attired, swagger stick and all, who, believe it or not, was exactly *six inches tall!* As he stared in disbelief, the bartender threw a red silk cord over the edge of the bar, the colonel pulled himself up hand over hand, and perched on the top with a whiskey and soda in his hand.

The guide was delighted. "What luck," he told the tourist. "You're going to meet Colonel Pringle, one of the most fascinating sights in all Africa!" Then he turned to the six-inch figure and boomed, "Be a good fellow, Colonel Pringle, and tell my tourist friend here about the night you told that witch doctor to go chase himself in the lake!"

* * *

162. Mrs. McDermott looked out of the window as the family was going on to dinner, and wailed, "Och, Sandy, here comes company. I bet they haven't eaten yet." Sandy, equal to the emergency, ordered, "Quick! Everybody out on the porch—with a toothpick."

* * *

163. The immigration authorities at Ellis Island were examining the credentials of a middle-aged Scotch couple that sought admission to our shores. The passport pictures caused trouble. "Mr. MacGregor," said the official, "this photograph of you is a perfect likeness, but I must say this other picture looks nothing like Mrs. MacGregor to me. Have you other substantiating evidence that this lady with you is indeed your wife?"

Mr. MacGregor sighed deeply and whispered to the official, "Laddie, if ya can prove she isn't, I'll gie ya twenty pounds."

164. An agricultural journal reports that a farmer in Wisconsin, who always complained that his wife didn't shoulder her share of the burden, agreed to run the household one day while his wife went to Madison for a medical examination. A methodical chap, he kept a minute record of his activities. It read as follows:

Open door for children: 106 times.
Shouted, "Stop, Johnnie": 94
Tied their shoes: 16
Stopped quarrels: 19

Provided glasses of water and Cokes: 26
Answered phone: 11
Answered questions: 202
Ran after children: about 4½ miles
Lost temper: 45 times.

The next day the farmer himself journeyed to Madison—and bought his wife the washing machine she had long coveted.

* * *

165. "My garden was such a success this year," boasted a gentleman farmer, "that my neighbor's chickens took first prize at the poultry show."

* * *

166. Three ladies at a Saratoga hotel, desperately seeking a fourth for bridge, finally appealed to a little old lady in an alpaca dress who was crocheting and minding her own business in a sheltered corner of the porch. Flustered but obviously pleased by the invitation, she said, "I'll play, but I warn you, I'm not up on all those new conventions." "Don't worry," they assured her. "None of us are members of the Regency Club either." On the very first hand, three consecutive passes left the bidding strictly up to the little old lady. She studied her hand carefully, cocked her head to one side and bid, "Two clovers."

* * *

167. George Allen, the White House jester, averred that he but carried on the tradition of his father, who practiced law, politics, and diplomacy in Booneville, Mississippi. One day a magistrate forgot his cue and had the gall to decide a case *against* Allen, Senior. The latter waved a volume of Blackstone under the justice's nose to emphasize his outrage. "Sit down, Mr. Allen," thundered the judge. "I know the law." "Of course you do," purred Mr. Allen. "I just wanted to read this paragraph to you to show you what a damn fool Blackstone was."

* * *

168. Publisher Richard Simon decided to include a half-dozen adhesives in a new juvenile called *Dr. Dan the Bandage Man,* and wired to a friend

at the Johnson and Johnson Company, "Please ship two million Band-Aids immediately." Back came a telegram reading, "Band-Aids on the way. What the hell happened to you?"

169. Old Colonel Archer, up from Kentucky, was describing his daily routine to a delighted group in Toots Shor's New York restaurant. "For breakfast," proclaimed the Colonel, "I ask only for a quart of bourbon, a pound of beefsteak, an' my ol' houn' dog." "What do you need the houn' dog for?" asked Toots. "The houn' dog," explained Colonel Archer, "eats the beefsteak."

* * *

170. Ed Laycock defines an intellectual snob as a man who won't speak to a beautiful girl on a train because he doesn't approve of the book she's reading. . . . William Butler Yeats characterized a literary movement as "two authors who live in the same city and hate each other." . . . Rebecca West described a pretentious society publisher as "every other inch a gentleman." . . . And bookmen who continually complain about the bad breaks they're getting might recall the words of Stephen Vincent Benét: "What some people call hard luck—well, we made New England out of it—that and codfish."

* * *

171. One of the many celebrities who dwell in Stamford, Connecticut, is editor Herbert Mayes, but his sumptuous home is so far from the town that servants are hard to find—and harder to keep. Mrs. Mayes finally latched on to a couple who seemed ideal, however, and after all arrangements had been concluded satisfactorily, led them in to meet Mayes in his study. Seeing the crowded bookshelves and piles of manuscripts, the butler was moved to inquire, "What's your line, sir?" Mayes answered, "I'm the editor of *Good Housekeeping Magazine*." "*Good Housekeeping!*" gasped the butler, heading for the door. "Come on, Hilda, this is no place for us!"

* * *

172. In Tulsa, an oil magnate, enamored of his secretary's chassis but appalled by her ignorance of literature, strove mightily to improve her I.Q. One morning she told him, "I took your advice. I borrowed a book from the library last night." "Great," enthused the magnate. "What was the name of it?" The secretary answered, "Dun and Bradstreet's."

* * *

173. A religious bookshop near the State Capitol in Boston put on a big Bible sale recently and quite a number of customers were lured by this bit of versification on a card in the window:

> Holy Scripture, Writ Divine
> At a dollar forty-nine;
> Satan trembles when he sees
> Bibles sold as cheap as these.

* * *

174. Dave Garroway is acquainted with a Chicago merchant who was summoned suddenly to a big business powwow in New York. It was scheduled to last four days, and he had to grab a plane at the Cicero airport within the hour. Problem: how to contact his wife, who was on

a shopping spree in the Loop? The merchant thought hard and suddenly came up with a brilliant idea. He ordered his secretary to cancel all of his wife's charge accounts. She called up in a rage twelve minutes later.

175. A little girl was having a hard time in Brentano's Bookstore selecting a book to be given to her mother as a birthday gift. "Does she like fiction?" asked the clerk. The little girl shook her head. "Biography? History? Books on art? Humor?" The little girl continued to register disapproval. Finally the exasperated clerk demanded, "Well, what on earth *does* she like?" The little girl said, "Men."

* * *

176. From Philadelphia comes the story of two suspender salesmen who were boasting of their products. "Five army mules pulled on either end of a pair of our braces," proclaimed one, "and they couldn't make them break."

"Paghh!" scoffed the other. "Yesterday I was rushing to catch a train at Penn Station in New York, and my suspenders got caught in a pillar on the platform. I made my train all right, but when the conductor opened the door in Philadelphia, those darn suspenders of ours snapped me right back to New York!"

* * *

177. A tourist bought a bolt of beautiful British cloth in the Bahamas and presented it to his Fifth Avenue tailor, asking, "Is there enough material here for you to make me a suit?" "No," said the tailor. The disappointed tourist headed for home, and passed a tiny sidestreet tailoring shop en route. "No harm to try again," he thought, and sure enough, the second tailor was confident he could make him a very adequate suit from the material available.

He was true to his word, and a fortnight later turned out a garment that fitted the tourist like a glove. Just as the latter was reaching for his pocketbook, however, the tailor's five-year-old son ran into the shop, garbed in a suit so obviously cut from the tourist's own material, the tailor didn't even attempt to alibi. "Yes, I made a suit for my boy from the goods left over," he said placatingly. "There wasn't enough to be of

"At fifty fathoms you'll see an old hull. Knock on the hatch and ask for Gladys."

509

any use to you anyhow!" At that moment the tourist bethought himself of Tailor Number One. Angrily charging into that worthy's establishment he cried, "Remember telling me I didn't have enough material for a suit? A competitor down the block not only made me a very fine one, but had enough cloth left over to make a suit for his five-year-old son!" "So what?" scoffed Tailor Number One. "*My* son is eighteen!"

* * *

178. A health crank, partial to yogurt and such like, felt a sudden craving for a plate of clam chowder, and what with it being a Friday, decided to indulge himself. He took the precaution, however, of presenting the waiter with two huge vitamin pills, and instructed him to dissolve them in the chowder before serving. When a half hour went by without a sign of chowder, the health crank collared the waiter and hollered, "Why am I receiving no service around here?" "You'll get your chowder, sir," soothed the waiter, "the minute we can get the clams to lie down."

* * *

179. Farmer Ekhamer owned a very tough ram, but discovered that music soothed its savage breast. Headed for town one day, Ekhamer reminded his son, "If that animal gets rambunctious just put a record on the Victrola." When he returned home he discovered that the ram had plunged against a stone wall and committed suicide. "Did you play music like I told you?" he demanded of the son. "I sure did," said the boy, "but the record I chose seemed to drive him crazy. It was Frank Sinatra singing, 'There'll Never Be Another Ewe.'"

* * *

180. Patricia Richardson's dog, "Faun," had an aggravating habit of curling himself up in his mistress' favorite easy chair, and feigning sleep when she attempted to dislodge him. Next door there resided a cat whom Faun abhorred, however, and Miss R. learned that by going to the window and crying "Here comes that cat," Faun could be persuaded to vacate the chair and vanish from sight without further ado. She had worked this dodge effectively on several occasions when, one afternoon, she sat dozing in her chair. Faun walked in, studied her with his head on one side, suddenly bounded to the door and began barking furiously. The

510

aroused Miss Richardson rushed to investigate. The street was absolutely empty. When she returned, Faun was curled up blissfully, his eyes closed, in the easy chair.

* * *

181. At one of those unbearably fancy new candy stores on Fifth Avenue, seemingly modeled after the boudoir of a big-time French courtesan, the wife of the editor of a Jewish newspaper wandered in to sample the wares. "I'll take five pounds of those chocolates over there," she decided. "Modom means the bon bons, no doubt," a suave clerk in a cutaway corrected gently. "I also would like five pounds of those cookies," continued the lady. "Ah," breathed the clerk, "our petits fours. Shall we deliver your purchase in our Rolls limousine now drawn up before the portals?" "Nah," said the lady. "I'll carry it home myself." This was too much for the elegant clerk. "Don't be silly," he burst out. "Why schlepp a package that big around the streets?"

"He was such a cute puppy—I can't believe
he's grown up."

182. A well-lubricated drummer staggered into a hotel lobby, and picked up a pen to register. As he did so a remarkable facsimile of a bedbug crawled across the desk. The drummer recoiled and informed the reception clerk, "I've been in lots of hotels, and I've been bitten by some mighty smart bedbugs, but—hic—this is the first time one ever came down to see what room I was getting!"

183. The Algonquin's famous boniface, the late Frank Case, loved William Faulkner personally, but was no admirer of his tortuous prose and grim pictures of depravity in the old South. Faulkner met him in the lobby one morning and complained, "I have kind of an upset stomach today." "Ah," sympathized Case, "something you wrote, no doubt?"

* * *

184. The manager of a swanky hotel at French Lick stumbled over a porter who was crouching in the corridor shining a pair of shoes. "Ichabod," remonstrated the manager, "haven't I told you a hundred times not

to clean shoes in the corridor, but to take them down to the basement?"
"Can't do it this time, boss," said Ichabod. "The man in this room says
he's from Scotland, and he's hanging on to the laces."

* * *

185. There are a number of allegedly living and solvent citizens (Jim
Marshall did the alleging) whose names and addresses make complete
sentences. Here's the evidence:

Hans R. Dirty, Jr., Goan, Wash.
Quoth D. Raven, Never, Mo.
G. Thirza Mighty, Pritty, Miss.
Ide Lamy, Down, N.D.
Lettice Finder, Shady, Del.
F. U. Pager, Income, Tex.
I. M. Phelan, Slightly, Ill.
Daniel Inner, Lyons, Tenn.
Wish I. Newther, Reese, N.Y.
C. U. Sunday, Early, Mass.
Allis Frenza, Deadan, Conn.
R. R. Crossing, Look, N.C.
Will U. Raider, Cookie, Ga.

* * *

186. There's a station on a one-track Maine branch line to which passengers descend via a rickety staircase. Alongside it is a chute used to
slide down packing cases and heavy baggage.

Local tradition has it that an elderly lady once came whizzing down
the chute, clutching her hat in one hand and a straw valise in the other.
At the bottom she pulled herself together and exclaimed, "You'd think a
big railroad company would make it a little easier for passengers to get
down to their ding-busted trains!"

* * *

187. One of the great stars of Hollywood cowboy sagas wired Toots
Shor, the restaurateur, "Arriving New York in time for dinner, November ninth. Reserve table for two." Shor cautiously wired back, "Are you
bringing your girl or your horse?"

513

188. When the conductor on an Arkansas local came through collecting tickets, an old gentleman simply couldn't find his in any pocket. Suddenly a man across the aisle laughed and said, "Jeb, you're holding it in your teeth." The conductor punched the ticket and passed on down the aisle. "Jeb, you're sure getting absent-minded," pursued the man across the aisle. "Absent-minded nothing," whispered old Jeb angrily. "I was chewing off last year's date."

* * *

189. Harpo Marx came down to the Pasadena station one day to see a friend off for the East. He was engaging in some characteristic clowning on the platform when he noticed two Helen Hokinson ladies gazing with undisguised horror from the diner on the train the friend was boarding. Impulsively, Harpo hopped aboard, rushed up to the ladies' table in the diner, sprinkled salt on their menu and gulped it down.

With no change of expression, one of them summoned the steward and commanded, "Will you kindly give us another menu. Somebody has eaten ours."

* * *

190. A returned traveler from Wales reports that whenever the through trains stop at Llanfechpwllgogerych the guards simply call out, "If anybody's getting out here, this is it."

* * *

191. Fulton J. Sheen relates that shortly after his elevation to the rank of Bishop he made the first of his many appearances on television, and stopped for a cup of coffee at the drugstore in the building where the studio was located, with his red cape already in place. The girl at the counter, obviously used to serving actors in every kind of costume, took the red cape very much in stride and asked blithely, "What's yours, Cock Robin?"

* * *

192. The first time Martha Raye ate at the famous Pump Room in Chicago, she was a member of a dinner party hosted by Jimmy Durante. When a waiter passed with a portion of shishkebab (lamb on a flaming sword—a specialty of the house), Miss Raye was startled and exclaimed,

514

"What on earth was that?" Durante explained, "A customer who only left a ten-dollar tip."

* * *

193. A group of world leaders in the Presbyterian Church met in Scotland for a conference and, on a warm summer's afternoon, went off to explore the beautiful countryside. Coming to a temporary bridge that spanned a swift-running stream, they started confidently to cross it. When they were half way over, the bridge keeper suddenly appeared and hollered that the bridge had been declared unsafe. The spokesman for the church party didn't quite hear the keeper's admonition and called back, "It's all right, my friend. We're Presbyterians from the conference." The bridge keeper replied, "If ye dinna get off the bridge this minute ye'll all be Baptists!"

* * *

194. The parson's wife in a small Connecticut town is a wonder at making a little go a long way, and boasts that she never throws away one

scrap of edible food. One of her dinners consisted entirely of leftovers. The parson viewed the food on the table with some distaste and began picking at his food in silence. "My dear," reproved his wife, "you've forgotten to ask the blessing." "If you can point out one item on the menu," he answered sharply, "that hasn't been blessed at least three times before, I'll see what a little praying can do for it."

* * *

195. When Parson Johnson saw Mrs. Sumter, whom he roundly detested, coming up his garden path, he sought refuge upstairs in the study and remained hidden for a full hour. Finally he risked calling down to his wife, "Has that horrible bore gone yet?" His wife, equal to any occasion, answered sweetly, "Yes, dear, she went long ago. Mrs. Sumter is here now."

* * *

196. There was a long line waiting to use the only public telephone booth in the neighborhood, and when a young thing with blonde curls and a huge vanity bag strapped over her shoulder prepared to enter, the experienced men behind her sighed in unison and resigned themselves to the inevitable. The young thing, however, sensed what was going on in their minds.

"Don't you all fret," she told them sweetly. "I'll only be a minute. I just want to hang up on him!"

* * *

197. A winsome chick gave up her job at the Copacabana night club to marry an auto executive in Detroit. "He's the knight I always dreamed would appear out of the West to win me," she gurgled. "He's tall, dark, and has some."

* * *

198. A dapper New Yorker—one of the ten best-dressed men in America—came to collect his six-year-old daughter at a birthday party. Taking hold of her hand to guide her across the street, he observed, "Goodness, Vicki, your hands seem mighty sticky today." "Yours would be, too," she informed him, "if you had a piece of lemon pie and a chocolate éclair inside your muff."

516

199. On the porch of Vanderschlitz Manor Mrs. Nussbaum mourned, "My boy never should have married that Davis girl. In a year she turned him into a pauper." "Really?" nodded Mrs. Gross pleasantly. "A girl or a boy?"

* * *

200. In these days when college football stadiums seat 90,000 or more spectators, it is interesting to note the comment made once by Andrew W. White, co-founder of Cornell University and its first president. Asked for permission to send the Cornell squad to Ann Arbor for a game, he replied indignantly:

"I will not permit thirty men to travel four hundred miles to agitate a bag of wind."

* * *

201. "Pop" Gabardine, coach of a Midwestern football team, had seen his charges trampled eight Saturday afternoons in a row, the last time by a humiliating score of 55 to 0. When the squad regathered the following Monday, "Pop" said bitterly, "For the last game of the season, we might as well forget all the trick plays I tried to teach you dimwits. We're going back to fundamentals. Let's go! Lesson number one: this object I am holding is known as a football. Lesson number . . ." At this point, Coach Gabardine was interrupted by a worried fullback in the front row, who pleaded, "Hey, Pop, not so fast!"

* * *

202. Between halves of a tough professional football game, three stars of the winning team fell to talking about the circumstances that surrounded their leaving college to play for money. "I was a senior at Cornell," said the first, "and got grounded on calculus. I couldn't even begin to know what the prof was talking about." "It was advanced trigonometry that did me in," said the second. "In fact, it ran me right out of Kansas State in my junior year." The third player, late of U.C.L.A., sat staring moodily into space. Suddenly he spoke. "Say, did you boys ever run into a subject called long division?"

* * *

203. A huntsman in Texas had a harrowing experience one night this fall. He had killed a huge rattlesnake outside his tent before supper, and,

517

just before going off to sleep, decided that the rattles would make a nice memento. With a practiced hand, he cut off the rattles in the dark.

The sight that greeted him the next morning stood his hair on end. The snake he had killed still had its rattles!

"Well, doggone! If somebody ain't gone and invented a helicopter!"

204. An intrepid bear stalker was recounting his triumphs to the boys around the cracker barrel one midwinter night. "I guess my closest shave," he recalled, "came the day I was walking unsuspectingly along a narrow mountain path when suddenly a giant grizzly crept up behind me, locked my arms in a tight embrace and then began squeezing the life out of me."

"What did you do?" obliged one of the boys with the expected show of suspense. "What the dickens could I do?" groaned the huntsman. "I had to marry his daughter."

* * *

205. The most believable golf story of the year appeared on the sports page of a Daytona Beach newspaper recently. It read, "At this point the gallery deserted the defending champion to watch Miss Blank, whose shorts were dropping on the green with astonishing regularity."

* * *

206. Nine times out of ten, when you think your favorite television actor is wearing a white shirt, it's actually light blue or some other neutral color. The color white reflects a glare from the powerful overhead lights and casts an unflattering shadow over the actor's neckline.

With that thought in mind, Paul Hartman, who usually performs his burlesque dance routines in white tie and tails, ordered two stiff-bosomed evening shirts in blue. The mystified shirtmaker followed instructions—at $25 per instruction.

Hartman used the shirts with conspicuous success, and then consigned them to the laundry. But they didn't come back with either that week's wash or the next. They finally were delivered, accompanied by a note from the unhappy laundryman.

"We scrubbed and scrubbed these shirts," it read, "and finally succeeded in getting most of the blue out of them. If they are not absolutely white, please don't blame us."

* * *

207. In a round-up of the year's funniest radio "fluffs," Joe Bryan awarded palm leaves with clusters to:

Jerry Lawrence for "When the King and Queen arrive you will hear a twenty-one sun galoot."

519

A commentator from Korea for "This brings back memories of the Bulgian Belch."

Mel Allen for "It's smope-piking time."

Ken Allyn for "Visit your nearest A and Poo Feed Store."

André Baruch for "Good evening, ladies and gentlemen of the audio radiance."

* * *

208. In *No People Like Show People*, Maurice Zolotow added another item to the Jack Benny saga. Jack was once so down on his luck that when his agent heard a New Jersey pop vaudeville palladium was offering twenty-five dollars for a novelty animal act, he cried, "I'll take it." He borrowed two mangy Pekingese pups from a friend, carried them on-stage in the Jersey theatre, tied them to a piece of scenery, and proceeded to wow the audience with funny stories and wheezings on his fiddle. The manager forked over the twenty-five dollars with the reservation that this certainly was the most peculiar animal act he ever did see. "Don't those pups do any tricks at all?" he demanded. "They sure do," said Jack airily, "but not at these prices."

* * *

209. Goodman Ace says he's discovered how really to enjoy television. "We do it all with a six-foot screen," he explains gravely, and when his visitor invariably expresses astonishment, he adds, "Yes, it's a Japanese screen, and we place it directly in front of the television set."

* * *

210. A young co-ed looked dreamily at the ceiling and declared, "The man I marry must be an outstanding personality, be musical, tell new jokes, sing and dance, stay home, neither drink nor smoke, and shut up when I tell him to."

Her caller arose, looked for his hat, and told her, "Lady, you don't want a husband; you want a television set."

* * *

211. Herb Shriner, the greatest thing in homespun wits since the days of Will Rogers, spends a good deal of his time discussing the town drunk back in his Indiana birthplace. The poor fellow wasn't always that way;

he simply took a nip now and then to "quiet his nerves." He finally quieted them so completely he couldn't move at all. "I don't even like the taste of the stuff," he confessed to Herb. "I just drink so's I can forget—and I got the best durn memory in Indiana."

The richest citizen in Herb's town made his fortune in a novel manner. He invented a dog food that tastes exactly like a letter carrier's ankle. For years, says Herb, this character's watch has lacked an hour hand. He's waiting for something else to bust on it so's he can get the whole thing fixed at once.

212. A Texas dowager presented herself at the Pearly Gates, and when Saint Peter asked for her credentials, proudly presented a membership card to the Symphony, receipted bills from Neiman-Marcus and the Shamrock Hotel, and a picture of herself shaking hands with Ted Dealey of the Dallas *News*. Saint Peter, duly impressed, remarked, "Come in, madam, by all means—but I don't think you'll like it."

213. An English visitor to Dallas, in a belittling mood, remarked, "You Texans don't do things as fast as I had been led to expect." "Zatso?" drawled Liz McMurray, the bookselling champion of the Southwest. "Just come down to Union Station with me and keep your eyes peeled." At the station, the superintendent was hurriedly drawing the redcaps into a single line. Just as the formation was completed, a streamliner whizzed by at a mile a minute. The Englishman got a fleeting glance at one passenger leaning out of a window with a notebook in his hand. "What was that chap trying to do?" demanded the Englishman. Answered Liz, "Just measuring the porters for new uniforms."

* * *

214. A boatman ran a ferry across a mountain stream full of whirlpools and rapids. During a crossing in which the frail craft was tossed hither and yon by the swirling waters, a timid lady in the boat asked whether any passengers ever were lost in the river.

"Never," the boatman reassured her. "We always find them again the next day."

* * *

215. There's a neat twist in this story of Sam Levenson's. A cloak and suit manufacturer, obviously born abroad, was taunted on his Americanism by a bigoted blue-blood. "What kind of American are you, after all?" sneered the blue-blood. "Why, my ancestors came over on the Mayflower." The cloak and suit man, unperturbed, replied, "Maybe it's lucky they did. By the time I arrived, the immigration laws were a lot stricter."

* * *

216. In a local election in Mississippi, officials tabulating the ballots were astounded to discover a Republican vote. There being no precedent for this phenomenon, the sheriff decided, "Let's hold it out till we get a full count." Then—wonder of wonders!—another Republican vote turned up. "That settles it," roared the sheriff. "The low-down varmint voted twice, so we won't count either of them."

* * *

217. A familiar character on Wall Street some years ago was a colorful broker named Pop Schwed. Pop loved nothing better than to reel off apocryphal tales of his youth in the wide-open town of Goldfield, Nevada, just after the turn of the century. There was one hellion there, he recalled, who went berserk every time he had six drinks inside of him, which was *usually*. An itinerant medico persuaded him that if he didn't forswear all hard liquor at once he'd be dead inside two months. One evening the reformed character was in the toughest dive in Goldfield, disconsolately sipping a beaker of ginger ale, when a prospector sashayed to the bar, pumped his faithless wife and her paramour full of lead, shot out the lights as a parting gesture, and vanished into the night. The paralyzed silence that followed was finally broken by Pop Schwed's reformed friend. "Waiter," he barked hoarsely, "for God's sake! A double order of ham and eggs!"

* * *

218. A couple who never before had ventured west of Hoboken were making their first transcontinental trip aboard a Canadian streamliner. At one stop far along the line they left the train for a little exercise, and inquired of a man on the platform, "What's the name of this town?" He

"I got a cold and can't get my feet wet!"

answered, "Sascatoon, Saskatchewan." "Goodness," marveled the husband, "we've come so far the natives don't even speak English here!"

219. What Henry Mencken would call a typical female motorist came tootling merrily down the wrong side of a crowded thoroughfare and ran smack into Mr. Jordan's brand-new convertible. While they were trying to untangle bumpers, the lady driver said grudgingly, "I'm afraid this was largely my fault."

"Nonsense," said Mr. Jordan with a gallant bow. "I assure you the blame rests entirely with me. I saw you fully three blocks away and had ample time to dart down a side street."

* * *

220. The late Albert Einstein, whose theories about relativity and the fourth dimension are said to be understood by only twelve people in the world besides himself, graciously allowed a film producer to take some shots for a documentary movie in his Princeton, N. J., residence not long ago.

Left alone momentarily in the library, the producer noticed a big blueprint on Dr. Einstein's desk.

Since he himself was having a new house built at the time, and had blueprints coming out of his ears, he felt an uncontrollable impulse to have a look at the Einsteinian conception.

Unable to make head or tail of it, he looked for the legend in the lower right-hand corner. Immaculately lettered, it read, "One inch equals a hundred million light years."

* * *

221. Orpah Anderson said this happened at a school in a northern Minnesota town. A strapping, healthy-looking girl appeared to register for a course in English. The recording clerk asked, "Have you a hobby?" The girl replied, "No, ay ban single."

* * *

222. Harry Oliver, editor of *The Desert Rat* (a newspaper published four times a year) swore that an Indian strode into a white man's court and pleaded to have his name shortened legally. "What's your name now?" asked the judge. "Chief Train-whistle," said the Indian. "And what do you want to shorten it to?" pursued the judge. The Indian folded his arms majestically and grunted, "Toots."

* * *

223. The father of every candidate for admission to Vassar is required to fill out a questionnaire regarding his daughter's qualifications. One of the questions is "Would you call your daughter a leader?" A father in Red Bank, New Jersey, meticulously honest, answered, "I have never noticed my daughter assume the role of leader, but I do know she is an excellent follower." Vassar's reply, as reported by the *Journal of Education*, was, "As our freshman group next fall seems to be composed almost exclusively of several hundred leaders, we congratulate ourselves that your daughter will also be a member of the class. We shall thus be assured of one good follower, at any rate. Her application is approved with enthusiasm."

525

"Hereafter when you come, dear, leave Rex home!"

224. A dean suffered the misfortune of sitting down on a newly painted bench just before graduation exercises began. He turned disaster into triumph, however, by opening his remarks with, "I had hoped to bring you an unvarnished tale this morning, but fate decreed otherwise."

* * *

225. Mingling with the throng that poured out of a California university stadium after a big game, a visiting Easterner enthused to his host, head of the chemistry department, "What a plant you have here! What a campus! How many students would you say you have?" The chemistry prof answered sourly, "About one in a thousand."

* * *

226. Two sweet co-eds at the University of Minnesota were happily carving up an ex-roommate over the telephone. "And, my dear," continued one, "who do you think she's been dating like mad the past month? Her X-ray specialist!" "Hmphh!" commented the other. "I wonder what he sees in her?"

227. Professor Irwin Edman, famed for his absent-mindedness, dropped in unexpectedly on his old friend, the family doctor, and chatted happily about his impending trip to France for almost three hours. Finally the doctor arose from his chair, and remarked pointedly, "Well, Irwin, I have an operation to perform at eight in the morning. I trust everyone in your household is well." "Good heavens," gasped Irwin, "that reminds me. I came here to tell you my cook is having a fit."

* * *

228. Preparing to attend a banquet given by Gwendolyn Cafritz, a Washington hostess, a Senator from a Rocky Mountain state slipped on the top step of a marble staircase and landed solidly on his posterior two floors below. The next morning he called from his bed of pain to apologize to the famous hostess.

"You're forgiven," she said, "but you ruined my seating arrangement." "*Your* seating arrangement," he exclaimed. "You ought to see *mine!*"

527

229. A staunch Republican from Maine was being shown the wonders of the Grand Canyon. "Yes, sir," said the guide. "It took about five million years for this awe-inspiring canyon to be carved out of the rocks." "Hmm," added the man from Maine. "Government project, I presume."

* * *

230. Every politician, suggests Carl Sandburg, should have three hats handy at all times: one for throwing into the ring, another for talking through, and a third for pulling rabbits out of if elected!

"All she says is: 'Just let anyone cough now!'"

231. Woodrow Wilson was a great reader of books, and the author he admired above all others was Mark Twain. When his presidential train passed through Hannibal, Missouri, therefore, Mr. Wilson ordered a three-hour wait-over that he might wander for a bit among the boyhood haunts of the famous humorist. Accosting a native, the President said, "I'm a stranger in these parts. Could you tell me where Tom Sawyer was supposed to live?" "Never heard of him," maintained the native. "Well, how about Huck Finn?" persisted Mr. Wilson. "Never heard of him nuther," declared the native. The President made one more try. "How about Puddinhead Wilson?" he inquired. The native's face brightened. "I heard of him all right," he said cheerfully. "In fact, I even voted for the durn fool."

* * *

232. Occasionally a writer comes along who can sit down at a typewriter and bang out a column or story at will. Most writers, however, can think of more ways to delay getting down to their work than even a temporary kitchen maid. Lee Rogow cites the case of one Hollywood scenario scripter who simply had to have a job completed by the following morning. His understanding wife disconnected the phone, inserted a fresh page in his typewriter, grabbed both kids by the hand and left him in sole possession of the premises. They rode to the end of the bus line and back, saw a double feature at the neighborhood movie, and came home at the tag end of the day to see how far Daddy had gotten. He hadn't done too badly. As they walked through the door, he was just polishing the last piece of their eighty-piece sterling-silver dinner set.

* * *

233. An author preparing an article on censorship unearthed the following interesting facts: In 1885 Concord, Massachusetts, home town of Thoreau, banned *Huckleberry Finn* as "trash suitable only for the slums." In 1929 Russia blacklisted Sherlock Holmes for his "disgraceful occultism and spiritualism." In 1931 China banned *Alice in Wonderland* on the ground that "animals should not use human language" and that it was "disastrous to put animals and human beings on the same level."

* * *

234. In the powder room of a Cambridge residence, Mrs. Cabot-Lodge preened herself and said loftily, "That South African gentleman says the nicest things! He remarked particularly on my birdlike appetite." "Hmmph," commented Mrs. Lowellstall. "He runs an ostrich farm!"

* * *

235. Erskine lounged into the office an hour late for the third time in one week and found the boss awaiting him, arms akimbo. "What's the story this time, Erskine?" he asked sarcastically. "Let's hear a good excuse for a change." Erskine sighed, "Everything went wrong this morning, boss. The wife decided to drive me to the station. She got ready in ten minutes, but then the drawbridge got stuck. Rather than let you down, I swam across the river (look, my suit's still damp), ran out to the airport, got a hitch in Mr. Harriman's helicopter, landed on top of Radio City Music Hall, and was carried here piggy-back by one of the Rockettes." "You'll have to do better than that, Erskine," said the boss, obviously disappointed. "No woman can get ready in ten minutes."

236. One of the most improbable anecdotes about the late George Bernard Shaw concerns an evening when a lady dramatist hornswoggled him into attending the tryout of her new play. "Now, you naughty man," she chided kittenishly, "you're not to sneak out in the middle of my drama." Shaw was planked down behind her and leaned forward to get a better view of the proceedings. Halfway through the first act, the author felt a tickling sensation on her neck. Groping in the dark, she felt a loose strand of hair and tucked it firmly into place with a big hatpin. Suddenly Shaw, thoroughly bored by this time, decided to fall back in his seat. He cried, "Ouch!" Then he told the authoress, "Madam, if you will kindly take my beard out of your hair, I promise I won't budge out of this seat until your confounded play is over."

* * *

237. Neal O'Hara visited an old pal whose equanimity was upset by his wife's dramatic announcement that she was so sick of wearing old rags she had marched into Filene's that afternoon and bought ten new dresses. "Ten!" shrieked the wounded husband. "What could any dame want with ten new dresses?" The wife answered promptly, "Ten new hats."

* * *

238. In Paris, John Woodburn negotiated a pun in French. He noticed that a lady's petticoat had slipped and was collecting dust as she promenaded down the Rue de la Paix.

Tapping her on the shoulder he pointed out, "Mademoiselle, your *quelque chose.*"

"Could I see your membership cards?"

239. Twain, says Vincent Starrett, once visited the celebrated Madame Tussaud's wax works in London, and was admiring a replica of Queen Victoria when he felt a sudden stab of pain in his posterior. Wheeling angrily, he found himself face to face with a flabbergasted British matron, her umbrella still pointed at him. "O lor', it's alive!" she gasped, and fled into the night.

* * *

240. Clyde Beck, erudite Detroit editor, presided at a dinner in honor of bibliophile John Winterich. Mr. Beck informed a large and enthusiastic gathering, "Our guest this evening needs no introduction," which was a lucky break, all things considered, because at this point Mr. Beck lost his balance and fell off the speaker's platform. Winterich restored order by assuring his audience, "Mr. Beck is an improvement in one respect. The last fellow who introduced me at a dinner suffered a heart attack."

241. Sam Himmell told about a new millionaire in Scarsdale who was showing a friend around his modernistic "push-button" mansion. "This is the best gadget of the lot," he exulted. "After a night out, I sometimes feel like stepping into a nice hot bath right here without the trouble of going into the bathroom. I just press this button—" He pressed the button and in rolled the bathtub, full of nice hot water—and the millionaire's wife.

* * *

242. An upstate social leader was expecting a large group of friends at her home one evening, and knowing her husband's propensity for using guest towels indiscriminately when he returned from the office, put a sign on the ones she had trotted out especially for the occasion that read, "If you use one of these towels, I'll slay you in cold blood." Unfortunately, she forgot to remove the note before the guests started arriving. At the evening's end she found the note still there—and not one towel touched.

534

243. A Governor of Iowa had a name that made rather a neat mouth-ful: Bourke Blakemore Hickenlooper. He himself told about a drugstore clerk who refused to charge ten cents' worth of asafetida to the Hicken-looper account. "Take it for nothing, boss," said the clerk. "I wouldn't write both asafetida and Hickenlooper for a dime."

244. When Pat O'Leary's wife presented him with his eleventh offspring in the space of thirteen years, the office force chipped in to present him with a well-earned gift—a silver tray with what they told him was the O'Leary coat of arms emblazoned thereon. "What's the idea of putting that funny lookin' duck on me coat of arms?" protested O'Leary. "That's no duck," explained the office manager. "That's a stork with his legs worn off."

* * *

245. Four men, one of them minus an eye, were playing poker in a West Texas saloon. Suddenly one of them yanked out a gat and intoned, "I ain't callin' no names, but the next rat I see dealin' from the bottom of the deck, I'm gonna shoot his other eye out!" . . .

* * *

246. A misguided lecture manager in Milwaukee once offered Hecht and Bodenheim fifty dollars apiece to stage a literary debate on any subject that appealed to them. They took the precaution of collecting their fees in advance, and strode onto the platform. "The subject of this debate," announced Bodenheim, "is, 'Resolved: that any person who pays good American cash to hear a literary debate is a blithering idiot.' I will uphold the affirmative, Mr. Hecht the negative." "I concede," cried Hecht. Then the two of them fled before the outraged audience could get to its feet. They haven't played Milwaukee since.

* * *

247. Vincent Starrett recalls one of the funniest incidents in the late Frank Harris' alleged autobiography, that amazing three-volume conglomeration of literary lore and sophomoric pornography that under-the-counter specialists peddle for as much as fifty dollars a set. Harris described a crucial international conference with all the wealth of detail that only a man who had not been present could supply. At the height of the confab an English munitions king let out a cry of anguish. His valuable timepiece had been hooked. The chairman—prime minister of a great European power—was properly outraged. "Gentlemen," he declared icily, "this will never do. The lights will be extinguished for five minutes. All of us will file out of this chamber in darkness. The thief, as

536

"Think hard, Henry! Are you sure you turned off the bathroom faucets?"

he exits, will place the watch on the table there beside the door, where the buhl clock now stands." Thereupon, concluded Harris, the delegates filed out in silence and darkness. Five minutes later the room was re-lighted. Not only was the watch still missing; the buhl clock also had disappeared.

* * *

248. Miss Josephine Austen, librarian at Forest Park, Illinois, declared that her profession provided a unique opportunity for souvenir-collecting. Readers use unbelievable objects for bookmarks, and frequently forget to remove them before they turn in the volumes. Miss Austen's collection includes violent love letters, nail files, playing cards, bobby pins—and most unexpected of all, a very, very thoroughly fried egg.

* * *

249. Cass Canfield of Harper's was approached one day in his editorial sanctum by a sweet-faced but determined matron who wanted very much to discuss a first novel on which she was working. "How long should a novel be?" she demanded. "That's an impossible question to answer," explained Canfield. "Some novels, like *Ethan Frome*, are only about 40,000 words long. Others, *Gone with the Wind*, for instance, may run to 300,000." "But what is the average length of the ordinary novel?" the lady persisted. "Oh, I'd say about 80,000 words," said Canfield. The lady jumped to her feet with a cry of triumph. "Thank God!" she cried. "My book is finished!"

* * *

250. John Daly says he can prove that men are warmer than women. Just consult a weather report. Doesn't it always read something like, "Max. 82; Min. 34"?

* * *

251. In times of stress there is always a tremendous upsurge of interest in ghost stories and tales that make the heart skip a beat. Several such collections have hit the best-seller lists recently, and Hollywood, which used to produce its so-called "Zombie" pictures at a cost of thirty cents (Confederate money) and regard them as a secret weapon to depopulate theatres, has now turned the attention of some of its fanciest directors and stars to the Trail of the Tingling Spine.

In the following pages I have set down a few of the memorable ghost stories and thrillers that have been told me in the past. One of them was narrated in the presence of a man who wears a toupee. He got so excited that in two minutes every hair on the toupee was standing on end.

Probably you have heard about the timid soul who was hurrying down a dark, dark corridor when he suddenly collided with a stout and shadowy personage whom he certainly had not seen approaching him. "Golly," said the timid one, "you gave me a fright! For a second I thought you were a ghost!" "What makes you think I'm not?" answered the other—and promptly vanished.

Try a few of these stories yourself at a dinner party one evening. The results are electrifying. Soon everybody is remembering a macabre story *he's* heard about a haunted house, or an ill-mannered ghost, or a thing that behaved in no fashion that was human. Give the spooks a chance, and they'll pay dividends. I have spooken.

"P-s-s-t, Miss Laverne!!!"

252. Two ladies from the faculty of a famous New England college for women decided to spend one of their vacations in an automobile tour to California and back. They traveled westward by way of the Petrified Forest and the Grand Canyon, and headed for home by the Salt Lake City route. They were two normal, unimaginative women, enjoying to the full a tour of their native country.

Late one evening, they were driving through the flat and monotonous fields of Kansas, intent upon reaching a hostel some thirty miles distant, when their car broke down. They were the kind of drivers who know nothing whatever about motors. They had no choice but to wait for some good Samaritan to come driving along and help them—and it soon became obvious that no other car was likely to come that way until the next morning.

539

It was then that one of the ladies noticed a two-story, unpainted farm-house, set back some distance from the road. They approached it gingerly, wary of watch-dogs, and knocked timidly on the front door. Nobody answered. The impression grew on them that the house was uninhabited. When they discovered that the door was unlocked, they entered, calling loudly, and flashing their pocket searchlight in every corner. They found the living room and kitchen in good order, but an undisturbed layer of dust indicated that no human being had been in them for days.

The ladies blessed their luck, and decided to spend the night in the living room. The couch was fairly comfortable, and they bundled themselves up in robes which they fetched from the stalled automobile. There were dry logs in the fireplace; the ladies soon had a roaring fire going, and, in the light of the flickering embers, went peacefully to sleep.

Some hours later, one of the ladies awoke with the distinct feeling that somebody had entered the house. Her friend jumped up at precisely the same moment. A chill seemed to run through the room, followed by the unmistakable scent of the salt sea, although the nearest ocean front was over a thousand miles away. Then a young man walked into the room! Rather he *floated* in, because they heard no footsteps. He was dressed in boots and oilskins; sea-spray glistened on his rough stubble of reddish beard. He moved to the dying fire, shivering violently, and knelt down before it.

One of the women screamed. The figure turned slowly, gave a sort of mournful sigh, and slowly dissolved into nothingness. The terrified women clutched each other desperately, and lay there until the morning sun poured through the dusty window panes. "I saw it; I know I did!" said one of them. "Of course you did; I saw it too," the other reassured her, and then pointed dramatically to the fireplace. Before it was a small puddle of brackish water, and a piece of slimy green weed.

The ladies made for the open air, but the bolder of the two snatched up the piece of weed before they bolted, and held it gingerly at arm's length. When it dried, she placed it carefully in her bag.

Eventually a car rattled along the highway, and the driver cheerfully consented to tow the ladies to the nearest garage. While the mechanic tinkered with the engine, the ladies asked him about the deserted house some miles back on the road. "That must have been the Newton place," he said with no special show of interest. "Been empty nigh on to two years now. When Old Man Newton died, he left it lock, stock and barrel to his son Tom, who said he didn't like farming, and lit out one day for the East. Spoke of taking to the sea, like his great-grandfather did. Ain't none of us seen hide nor hair of him since that day!"

When the ladies returned to their college, they took the green weed, which still seemed clammy and damp, to the head of the botany department. He readily confirmed their suspicions. "It's seaweed, all right," he told them. "Furthermore, it's a kind that's only found on dead bodies!" The ship news reporter of the *Evening Sun* reported that a Thomas Newton had sailed as first-class seaman on a freighter called the *Robert B. Anthony* on April 14, 1937. It had gone down with all hands aboard in a storm off the Greenland coast six weeks thereafter.

"Here, sir!"

541

253. A young lady dreamed one night that she was walking along a strange country lane. It led her up a wooded hill whose summit was crowned with the loveliest little white frame house and garden she ever had seen. Unable to conceal her delight, she knocked loudly on the door of the house, and finally it was opened by an old, old man with a long white beard. Just as she started to talk to him, she woke up. Every detail of this dream was so vivid in her memory that she carried it about in her head for days. Then, on three successive nights, she had precisely the same dream again. Always she awakened at the point where her conversation with the old man was about to begin.

A few weeks later, the young lady was motoring to Litchfield for a week-end party, when she suddenly tugged at the driver's sleeve, and begged him to stop. There, at the right of the concrete highway, was the country lane of her dreams! "Wait for me a few moments," she pleaded, and, her heart beating wildly, set out on the lane. She was no longer surprised when it wound to the top of the wooded hill, and the house whose every feature was now so familiar to her. The old man responded to her impatient summons. "Tell me," she began, "is this little house for sale?" "That it is," said the man, "but I would scarcely advise you to buy it. You see, young lady, this house is haunted!" "Haunted," echoed the girl. "For heaven's sake, by whom?" "By you," said the old man, and softly closed the door.

* * *

254. Monte Carlo was the scene of a strange occurrence one night many years ago. An elderly gentleman took a seat in the casino and ventured fifty francs on Number 17. The number came up. The old man pointed at Number 17 again and made no move to rake in any of his winnings.

Again the little silver ball came to rest at Number 17! The croupier looked questioningly at the old man, who sat with his head down on one arm and his finger pointed at Number 17 on the board. Five more consecutive times the wheel hit Number 17. The old man's pile of chips was enormous. The crowd stood silent with admiration for his nerve. The croupier had a hurried consultation with the directors, and announced that the bank was broken and the roulette game was at an end.

But the winner of the fortune never stirred. He was dead. Furthermore, a doctor testified in court he had been dead ever since the second spin. A dead man broke the bank at Monte Carlo!

542

*"Good gosh! Wasn't this crate inspected before we
left Miami?"*

255. On a radio program once, Fred Allen introduced one character
as his "molehill man." "Every morning," he vouchsafed by way of
explanation, "this fellow arrives at his office and finds a molehill on his
desk. It's his job to make a mountain of it before 5 P.M. comes around."

Allen says his next sponsor will be the manufacturer of Lumpo Soap:
"It doesn't lather. It doesn't float. It contains no secret oils. It is designed
solely to keep you company in the tub."

* * *

256. When John Mulholland, one of the great prestidigitators of our
time, was a youngster, he was added as an afterthought to a program at
the National Arts Club, and forthwith gave a very creditable performance. When it was over, however, an old killjoy with a perverted sense
of humor asked if the young magician could do the same tricks with any
old pack of cards. Mulhholland brazened it out, and found an unopened

pack of cards, with the National Arts device on their orange backs, thrust into his hands. To the astonishment of the members, he performed some tricks with the new cards that eclipsed any he had done with his own prepared deck—more mystifying, indeed, than any he has been able to do since. It appears that when Mulholland unwrapped the deck he noticed (although he did not see fit to call it to the attention of the members) that a singular error had occurred at the factory in the assembling of that pack. It was made up of fifty-two aces of spades.

* * *

257. Lucius Beebe tells of Jack Miley's visit to the Pump Room in Chicago. Miley was sports editor of the New York *Daily News.* On the day in question, he was fried. The Pump Room specializes in flaming foods served on swords, spears, bayonets, and what have you. Miley watched the spectacle for a few moments and commanded, "Waiter, bring me a double order of scrambled eggs, extra soft, and listen, fellow, bring them on a *saber.*"

* * *

258. Cullman has developed a neat technique which may give executives who read these lines an idea. At eight-thirty sharp he calls his office and has his secretary read the mail to him over the phone. He dictates his answers before he hangs up. Recipients of these notes think "Jiminy cricket, but that Cullman is a ball of fire." Frequently the ball of fire has meanwhile turned over and peacefully gone back to sleep.

* * *

259. For years Howard Lindsay engaged in a bitter feud with an actor who had let him down and wouldn't even stay in the same room with him when they accidentally met at a party. Then one night Lindsay's wife, Dorothy Stickney, was amazed to find him in close and harmonious conversation with the actor at the other end of a Hollywood drawing room.

The conference ended in a burst of laughter, and Lindsay clapped the actor on the back. "I wonder what caused Howard to forgive him?"

thought Mrs. Lindsay. At this moment, Lindsay whispered hoarsely in her ear, "Who *was* that fellow I just was talking to, anyhow?"

*"If it doesn't break up your cold, you'll at least
have a lot of fun trying."*

260. A fantastically henpecked husband finally did something entirely on his own initiative. He dropped dead. His nagging wife mourned his loss—and the fact that she had nobody left to badger. A visitor sympathized, "How you must miss dear Wilbur." "Yes," said the widow wistfully, "it seems but yesterday that he stood at that very door, holding it open until two flies got in."

* * *

261. A poker-loving spiritualist wanted another player for a Saturday-night session and summoned the ghost of a departed companion. The ghost was delighted to sit in on the game, and on the very first hand drew five beautiful hearts. He bet his stack.

Unfortunately, one of the flesh-and-blood players had a pat full house and raked in the pot—just one more time when the spirit was willing but the flush was weak.

* * *

262. Mrs. Gabor and her three talented and beautiful daughters, Eva, Zsa Zsa and Magda, attract publicity and men with equal facility. Recently one gentleman caller expressed a need for food to help him cope with the girls.

"Raid the icebox," suggested Mama Gabor. "It's always full of good things to eat." The visitor found that the entire contents of the icebox consisted of two dozen orchids and a salami.

"How does a moose call go again?"

263. "A pessimist," explained Grover Whalen at a dinner for traffic regulators, "is a female who's afraid she won't be able to squeeze her car into a very small parking space. An optimist is a male who thinks she won't try." Lee Gillespie, of Council Bluffs, wrote, "I've discovered how to get rid of a noise in your car. Let *her* drive." Allan McMahon, the Fort Wayne capitalist, said you can always pick out the owner of a car in which six ladies are riding. She's the one who, after somebody pulls the door shut, always opens it and slams it harder.

* * *

264. My Uncle Herbert loves to rough it in the woods every summer, communing with nature in an outfit that sets him back about three hundred dollars at Abercrombie and Fitch. Last year we were gradually freezing to death in an overnight cabin in Maine when I suggested that Uncle Herbert blaze a trail to the kitchen and light the stove. A couple of moments later he was back with his impeccable costume strangely tattered and torn. "I thought you were going to light the stove?" I grumbled. "I did," maintained Uncle Herbert, "but it went out." "Well," I said impatiently, "light it again." "I can't," said Uncle Herbert. "It went out through the roof."

* * *

265. Andrew Carnegie once was showing a delegation through his plant when he stopped to talk to a stooped, gray-haired employee. "Let's see, Wilson," he said. "How many years exactly is it that you've been with me now?"

"Thirty-nine, sir," beamed Wilson. "And may I add that in that entire time I made only one trifling mistake?" "Good work," grunted Mr. Carnegie, "but from now on, please be more careful."

* * *

266. The most sensational trial of the year was in progress in Iceland, country of the midnight sun. The prosecuting attorney shook a bony finger in the face of the accused and thundered, "I ask you again, sir: where were you on the night of November 8 to March 16?"

"He's down a considerable time. I wonder what he found."

267. It's difficult to keep up with the adventures of an absent-minded publisher of the *Saturday Review*, Hal Smith. His exploit took place at the corner of Fifth Avenue and 23rd Street. While the traffic light was red, a man planted himself directly in front of Hal's jalopy. The light turned to green, but the gent moved nary a step. Finally Hal leaned out of the car, and gently reminded him, "Say, bud, the light is green. How about getting the hell out of my way?" "Sorry, I can't oblige," replied the character. "Your car is on my foot!"

* * *

268. A young banker picked up the telephone. His end of the conversation went as follows: "No. No. *No.* No. No. No. *Yes.* No. No. No." Finally, with a last explosive "No" he hung up the phone. The vice-president of the bank overheard him and grumbled, "What d'ya mean by saying yes to that fellow?" "I had to," explained the other. "He asked me if I could hear him."

* * *

269. The late Cardinal Hinsley of Great Britain and the Archbishop of Canterbury attended the same dinner party and later shared a taxicab into town. "It is quite fitting that we take the cab together," smiled the Archbishop. "After all, we both serve God." "Yes, yes," agreed the Cardinal heartily. "You in your way; I in His."

Cardinal Hinsley liked to tell the story of two brothers who studied for the ministry. One was a little too flippant and whimsical to reach the heights; the other, a pompous and heavy-handed party, became a bishop in due course. "My brother," the whimsical one explained, "rose because of his gravity; I was held down by my levity."

* * *

270. There was a total eclipse of the sun in 1932, and a newsreel company sent two expeditions to South America to get authentic pictures of it. Bad weather prevented their getting any shots worth exhibiting. The company had to have a picture, however, and put the problem to its technical expert. "I'll manufacture a picture of an eclipse for you right in my laboratory," he promised, and he was as good as his word. There was one flaw. When the picture was run off, the word "Mazda" appeared on the face of the sun.

549

271. There was a daily columnist in Hollywood who just doted on printing long lists of notables seen at important picture premieres. She missed the opening of *Going My Way*, but a supposed friend volunteered to supply her with a list of big shots in the audience. She printed his story unedited. It began with a bang. "Among those present," it read, "were Miss Lizzie Borden, Mr. Marcus Aurelius, Mr. Ethan Frome . . ." Most readers got no farther.

* * *

272. In the summer of 1929 The Viking Press imported five hundred copies of a couple of expensive, beautifully printed and bound editions of obscure English poets. After the market crash in the fall of the same year, "limited" editions of this sort were a drug on the market.

George Oppenheimer, now of Hollywood, then an officer of The Viking Press, was visiting a young couple he knew in Buffalo when he spied copies of the special editions on the bookshelf. He roared with laughter, and exclaimed, "How did you ever get stuck with those lemons? We couldn't *give* them away." The lady of the house turned a cold eye on him. "They were your wedding gift to us," she reminded him.

* * *

273. An American tourist in England asked the gardener at Kensington Gardens, "How do you ever get lawns as perfect as that?" The reply was, "Well, madam, the first thing you have to do is begin about 600 years ago."

* * *

274. At the opening of a Bankhead play, Heywood Broun once whispered into the star's ear, "Don't look now, Tallulah, but your show's slipping!"

* * *

275. Nick Agropopolus, who did a mite of farming down Maryland way, received a notice from the town council that the license to maintain a cow on his premises had expired. Agropopolus took pen in hand and replied, "My cow she beat you to it. She expire two weeks ago. Much oblige: Your truly . . ."

276. The late S. S. McClure, pioneer magazine and book publisher, was waylaid on the way to his inner office one morning by a determined lady who demanded, "Did you keep your promise and read the manuscript I gave you?" To be rid of her, he answered, "I did. We can't use it." She appeared crestfallen and murmured, "I suppose the little verses at the beginning of each chapter detracted from the story. Maybe they should come out." "No, no," said the publisher suavely. "Those little verses add to the interest. I'd leave them in by all means."

"Mr. McClure," the lady answered triumphantly, "there *are* no little verses at the head of each chapter. You simply haven't read the manuscript as you said you would and I'm going to sit right here until you do." McClure realized he was trapped, and with a sigh, sat down to skim through the manuscript as quickly as possible. He decided to accept it, however. The lady was Mrs. Ovid Butler Jameson of Indianapolis, determined to set her brother astride the high road to literary fame. Her brother's name was Booth Tarkington. The manuscript was *Monsieur Beaucaire.*

"Oh, I'll bet you tell that to all the squirrels!"

552

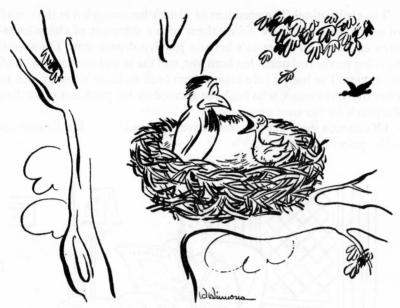

"Mom, what's all this stuff I hear about the birds and bees?"

277. The court house at Stephenville has a large clock that is the pride of the town. It is illuminated at night. One citizen staggered up to a mail box, dropped a penny in the slot, glanced at the clock, and exclaimed, "Jehoshaphat, I'm nine pounds overweight." . . .

* * *

278. A lady and her daughter are sauntering down Fifth Avenue. In front of Tiffany's the young girl's "pearl necklace" breaks, and the pearls roll all over the street. She reclaims them, and suggests giving them to Tiffany's for stringing.

"We can't ask Tiffany's to restring things like that," protests the mother. "After all, the whole necklace cost only $12.98 at Blank's." Anyhow, they enter Tiffany's. The man at the repair desk takes one look at the loose pearls, asks to be excused for a moment, and returns with the general manager, who offers the startled lady fifty thousand dollars for the lot.

The explanation? The president of Blank's has smuggled in the strand of pearls for his wife by hiding them with a shipment of cheap imitations addressed to the store's bargain jewelry department. The special marking on the real pearls has been lost, and the strand mixed up with all the others. The honest lady brings them back to Blank's just in time to clear the saleswoman, who has been accused by the president of stealing the pearls for her own purposes.

Of course, a story like this *could* have happened in real life. Reasonable odds against it: 4000 to 1.

279. Most jewel thieves and smugglers are apprehended sooner or later, but one clever fraud has gotten away scot-free. He came into a famous New York jewelry shop and said he was looking for a special pearl for his wife's birthday. The price made no difference, he declared; he was a Texas oil millionaire, and had credentials to prove it. He finally picked out a beautiful pearl and paid $5,000 cash for it.

A few weeks later he was back. His wife was crazy about the pearl; wanted to match it for a pair of earrings. The manager of the store said he doubted whether a duplicate could be found. "Advertise," suggested the customer. "I'll pay up to $25,000 for a duplicate of that pearl." It developed that a lady in Chicago had just such a pearl, which she was willing to sell for $20,000. The store bought it from her—but is still waiting for the "Texas millionaire" to claim it. What he had done, of course, was to sell back the store's own pearl for four times the purchase price. Even if they find him, they'll have a hard time convicting him of any crime.

* * *

280. A poet came into the Doubleday office recently and asked, "What do you pay for blank verse?" The telephone operator had the proper reply: "Blank checks."

* * *

281. John Barrymore and Richard Bennett, reports Gene Fowler, spent an evening together in London that included liquid refreshments of many descriptions and copious quantity. Bennett woke up the next morning, gingerly felt his head, and wondered if Barrymore had gotten to his home without bodily injury. He phoned him, and, when several seconds passed without an answer, called angrily into the instrument, "Hello! Hello!"

Barrymore's voice, very sleepy, replied, "Hello."

"Are you all right?"

"I'm fine. How are you?"

"Fine. But I've had the devil of a time getting your room. Are you in it, or down in the lobby?"

"I don't know."

"What in hell do you mean, you don't know? Where *are* you then?"

"Here, I suppose," said Barrymore, poking his head out from beneath Bennett's own bed.

* * *

282. Heywood Broun loved the theatre, and the majority of his reviews were gentle and encouraging. One evening, however, an actor named Geoffrey Steyne gave a performance that displeased him. Broun allowed that Mr. Steyne was the worst actor on the American stage. Mr. Steyne sued. The whole principle of dramatic criticism was at stake in this suit; if the actor won it, obviously, a dangerous precedent would have been established. The case was dismissed, and it remained only to see what Heywood would say about Mr. Steyne on the occasion of his next New York appearance. The big night finally arrived, and the next morning initiates turned eagerly to Broun's review. He did not so much as mention Geoffrey Steyne until the last sentence of his last paragraph. This read simply, "Mr. Steyne's performance was not up to his usual standard."

* * *

283. Gene Fowler, novelist and biographer, suffered from too many visitors who barged into his private office to exchange quips and keep him from his work. The sign he painted outside his door read "Horace Witherspoon, Jr.: Famous Polish Impersonator." Nobody came near him for weeks.

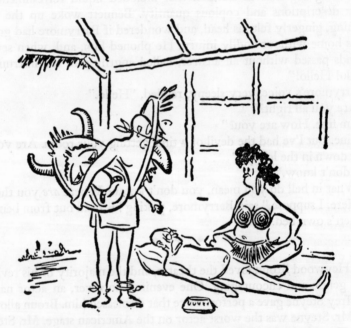

"Don't worry, ma'am—if everything else fails, we can always fall back on penicillin."

284. In private life, Jimmie Durante is so friendly, unassuming, and generous that everybody in show business loves him. Fred Allen calls him "The Riff-Raff's Caruso." "His voice," reports Allen, "can only be described as a dull rasp calling its mate, or an air-raid signal blasting through two layers of gravel." He hasn't much hair left, and refers to himself as "The Surrey with the Fringe on Top." He wears glasses now ("to read de racin' form"), plays piano duets with men like Professor Einstein and Deems Taylor, and explores esoteric dishes at exclusive restaurants. He had his first cheese soufflé at an expensive French eatery not long ago. After one bite, he registered ecstasy, and summoned the head waiter. "Where has dis been all my life?" he demanded. The waiter looked very pained. "I do not know, sir," he apologized.

* * *

285. Voltaire had a visitor who remarked that he had encountered another literary notable of that era on the way. "Ah," said Voltaire, "a

very able man, a fine character." "That's very kind of you," said the visitor, "because he said that you were a villainous old wretch." "Well," said Voltaire with a smile, "perhaps we are both mistaken."

When Rousseau wrote his ode "To Posterity" he sent an advance copy to Voltaire. Voltaire read it with a frown and remarked, "This poem will never reach its destination."

* * *

286. Frank Case, amiable Boniface of the Algonquin Hotel, tells the story of the day the late DeWolf Hopper protested to him that nowhere in New York could he find his favorite dessert, brown betty, on the menu. "I'd have it here for you," Case said, "if I thought there would be a reasonable demand for it." "You put it on your menu tomorrow night," proposed Hopper, "and I'll see to it personally that the demand develops." The next night brown betty was duly added to the Algonquin bill of fare, and Hopper, much gratified, made a personal tour of every table in the dining room. "I am DeWolf Hopper," he announced to the surprised patrons, "and I personally urge you to sample the brown betty this evening. It's delicious!" Hopper then repaired to his own table, toyed with a beefsteak, and summoned his waiter. "Now," he said, rubbing his hands in anticipation, "I'll have a double order of brown betty." "I'm very sorry, sir," said the waiter. "It's all gone."

* * *

287. A persistent playwright forced the same manuscript on the late producing wizard, David Belasco, seven times, always claiming that important revisions had made it the stuff from which sure hits were fashioned. "It's awful," Belasco said finally. "All the great playwrights combined couldn't doctor it sufficiently." "Isn't there some way you can put it on the stage?" persisted the playwright. "Yes," snapped Belasco, his patience exhausted. "Give me the script." He tossed it to his assistant and ordered, "Chop this up and use it as the snowstorm tonight."

* * *

288. Another memorable incident at the Dutch Treat Club centred in the appearance of Gertrude Lawrence, who was starring at the time in the very successful *Susan and God*.

Miss Lawrence expressed girlish embarrassment at finding herself the only female in a gathering of some three hundred handsome gentlemen. "Instead of making a silly speech," she suggested, "how would you like it if I raffled off two seats in the fourth row centre for Saturday night's performance of *Susan and God*?" The crowd roared its approval. "O.K.," said Miss Lawrence. "Every one of you has a green hat-check. I'll call out a number at random. The man whose hat-check number corresponds with it gets the ducats." Followed the business of three hundred gentlemen fishing in their jeans for their hat-checks.

"Ready?" asked Miss Lawrence. "The number I pick is 171."

"That's mine," said a happy voice from the back of the room. It belonged to Mr. John Golden, owner and producer of *Susan and God*. Thereupon Miss Lawrence and Mr. Golden escaped from the room before the stunned audience could translate its mute rage into positive action.

"He's fine until his arms get tired; then he stutters!"

"Well, Madam Onyx, it all happened—Just the way you said."

289. Samuel Johnson blundered into a musicale at Mrs. Thrale's house one night; registered acute nausea when a soprano mutilated an aria. "Come now," said Mrs. Thrale, "make some allowances. You don't realize how very difficult that piece is." "Difficult, Madam," snorted Johnson. "I wish it were impossible!"

* * *

290. One place during the war where they really took their music seriously was aboard a certain British airplane carrier. Each day at four, unless there was a heavy gale or the enemy had actually engaged the ship, there was a concert on deck. The band sat on the principal plane elevator, which is depressed about two feet so the musicians might follow better the baton-wielding of the conductor. He stood at the edge of the deck above, his back to the audience, which was always ample, since every man who could be spared was there under official orders.

On the afternoon in question, the carrier was coursing lazily through Mediterranean waters, and the concert was in full cry. Suddenly a mechanic in the control room noticed the plane-elevator indicator, which registered the fact that it was not quite flush with the deck. Afraid that the mechanism was out of kilter, he pressed a button hard. The ship's band, in the middle of the overture from *Carmen*, suddenly disappeared from the view of the entranced audience and plunged into the bowels of the ship. The mechanic, horrified when he saw what he had done, hastily pushed another button. The elevator shot skyward. It came to the surface with a jolt that sent every musician bouncing at least three feet in the air. But ah, those imperturbable British! Not one man stopped tooting his instrument for a moment during the entire round trip. The leader never lost a beat. When the overture was concluded, the unsmiling ship's company applauded politely.

* * *

291. A visitor from Australia walked into the Rolls-Royce showroom and paid cash on the line for the most expensive limousine model. "Ship it to my sheep ranch outside of Sydney," he instructed the sales manager. A year later he was back to order another car. "Best model I ever saw," he exclaimed, "and you can quote me on that. I particularly approve of the glass partition between the front and rear seats. Most ingenious feature of the whole car." "Why do you say that?" inquired the Rolls-

Royce representative. "It's like this," explained the Australian. "I roll that window up, and I'd like to see the damn sheep that can lick the back of my neck while I'm driving it to market!"

* * *

292. A five-year-old lad in Minnesota was watching his mother change the baby. When she overlooked sprinkling the tot's backside with talcum powder and hurried him into his diaper, the five-year-old reproved her sharply, "Hey, Mom, you forgot to salt him!"

* * *

293. A railroad claim agent was teaching his wife to drive, when the brakes suddenly failed on a steep downhill grade. "I can't stop," she shrilled. "What'll I do?" "Brace yourself," advised her husband, "and try to hit something cheap."

* * *

294. A fine distinction between acquaintanceship and friendship has been established by such Southern tobacco auctioneers as haven't been exported to New York for radio appearances. Several were convening in a backwoods bar, when a newcomer approached. One of the group patted him on the back and said, "Russ, you know Joe Arbuckle, don't you?" Russ grudgingly extended a hand, and allowed, "We've howdied but we ain't shook."

* * *

295. The going was even rougher than usual at the Guggenheims' weekly bridge joust with the Loebs. "Will you tell me," demanded the exasperated Mrs. G. of her spouse, "how you could make an original bid of three no-trumps when I was sitting there with all four aces and a king in my hand?" "If you must know," admitted the harassed Mr. Guggenheim, "I bid on three queens, two jacks and four highballs."

* * *

296. Latest "kibitzer" story tells of one of the most persistent of the breed, who hovered behind a card player for three solid hours giving advice. What's more, the player won consistently. Suddenly he found himself in a quandary. Turning to the kibitzer, he whispered, "Well,

562

smart guy, what do I play now, the ten or the queen?" The kibitzer answered, "First you've got to tell me this: What game are you playing?"

* * *

297. A couple of legal eagles in Reno, Nevada, write to say that while business never has been better, it does grow somewhat boring to be handling the same kind of cases all the time. Is divorce, they ask plaintively, the *only* subject engaging the attention of the Law in America today?

At any rate, while waiting for the Truckee River to unfreeze last winter, so they could resume fishing for the gold wedding rings divorcees impulsively throw in when their decrees are granted, the impatient attorneys composed these pertinent couplets:

Mrs. Camp's bereft today. She always knew a shorter way.

No longer wed is Mrs. Thorne. She hogged the bathroom every morn.

Each week poor Sue found some new diet. Worse still, she made her husband try it.

Marriage, thought Jones, was sure and stable. But then he fed the dog at table.

She left him flat and deserted the scene. He ended each sentence with "See what I mean?"

Their marital break was grim and gory. She never would let him finish a story.

The Campbells are no longer lovers. She always woke up with no bed covers.

In Reno, John Doe is slowly reviving. He couldn't stand the backseat driving.

* * *

298. Somerset Hemingwell sat happily typing the final pages of his new novel. In the yard, his nine-year-old son had just tripped over a tree root and broken his leg. The boxer puppy had chewed up Mrs. Hemingwell's best curtain, the twins had spilled a can of paint in the parlor and were now trying to pull each other's hair out, and the nurse had given notice. Mrs. Hemingwell paused in front of her husband's door and called out, "Lunch will be ready in a few moments. How far have you gotten with your manuscript?" Mr. H. answered, "It's going like a house-afire. The hero is just proposing to the heroine." "Give it a happy ending," begged Mrs. H. earnestly. "Have her say 'no'!"

563

TITLE INDEX

A

ALIENIST, THE, *Keith Preston* 32
ANECDOTAGE, *Richard Armour* 354
ANTHOLOGISTICS, *Arthur Guiterman* 170
AUNT AGATHA SPEAKS HER MIND, *P. G. Wodehouse* 251
AWAKE, AWAKE!, *Robert Benchley* 370

B

BEAUTY'S SISTER, *Owen Johnson* 298
BEWARE THE BRAZILIAN NAVY, *Ruth McKenney* 23
BODY BEAUTIFUL, THE, *Cornelia Otis Skinner* 1

C

CALLING DR. KILDARE! CALLING DR. PASTURE!, *Arthur Kober* 365
CHANGE OF TREATMENT, A, *W. W. Jacobs* 357
CHRISTMAS OF THE FUTURE, THE, *Frank Sullivan* 294
COMPLETE DANGLER, THE, *John Mason Brown* 219
CONSTABLE SAM AND THE UGLY TYKE, *Eric Knight* 54

D

DR. ATWOOD AND MR. ED, *Walter Brooks* 188

E

EIGHT BOTTLES OF LINIMENT, *Frances Eisenberg* 181
EXPERIENCE, *Dorothy Parker* 53

F

FIGHTING WORDS, *Dorothy Parker* 33
FILLING THAT HIATUS, *Robert Benchley* 81
FIREFLY, THE, *Ogden Nash* 22
FOWL PLAY, *Ian Hay* 397

G

GREAT PANCAKE RECORD, THE, *Owen Johnson*   152

H

HELL'S BELLS, *Margaret Fishback*   227
HI, ROVER, OR, OLIVER AMES WANTS A DOG, *Phyllis McGinley*   34
HIPPOPOTAMUS, THE, *Ogden Nash*   218
HORSES, *Richard Armour*   425
HOW BEAUTIFUL WITH MUD, *Hildegarde Dolson*   401
HOW DOES IT FEEL?, *David Burnham*   133

K

KENNEL AND THE CAT COOP, THE, *Ellis Parker Butler*   324

L

LADIES, THE, *Richard Armour*   270
LAST DAY, THE, *Robert Benchley*   241

M

MOMENT MUSICALE, *Margaret Fishback*   354
MONEY, *Richard Armour*   187
MR. POTTLE AND THE ONE MAN DOG, *Richard Connell*   271
MY NEXT GIRL, *Max Shulman*   39

N

NEED OF CHANGE, THE, *Julian Street*   372
NEW YEAR WISH, A, *Laura Lee Randall*   80

O

ON RIDING, *Cornelia Otis Skinner*   419

P

PAIR OF SEXES, A, *Franklin P. Adams (F.P.A.)*   168
PENSIVE PEN, THE, *Keith Preston*   342
PIGS IS PIGS, *Ellis Parker Butler*   171

R

RANSOM OF RED CHIEF, THE, *O. Henry*   408
RICH MAN, THE, *Franklin P. Adams (F.P.A.)*   269
RING OUT, WILD BELLS, *Wolcott Gibbs*   320
ROMAN GUIDE, A, *Mark Twain*   314
ROOF SITTER, *Frances Eisenberg*   9

S

SONG OF THE OPEN ROAD, *Ogden Nash*   250
SPRING OVER BROOKLYN, *Zachary Gold*   206
SPRING TONIC, *Margaret Fishback*   217

T

TACT IN ENTERTAINING, *Franklin P. Adams (F.P.A.)*   36
TERMITE, THE, *Ogden Nash*   341
THOSE TWO BOYS, *Franklin P. Adams (F.P.A.)*   32
THREE MUSKETEERS, THE, *Rudyard Kipling*   346
TO A SMALL BOY STANDING ON MY SHOES
    WHILE I AM WEARING THEM, *Ogden Nash*   340
TO A THESAURUS, *Franklin P. Adams (F.P.A.)*   150
TO A LADY TROUBLED BY INSOMNIA, *Franklin P. Adams (F.P.A.)*   369
TO A YOUNG MAN SELECTING SIX ORCHIDS, *Margaret Fishback*   132
TRANSFERRED GHOST, THE, *Frank R. Stockton*   343
TREASURE HUNT, THE, *Mary Roberts Rinehart*   84
TRIAL AND ERROR, *Phyllis McGinley*   269

U

UNCLE PODGER HANGS A PICTURE, *Jerome K. Jerome*   355

V

VERSES FOR A GREETING CARD, *Phyllis McGinley*   297
VISION FOR WILLY, A, *Marion Sturges-Jones*   73

W

WANTED: ONE CAVE MAN WITH CLUB, *Margaret Fishback*   119
WIDOW'S CRUISE, THE, *Frank R. Stockton*   228

Z

ZENOBIA'S INFIDELITY, *H. C. Bunner*   120

AUTHOR INDEX

ADAMS, FRANKLIN P. (F.P.A.)
Pair of Sexes, A   168
Rich Man, The   269
Tact in Entertaining   36
Those Two Boys   32
To a Lady Troubled by Insomnia   369
To a Thesaurus   150

ARMOUR, RICHARD
Anecdotage   354
Horses   425
Ladies, The   270
Money   187

BENCHLEY, ROBERT
Awake, Awake!   370
Filling That Hiatus   81
Last Day, The   241

BROOKS, WALTER
Dr. Atwood and Mr. Ed   188

BROWN, JOHN MASON
Complete Dangler, The   219

BUNNER, H. C.
Zenobia's Infidelity   120

BURNHAM, DAVID
How Does It Feel?   133

BUTLER, ELLIS PARKER
Kennel and the Cat Coop, The   324
Pigs Is Pigs   171

CONNELL, RICHARD
Mr. Pottle and the One Man Dog   271

DOLSON, HILDEGARDE
How Beautiful with Mud   401

EISENBERG, FRANCES
   Eight Bottles of Liniment   181
   Roof Sitter   9

FISHBACK, MARGARET
   Hell's Bells   227
   Moment Musicale   354
   Spring Tonic   217
   To a Young Man Selecting Six Orchids   132
   Wanted: One Cave Man with Club   119

GIBBS, WOLCOTT
   Ring Out, Wild Bells   320

GOLD, ZACHARY
   Spring over Brooklyn   206

GUITERMAN, ARTHUR
   Anthologistics   170

HAY, IAN
   Fowl Play   397

HENRY, O.
   Ransom of Red Chief, The   408

JACOBS, W. W.
   Change of Treatment, A   357

JEROME, JEROME K.
   Uncle Podger Hangs a Picture   355

JOHNSON, OWEN
   Beauty's Sister   298
   Great Pancake Record, The   152

KIPLING, RUDYARD
   Three Musketeers, The   246

KNIGHT, ERIC
   Constable Sam and the Ugly Tyke   54

KOBER, ARTHUR
   Calling Dr. Kildare! Calling Dr. Pasture!   365

McGINLEY, PHYLLIS
   Hi, Rover, or, Oliver Ames Wants a Dog   34
   Trial and Error   269
   Verses for a Greeting Card   297

McKenney, Ruth
  Beware the Brazilian Navy   23
Nash, Ogden
  Firefly, The   22
  Hippopotamus, The   218
  Song of the Open Road   250
  Termite, The   341
  To a Small Boy Standing on My Shoes While I Am
  Wearing Them   340
Parker, Dorothy
  Experience   53
  Fighting Words   33
Preston, Keith
  Alienist, The   32
  Pensive Pen, The   342
Randall, Laura Lee
  New Year Wish, A   80
Rinehart, Mary Roberts
  Treasure Hunt, The   84
Shulman, Max
  My Next Girl   39
Skinner, Cornelia Otis
  Body Beautiful, The   1
  On Riding   419
Stockton, Frank R.
  Transferred Ghost, The   343
  Widow's Cruise, The   228
Street, Julian
  Need of Change, The   372
Sturges-Jones, Marion
  Vision for Willy, A   73
Sullivan, Frank
  Christmas of the Future, The   294
Twain, Mark
  Roman Guide, A   314
Wodehouse, P. G.
  Aunt Agatha Speaks Her Mind   251

SUBJECT INDEX, TOASTMASTER'S HANDBOOK
(Number for anecdote indicated)

ACTORS AND ACTRESSES
5, 6, 7, 8, 9, 14, 40, 42, 81,
82, 142, 144, 288

ANIMALS
179, 180

ARMED FORCES
85, 129, 130, 131, 133, 135,
136, 137, 138, 290

AUTOMOBILES
61, 75, 76, 219, 263, 267,
291, 293

BROADWAY
10, 22, 36, 134, 143, 208,
259, 262, 274, 282, 287

CHILDREN
23, 41, 72, 119, 120, 121,
149, 150, 151, 152, 175,
198, 292

CLUBS
33

DOCTORS
155, 157

FUNNY BUSINESS
26, 31

GAMING
79, 100, 166, 245, 261, 295,
296

GRAB BAG
4, 19, 21, 50, 51, 53, 54, 55,
56, 59, 63, 64, 66, 84, 116,
117, 122, 123, 124, 126,
127, 128, 139, 145, 146,
147, 153, 154, 156, 158,
161, 162, 163, 165, 169,
178, 181, 182, 184, 185,
193, 194, 204, 212, 214,
215, 216, 222, 229, 230,
238, 243, 244, 247, 256,
257, 264, 266, 269, 273,
275, 278, 279, 286, 294,
297

HILLBILLY
32

HISTORY
83, 101

HOLLYWOOD
1, 11, 12, 13, 15, 16, 17, 18,
160, 187, 189, 192, 271,
283, 284

INTOXICANTS
39, 45, 125, 132, 211, 217,
277, 281

LITERARY LIFE
2, 3, 20, 22, 25, 27, 28, 29,
30, 31, 34, 35, 36, 37, 38,
40, 41, 44, 65, 67, 68, 69,
74, 78, 82, 168, 170, 171,
172, 183, 232, 233, 236,
239, 246, 248, 249, 272,
276, 280, 283, 285

MARTS OF TRADE
24, 31, 58, 60, 62, 77, 173,
176, 177, 258, 268, 270

M. C. QUIPS
46, 240

MUSIC
71, 73, 289

RAILROADS
186, 188, 190, 213, 218,
222

RICH MAN, POOR MAN
43, 47, 70, 80, 241, 265

ROMANCE
148, 199

SHAGGY DOG
102, 103, 104, 105, 106,
107, 108, 109, 110, 111,
112, 113, 114, 115, 118

SPORTS
52, 89, 90, 91, 92, 93, 94,
95, 96, 97, 98, 99, 159, 200,
201, 202, 205

STRICTLY PROFESSIONAL
57

TELEVISION AND RADIO
10, 21, 191, 206, 207, 209,
210, 255

TINGLING SPINE
203, 251, 252, 253, 254

UNIVERSITY
141, 220, 221, 223, 224,
225, 226, 227

VIP's IN WASHINGTON
48, 86, 87, 88, 167, 228,
231, 250

WOMEN
33, 49, 140, 164, 174, 195,
196, 197, 234, 235, 237,
242, 260, 298